G000167053

WEATHER PATTERNS OF EAST ANGLIA

WEATHER PATTERNS OF EAST ANGLIA

by

ALFRED GLENN

TERENCE DALTON LIMITED
LAVENHAM . SUFFOLK
1987

Published by
TERENCE DALTON LIMITED
ISBN 0 86138 044 4

Text photoset in 11/12 pt Baskerville

Printed in Great Britain at
The Lavenham Press Limited, Lavenham, Suffolk

© Alfred Glenn, 1987

Contents

Preface

IN no sense is this a textbook, nor does it add one iota of knowledge to the complex science of meteorology. It contains no gems of discovery; simply assorted pebbles of information washed ashore by the tides of experience in a part of England which I know and have learned to love.

Alfred Glenn
Rushmere St Andrew
Suffolk

September, 1987

To my wife Mary

Acknowledgements

I AM grateful to my brother Walter, who for many years shared our first weather station and who spent many hours researching past records, and also to Richard Wilson of Belstead Hall, Ipswich, who was generous and trusting enough to let me retain for a long period his priceless and irreplaceable registers of continuous weather records at Copdock and Belstead from 1902 to date.

I am also indebted to many other individuals and organisations, including Casella (London) Ltd, Fisons Ltd (Levington Research Station), Suffolk Record Office, *East Anglian Daily Times*, the Meteorological Office, Bracknell, the Editor of *Weather* (Royal Meteorological Society), K. E. Blowers, Dr C. E. Briscoe, David Brooks, R. J. Prichard, Gerald Ralph, Dr G. T. Meaden, Keith Watson, John Loughton, Tony Ray, Brian Hayes, R. A. Robson, R. Snowling, S. Bartholomew.

The tables in appendices four, five, six and seven are reproduced by courtesy of the Meteorological Office.

I make no apologies for all temperatures being quoted in degrees Fahrenheit instead of Centigrade or Celsius. The decision was not taken lightly — and my reasons are given with the temperature conversion table in appendix one.

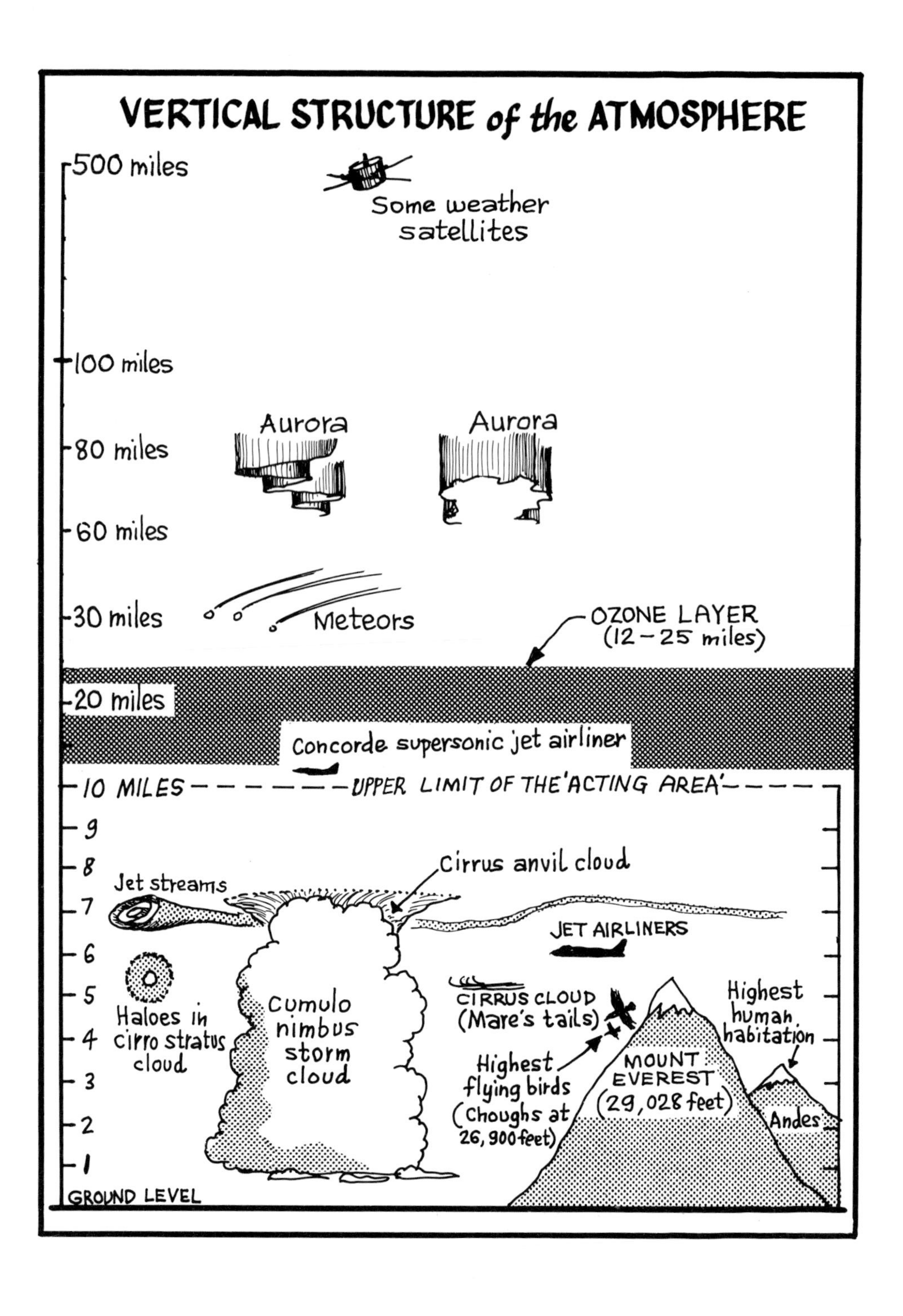
VERTICAL STRUCTURE of the ATMOSPHERE
500 miles
Some weather satellites
100 miles
Aurora
Aurora
80 miles
60 miles
30 miles
Meteors
OZONE LAYER (12 – 25 miles)
20 miles
Concorde supersonic jet airliner
10 MILES
UPPER LIMIT OF THE 'ACTING AREA'
9
8
Cirrus anvil cloud
Jet streams
7
JET AIRLINERS
6
5
4
3
2
1
Haloes in cirro stratus cloud
Cumulo nimbus storm cloud
CIRRUS CLOUD (Mare's tails)
Highest flying birds (Choughs at 26,900 feet)
MOUNT EVEREST (29,028 feet)
Highest human habitation
Andes
GROUND LEVEL

CHAPTER ONE

What Causes our Weather?

METEOROLOGY is, by common dictionary definition, the scientific study of atmospheric phenomena (called meteors) and has no direct concern with astronomical meteors, shooting stars and the like.

It is easy for us when browsing through old books to smile indulgently at some of the quaint, often melodramatic, theories as to the nature and causes of meteorological phenomena. To give a typical example, William Pardon in his *Dictionary* of 1740 describes lightning as being "sudden flashes of exceeding subtle light or fire generated in the air" and thunder as "a noise made in the air like a roaring cannon, occasioned by a commixtion of disagreeing vapours that generate noisy explosions".

Lightning is, indeed, an exceeding subtle light. So subtle that centuries after an almost suicidal experiment with a kite by Benjamin Franklin in July, 1752, by which he discovered that lightning was caused by a build-up of positive and negative charges in the atmosphere we still do not know how that build-up occurs. It is clear enough that a thundercloud is like a natural electro-static generator but, although the meteorological conditions conducive to the formation of thunderstorms are easily definable, we have yet to discover precisely how the electrical potential develops. There are many other aspects of our weather the causes of which are still not fully understood.

Being a branch of physics, meteorology is much concerned with mechanics and it is not medieval mumbo-jumbo to describe the earth's atmosphere as a machine, manufacturing weather. And, like all machines, our atmosphere needs a source of energy to provide the driving force. That energy is derived solely from the sun, which has a temperature of over 10,000 degrees Fahrenheit (6,000 degrees Centigrade). Such a temperature may seem (and is) out of this world but the commonplace spin-off in a thunderstorm (often caused by the direct heat of the sun) is even more startling. A single flash of lightning can raise a temperature of 27,000 degrees F. (15,000 degrees C.) in a few millionths of a second. The sun's heat is 93 million miles away; lightning can strike our house or the metal golf clubs we are carrying.

Our atmosphere (its weight being measured by the barometer) is at its most dense at the earth's surface, thinning out until it merges into space at a height of a hundred miles or so. At sixty miles high the air is so rarefied as to have become almost a vacuum. More than ninety-nine per cent of our atmospheric pressure is exerted within twenty-five miles of the earth's surface and about half the atmosphere's weight is contained in the lower three-and-a-half miles. In the idiom of the theatre, the acting area is mainly confined to a bottom layer of about ten or eleven miles in depth. In this shallow area we experience the action, the drama and sometimes the tragedies of our weather, and we can see at least some of the events going on above us in the shape of cloud formations, haloes and the like.

An important factor is that the temperature is normally at its highest nearest the earth's surface, the usual decrease with height being something like three to four degrees F. for every 3,000 feet. This causes a natural tendency for the lighter, surface air to rise. Sometimes a layer of warmer air develops above us (a temperature inversion) which tends to trap the cool air below it. Persistent fog in quiet weather is often due to a temperature inversion.

The reason for the falling off of temperature with height is that the sun's heat as it travels through space is not immediately apparent but is to some extent convertible — rather like a cheque which is a worthless piece of paper until it reaches the conversion point of our bank counter. The sun's rays, travelling through space, are not substantially converted into heat until they reach a conversion point — something of substance. Minor conversions take place as the sun's rays mingle with traces of gases and minute particles of dust and moisture in the rarefied air of our upper atmosphere, but the first major conversion takes place when the sun's rays strike the all-important ozone layer, high in the atmosphere. In the process the ozone layer absorbs large quantities of the ultra-violet rays which, if they reached us undiluted, would prove fatal to all living organisms.

The various layers of clouds provide other conversion points for the sun's heat, but the very solid earth's surface is the final conversion point — as is easily apparent on a hot, sunny day by feeling with your hand the heat of bare soil or finding the roof of one's car too hot to touch.

Largely because of the tilt of the earth distribution of the sun's heat is uneven, with great warmth at the equator and masses of accumulated cold air at the poles. This imbalance provides the thermo-dynamic factors which drive the circulation of our atmosphere, making the weather machine work. If everything were simple, the atmospheric circulation of the earth might consist of a uniform system of temperature control in which the cold (and heavier) air from the poles would travel towards the tropics to push away the hot equatorial air which, being lighter, would rise and flow out to the poles; becoming colder and heavier, it would sink and return to the equator for re-heating and re-distribution, rather like a well-planned domestic central heating unit.

Things are not as simple as that. Our air circulation runs into all sorts of traffic problems, creating disruptions in the circulatory flow with actual confrontations, sometimes violent, between the conflicting air masses. Temperature is by no means the only factor; differences in barometric pressure (resulting in areas of high and low pressure, anticyclones and depressions respectively) are ultimately the most important factor and our weather is largely dependent on the movement and behaviour of the "highs" and the "lows".

Fortunately, nature has evolved a neat way by which, largely due to the rotation of the earth, the air currents (in the northern hemisphere) are steered anti-clockwise round the depressions and clockwise round the anticyclones — rather like our system of traffic islands which transform head-on and criss-cross confrontations into circulatory traffic. In the southern hemisphere the air circulation is the other way round. The various weather systems can be seen in synoptic form on the weather maps on the televison screens and in some of the daily papers.

A simple and relatively uncomplicated type of low pressure area (or depression) provides a good example of the battle between the warm and cold air masses, the advance guard of each air mass being known respectively as a "warm" and a "cold" front. (Map "F" in "East Anglia and the Daily Weather Maps" demonstrates this.)

Comparatively warm air arriving with a warm front (usually from the south-west) in the front of a depression rises because, being warmer, it is lighter than the surrounding air. Barometric pressure (like temperature) falls with height so, as the warm air rises into regions of lower barometric pressure, it expands. Because of its expansion, it cools. When it is cooled to saturation point (the more air is cooled the less moisture it can hold), precipitation occurs in the form of rain, sleet or snow.

The cold front is generally a far more vigorous affair, the advancing heavier cold air, sweeping (usually) from the north-west in the rear of a depression, unceremoniously jerking the warmer and lighter air upwards, often causing heavy showers and sometimes thunderstorms. Most of East Anglia's tornadoes, waterspouts and other violent occurrences are associated with the line of a cold front. (See chapter three "Wind".)

But fronts are not always as simple as that. There are many, often confusing, variations. Frequently a depression becomes stationary or very slow moving while within its system a series of cold and warm fronts may be circulating, rather like the spokes of a wheel. On or near the spokes there may be rain. The incidence of the rain belts, usually spaced several hours apart, means that we may — by good or bad luck — get the fair weather by day and the rain at night; or vice versa. Whether in East Anglia or elsewhere, we talk of this type of weather as being unsettled, whereas in fact it is a familiar pattern into which are woven rhythms of varying speeds and intensity. Often the fronts are by no means aggressive and the weather situation becomes less of a battlefield and more a state of lightly armed neutrality in which the fronts reveal themselves as indeterminate wiggles on the weather map causing equally undistinguished weather, generally of a rather unpleasant kind but often with little more than an increase in cloud and a risk of light rain.

In such slack conditions, the fronts often drift aimlessly around like disillusioned discontents having lost their aim in life. Their movement is usually anti-clockwise within the depression. If the depression lies to the west of the British Isles we can expect the fronts to move towards East Anglia from the south-west; if the depression is to the east, the fronts will most likely arrive from the north. In both cases, even if rain does occur, changes in the barometer are usually very slight, thus denying us much warning.

East Anglia comes off badly when, as sometimes happens, a front drifts eastwards into the North Sea giving rain on its way, and then drifts back again giving us, as it were, the same rain all over again. Further complications often arise when a cold front catches up with a warm front, when they merge and become "occluded". Usually an occlusion is a rather faded affair; sometimes it may be bad-tempered enough to organise the development of a new low pressure system.

The erratic behaviour of fronts is one of the most common causes of inaccurate forecasts. Even when the forecasters have got their sums right, the timing may let them down. Vagrant fronts sometimes even invade the sanctity of an anticyclone. Perhaps a little overawed by their surroundings, they rarely cause much upset; when pressure is high they tend to be weak but can still give areas of cloudy, doubtful looking weather in what would otherwise be a settled fine spell.

Precipitation in the form of rain, snow, sleet and hail is almost always caused by rising currents of air (with or without the aid of a front). When the rising currents are sufficiently strong they can cause thunderstorms which, by their nature, are usually easy to predict even though the precise mechanics are still not fully understood.

The aptly named "heat" thunderstorm is an example. On a hot Summer day the earth's surface and the local layers of air become excessively heated. The hot air, lighter than the air above it, starts to rise on the same principle as the buoyancy of a hot-air balloon. Surface heating sends up columns of warm air. If the air is cooled to its dewpoint,

Just as the hot air produced by the gas burners causes the balloon to rise, so air heated by the sun rises into the colder air — and thunderstorms can result. *East Anglian Daily Times*

we see the formation of small "fine weather" cumulus clouds at the top of the columns. They are harmless enough but, if the heating is considerable, the columns of air continue their upward thrust and the clouds build in size until they reach the point where raindrops form and showers develop. When the uprush of air is strong (vertical speeds of well over 20 m.p.h. are common) the showers can be very heavy, often accompanied by hail and thunder. During the Autumn of 1982 a parachutist practising for the Commonwealth Games jumped from his aircraft to find himself going up instead of down as he was hurled upwards for 6,000 feet in the fierce turbulence of a thundercloud, bombarded by huge hailstones. Knowing that he could be whisked to a height of 25,000 feet or more (and "flake out" through lack of oxygen) he released his main 'chute for a free-fall down to a safe height, at which he opened his reserve 'chute. He landed unharmed about five miles away from his intended target.

The cause of lightning, which in turn causes the sound of thunder, is still not completely understood. Benjamin Franklin's kite experiment established the presence of a highly developed positive–negative potential in a thundercloud. It is widely thought, though not definitely proved, that the positive element is at the top of the cloud and the negative one at the bottom, but exactly how this happens remains a mystery. Text books on meteorology either evade the issue or generalise with such phrases as "the turbulent conditions in a stormcloud can eventually lead to a build-up of electrical charges, thus triggering off a thunderstorm".

One theory is based on the fact that when the uprush of air is enough, the raindrops may not be heavy enough to fall through the violently rising air-currents, so they are tossed still higher. If they have become larger but still not heavy enough to fall they become unstable and break (a raindrop rarely exceeds a quarter-inch in diameter without splitting). Every time a raindrop breaks, one half acquires a positive electrical charge and the other half a negative one, the "positive" drops going to the top of the cloud while the "negative" drops remain at the bottom. If the storm is a severe one and the breaking-up process is repeated several times the potential builds up to the point of causing an electrical discharge — the first flash of lightning and the beginning of a thunderstorm. Well, that is one theory. There are others — some contradictory — but we do know that the initial cause of a thunderstorm is vigorously rising currents of air.

Heat is by no means the only cause of a thunderstorm. In the Winter, air warmed by the sea can rise rapidly into the colder air above. The principle is the same. Just as the atmosphere becomes "top heavy" when the lower layers are heated, so it does if the upper layers become markedly cooled. Even on a chilly Winter's day, the arrival of much colder air above us will create a similar thermal instability to that of a "heat" thunderstorm. Long before the Common Market, a frequent and troublesome import from France (and Spain) was layers of cold air moving northwards over our own weather. This can happen at any time of the year but is most frequent in the Summer and Autumn. These high-level invasions of cold air can cause some very severe thunder-

These big hailstones fell during a severe storm which swept across the Woodbridge area of East Suffolk on 22nd August, 1987.

East Anglian Daily Times

storms, often in the early hours of the morning. Southern England and East Anglia are particularly vulnerable target areas. The Kent peninsula is usually in the front line of attack and, even if the spread of cold upper air does not always reach East Anglia, we are often treated to a spectacular night display of sheet lightning over our southern horizon (the apparent difference between sheet and fork lightning is explained in chapter four).

Why in the middle of a scorching heatwave — and usually in a thunderstorm — are we sometimes bombarded with hailstones, which are really frozen drops of rain? On 23rd September, 1976, following a famous hot Summer, with shade temperatures well into the mid-60s, residents in the Westleton and Blythburgh area of Suffolk were alarmed by a particularly severe hailstorm which, according to reports, produced hailstones the size of marbles drifting to a depth of four feet.

The combination of heat and hail is simple. Paradoxically, it often happens that the greater the heat, the more the likelihood of hail. If the uprush of air in a cumulo-nimbus thundercloud, often triggered off by great heat, is strong enough the raindrops will be tossed higher and higher until eventually they reach the upper layer of freezing temperatures (the top of a cumulo-nimbus can easily reach a height of five miles or so). There the raindrops become frozen, eventually falling to the ground as hail. In very severe storms, the upward currents are often too strong to allow the hailstones to fall and they may be tossed up time and again, each time acquiring a fresh coating of ice before finally becoming heavy enough to fall to the ground (hence the very large stones in a severe storm). If anyone in that Westleton and Blythburgh storm of 1976 had picked up a hailstone and quickly sliced it in two, he would almost certainly have found separate layers of ice which, like the rings in the trunk of a felled tree, would have given some indication of its life history.

The difference between hail, rain, sleet and snow is worth noting. Hail is simply rain which has become frozen either by the tossing-up process or by falling through a freezing layer of air near the ground; snow is formed when condensation takes place below freezing point; sleet is usually either flakes of melting snow or a mixture of rain and snow and generally occurs with air temperatures between about 37 and 39 degrees F.

A common form of precipitation is mist or fog. At one time there was a sinister difference between the inoffensive fogs and mists of the countryside and the pea-soup fogs of the Victorian cities. Even during the present century, choking fogs have sometimes proved lethal. One of the worst of all time was in London between 5th and 9th December, 1952. The fog thickened as a temperature inversion made it impossible for the smoke to rise (the word "smog" was coined to describe a fog of high smoke density) and the resultant mixture of water drops, oxygen and sulphur dioxide formed a deadly sulphuric acid; thousands of people, mostly elderly and chest sufferers, died in that one dreadful fog. In January, 1981, Denmark — particularly Copenhagen — experienced its worst ever smog due to the warmer air of a thaw trapping the colder layers of air which still lay over the half-frozen ground.

Fortunately smoke pollution regulations have largely eliminated city fogs. Far from large industrial towns, rural East Anglia can happily accept the official meteorological criterion that the only difference between mist and fog is one of density, "fog" describing a visibility limited to 1,100 yards. Mist and fog are both due to air having been cooled to saturation point. The condensation of warm, moist air blowing across a cold earth surface is a common cause. Fogs caused on "radiation" nights by the condensation of the lower layers of air losing heat to the sky are usually shallow and, because of their patchy nature, the most hazardous type for the motorist (see chapter four). Sea fogs usually occur when comparatively warm air is cooled to its dew-point over a comparatively cold sea. With an onshore wind, sea fogs can penetrate several miles inland — and East Anglia is particularly vulnerable in the Springtime, when warm air flowing across the North Sea (still cold from the Winter) is more than usually chilled. Freezing fogs are usually radiation fogs formed at a temperature below freezing point; their only pleasant aspect is when every branch and twig becomes coated with ice to form a beautiful filigree of rime.

Dew, one of the most gentle forms of precipitation, is another result of loss of heat by radiation by which comparatively warm and moist air condenses on the cooler leaves and blades of grass. When the precipitation occurs below freezing point the result is hoar frost, which, because of its whiteness, gives the motorist ample warning of its presence. Most sinister is the dreaded "black ice", simply frozen water through which, because of its transparency, the dark road surface shows black. The Race Relations Board once received a complaint that the phrase was derogatory. Even though the description is scientifically inaccurate, it has a descriptive potency that justifies its use in traffic warnings and weather forecasts.

Despite all the variations of our weather and its attendant hazards, nature does achieve a remarkably efficient overall balance. During the day the sun pours warmth into our atmosphere, the amount being fairly stable and known as the "solar constant". At night, the earth usually returns heat into space — the earth's "radiation loss".

Short-term variations of income and loss of heat are considerable even in the comparatively small area of East Anglia. On an overcast night the heat sent back by the earth is intercepted and trapped by the clouds, but on a clear night the radiated heat is given a free passage and is almost completely lost into space — the most common cause of severe night frosts. The amount of radiation loss can be indicated by two thermometers, one sheltered and the other close to short grass and fully exposed to the sky. On a cloudy night with no radiation loss both thermometers will read approximately the same, but with a clear sky the grass thermometer registers temperatures several degrees below that of the sheltered instrument — sometimes 15 degrees F. or even more. Alert

Fine-weather cumulus like this seen at Foxhall, near Ipswich, on a pleasant summer's day does nothing to spoil the holidaymaker's enjoyment.

Fine-weather cumulus forming over Rushmere St Andrew. A few miles away at Felixstowe there are probably no clouds because there is less heating of the air over the sea.

gardeners will already be aware that a sharp ground frost can occur even while the sheltered air temperature remains above freezing point.

Loss of heat by radiation often begins during late afternoon even before the sun has set. From Autumn to Spring I have very frequently registered at Rushmere St Andrew a mid-afternoon air (or "screen") temperature of 40 degrees F. and over, while the grass thermometer has already dropped to well below freezing point. Although a fresh wind makes the weather seem colder than it really is, the most severe radiation frosts occur on calm nights, the lack of wind allowing the air to settle on the cold ground. The cold, heavier air then drains down into the lower ground, causing the frost hollows which are such a hazard to gardeners and allotment holders. Dry, sandy hollows are particularly vulnerable.

Despite all the extremes we experience in these heating and cooling processes — both globally and locally — nature manages to achieve a most remarkable balance-of-payments act. If nature's thermal income and expenditure account had been gradually going wrong one way or another by even so much as a fraction of a degree over the centuries we would by now have been either frozen or sizzled to death. As it is, there is no evidence of any defects in nature's thermal control.

The following figures show the mean annual temperatures for eight decades in Suffolk as registered in the Belstead/Copdock region, near Ipswich. The "mean" temperature is simply the average 24-hour maximum and minimum readings added together and divided by two. It gives no indication of the daily range of temperature but is the recognised method of assessing the average overall situation.

MEAN TEMPERATURES
Belstead/Copdock

	Degrees F.
1902–1911	49.1
1912–1921	49.1
1922–1931	49.1
1932–1941	49.7
1942–1951	50.0
1952–1961	49.5
1962–1971	48.8
1972–1981	49.2
80-year average	49.3

There was a tendency for slightly warmer weather between 1932 and 1961 but it does not appear to have been of a developing character. Eighty years is too short a period in which to search for any significant climatic changes, but scrutiny of much older records shows a similar pattern of minor variations with no evidence of any developing changes.

So far, we have looked at some of the basic elementary facts behind the behaviour of our weather. These are only broad generalisations, and despite some recent discoveries there are still large areas of meteorology which remain a mystery. Climate is the overall product of weather variations. Why do the two often appear to be at odds with each other? It is not the intention of this book to delve into the technicalities of a very complex subject but simply to relate wherever possible the weather of East Anglia to the broad background I have outlined.

In Kenneth Grahame's book *The Wind in the Willows*, when Mole and Rat were struggling through deep snow in search of Badger's home, Mole suddenly hit his shin painfully against a hard object. While he hopped around in pain, Rat solicitously inquired as to the cause, to which Mole replied "Never mind what done it, it hurts just the same, whatever done it". But when something happens to our weather it is interesting and sometimes useful to know "what done it". The chances are that it has all happened before, so we should not worry unduly about the possibility of a changing climate.

CHAPTER TWO

Weather Proverbs — True or False?

ONCE, when I was very young, I dreamt that I had fallen out of bed; when I woke, I found that I had. Some weather proverbs are like that; however fanciful they seem, they may be based on fact.

Sadly, however, there are very few reliable ones. Yet even those sayings with little forecasting value should not be decried, for they are a part of world-wide folklore, enriching our literature with expressions of mankind's eternal search for knowledge and guidance.

Many over-enthusiastic proverbs are overgrown with the deceptions of doggerel, compulsive rhyming and a confusion of contradictions. Irony plays a part, as in this Suffolk example of the ultimate in pessimism:

The west wind always brings wet weather;
The east wind wet and cold together;
The south wind surely brings us rain;
The north wind blows it back again.

According to that piece of rhyming nonsense, a dead calm would be Suffolk's only hope of justifying its place on the dry side of Britain. The BBC television programme *Weekend* promoted a contest for new East Anglian songs, a selection of entries later being published by Yoxford Publications in a booklet *New Songs of East Anglia* — including this chirpy little ditty by Henry Joseph Hinds, set to the tune of Bunessan (*Morning has Broken*):

Essex Weather Forecast

Morning has broken in Thorpe-le-Soken,
But there's a haze at Walton-on-Naze;
Snow is descending at Weeley and Tendring,
With frostbitten toes at Beaumont-cum-Moze.

Pressure is falling, the weather's appalling,
By about six you'll get it at Wix;
Drive very gently round Frating and Bentley,
The weather looks bleak till the end of the week.

Tomorrow morning, just about dawning
Clouds will be forming o'er Clacton-on-Sea;
Here's something funny — its suddenly sunny
Over Harwich and old Parkeston Quay.

Weather sayings of more serious intent should be treated with caution. Many arise from local conditions and are often used out of context. Mankind has always sought means of prophesying the weather (the word "forecast" was not used meteorologically until around the mid-nineteenth century) and weather prophets were active in the Middle and Far East some 4,000 years ago.

Many proverbs are based on superstition or a belief that some of the saints or religious festivals have an influence on the weather. Some are no more than wishful thinking. Their survival may be due to our selective memory of the occasions when the proverbs proved correct, conveniently forgetting the majority of errors. Dr Johnson observed that there is a tendency "to represent as perpetual what is only frequent, or as constant what is really casual".

Some weather lore contains scientific truths and, if used with a little knowledge of meteorology, has practical value. Any seaman or countryman who has the "feel" of the local weather can on occasion prove a match for the professional forecaster. The time allotted to the national forecasters on television and radio is far too short for local variations to be dealt with adequately.

The late Henry Blogg, heroic coxswain of the Cromer lifeboat, regularly checked his barometer before going to sea and he always listened to the official weather forecasts, to which he added his own pinch of salty wisdom. He talked of the water turning sheer (clear) as a sign of an impending onshore wind and he reckoned a "mackerel sky" to be a sign of wind.

There are many variations of "Mackerel sky, mackerel sky, never long wet and never long dry". A mackerel sky describes the wavy sheets of cirro-cumulus or alto-cumulus clouds, usually at a height of 15,000 feet or more, which have a broadly rippled appearance. These clouds do not belong exclusively to either a fine or a wet weather system but are frequently associated with weather fronts. The rain-bearing fronts are often separated by one or two days of dry weather, so the old saying is basically a good one, even though the timing may not always be reliable.

The element of superstition in some weather sayings is understandable. On the rare occasion of a total eclipse of the sun many years ago, my wife and I — far from East Anglia, holidaying in Devon — took a picnic lunch up to the highest point of Dartmoor to ensure a grandstand view. As the intervening moon took its first few bites from the sun we were more interested than impressed — and we knew to a second when finality would occur. But, as the grim darkening of total eclipse swept upland, accompanied by a chilly, whistling wind and the almost complete cessation of bird song, the security of our smug twentieth-century

A mackerel sky, alto-cumulus clouds, over Rushmere St Andrew. These clouds are often associated with weather fronts.

knowledge seemed to be spirited away, leaving us as vulnerable as any Stone Age people. Alone in the darkened silence of a bleak moor, despite our knowledge that light would soon return, we found ourselves sharing some primeval feeling with those early builders of the hut circles; creatures who had a fearful respect for the unknown, the elemental and astronomical events. Even the gradual return of full daylight had its eerie moments, and it was not until the sun was fully restored and we opened our luncheon basket to sip our wine at correct moor temperature that we felt the comforting return of normality.

Despite an age-old respect and worship of the sun (which, after all, is the prime generator of our weather), the sun itself plays a surprisingly minor role in weather lore; the moon and its phases attract more attention. Although the pull of the moon is strongly linked with the tides (a full moon coinciding with high tides and strong winds can have a disastrous surge effect on the sea), its influence on barometric pressure is insufficient to affect our weather.

An old Norfolk saying "Saturday's change and Sunday's full; never brought change and never wull" (also paraphrased in the Peterborough area) is obviously irrelevant because of its reliance on a specific day of the week. The late Walter Woodcock, Radio Orwell's much-respected gardening expert, was a firm believer in some forms of moon–weather relationships and he once told me that peas, beans and plants which produce fruit above the ground should always be sown when the moon is going to the full. "But," he added, "potatoes and root crops should always be sown when the moon is low and below the earth."

One strongly held belief is that a full moon causes frosts in Spring, Autumn and Winter. A clearly visible full moon is a fairly reliable frost warning, but the moon itself is not the cause of the frost. The real reason is that a clear night sky allows considerable loss of heat, often resulting in radiation frosts. If the sky is cloudy we probably escape a frost — and we see no moon. A crescent moon might pass unnoticed even in a clear sky but a full moon is strikingly evident — and gets blamed for the frost.

This moon–frost relationship is a good example of cause and effect in weather happenings being misinterpreted. It can be illustrated very simply:

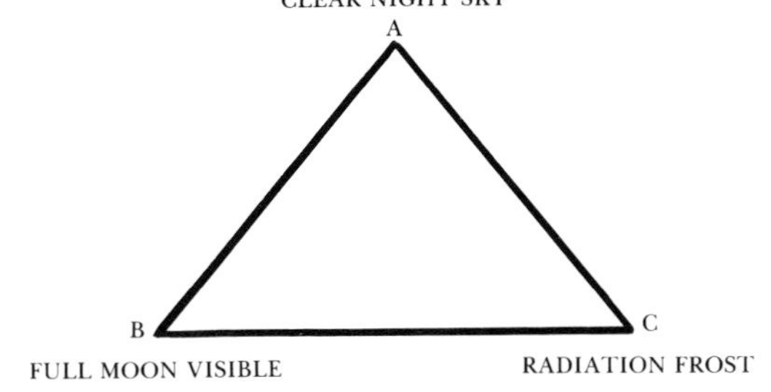

Neither B nor C affects the other; both are the result of A. Similar triangles of cause and effect frequently occur. In a blistering heatwave, a Lowestoft chemist might be busy treating incautious holidaymakers suffering from sunburn, while Waveney District Council is having trouble with melting tar on the roads. Melting tar near Beccles does not cause sunburn at Lowestoft, nor vice versa, but the connection is clear. A naive example, maybe, but there are many at present unknown "A" factors responsible for our weather and researchers would be foolish to ignore any correlation of events, however dissociated they may seem to be, without searching for the possibility of a common cause.

Early in the present century, meteorologists noticed an apparently irrational relationship between the level of Lake Victoria in Africa and rainfall at Kew Observatory. The mystery was solved to some extent by the discovery that both factors were closely linked with the 11.1-year cycle of the numbers of sunspots (the "A" factor). Like many weather patterns, the relationship lasted only a few years and has not, to my knowledge, recurred. Sunspots are enormous disturbances in the sun's atmosphere whose cycles of occurrence have long interested climatologists but I know of no lasting connection with our weather.

Proverbs based on the belief that a single day's weather can have an effect on the future are untrue. One of the most famous, based on superstition, is that a wet St Swithin's Day (15th July) foretells forty days and nights of rain. This is manifestly absurd and I can find no trace of forty consecutive days of rain having ever occurred in East Anglia at any time of year. Away from some of the mountainous regions, a forty-day spell of continuous wet weather would be a most unusual happening anywhere in the British Isles. In contrast, I would think that there are few if any places in East Anglia which have not at some time experienced at least one spell of forty consecutive dry days. In 1972 at Rushmere St Andrew I registered a forty-day drought from 19th September to 28th

October. The only grain of reason in the St Swithin's legend is that our weather does develop patterns and there is evidence that mid-July is a likely time for a change of mood.

Another well-known saying associated with a religious feast day is that of 2nd February, Candlemas Day. "If Candlemas Day be fair and bright, Winter will have another flight" has many variations, all with the same meaning. Radio Orwell and Saxon Radio provide daily traffic reports from the Suffolk Police HQ at Martlesham; Mrs Jean Denny, of Stowmarket, told me she was once tempted to ring up Radio Orwell in dismay when, on the morning of Candlemas Day, 1979, she heard the duty officer at Police HQ happily announce that "It's a lovely sunny day out here". That was just after a very wintry January. Then had followed a brief spell of milder weather — including that fair and bright 2nd February — and within two weeks East Anglia was almost buried by some of the worst blizzards and snowdrifts in living memory. But that was exceptional.

As for compulsive rhyming, the most popular example is that of the oak and the ash. Ash, splash, oak and soak rhyme most temptingly, but the rhyming medium so often distorts the message that we get complete contradictions in many parts of the British Isles. One saying, originating in the Peterborough area, is:

If the ash before the oak,
Then there'll be a regular soak;
But if the oak before the ash,
Then there'll only be a splash.

This is contradicted by a Shropshire saying:

When the ash is out before the oak,
Then we may expect a choke;
When the oak before the ash,
Then we may expect a splash.

"Choke" means drought, and elsewhere in England this saying is repeated in even more aggressive rhyme:

The ash before the oak,
Choke, choke, choke.
The oak before the ash,
Splash, splash, splash.

In the doggerel bedlam of oaks, soaks, chokes, ashes and splashes I do not believe that the behaviour of trees has anything to do with the weather to come. It seems more likely that the leafing is affected by previous weather; it has been said that the oak comes into leaf before the ash if the subsoil is in a moist state.

Some rhymes such as "Rain before seven, leave off by eleven" contain an element of truth in a rather sneaky manner. Because we associate weather proverbs with shepherds, sailors and people who get up early, we generally assume the proverb to mean seven in the morning; it could be seven at night — and therein lies the catch and the element of truth. In East Anglia rain does not usually last much longer than four or five hours, so it would be equally fair to say "Rain before eight, leave off by twelve" and so on. But seven and eleven are the only hours which rhyme, so — presto — we have a rhyming prophecy on our hands which does no more than describe a fairly common occurrence.

Among the lesser-known sayings is:

When the wind's in the west
The weather's at its best.

That has some truth so far as East Anglia is concerned, for westerly winds, often accompanying rain-bearing Atlantic depressions, usually shed a good deal of their rain in the Welsh mountains and have often dried out by the time they reach East Anglia. More generally, however, the westerlies bring unsettled conditions with no reliable indications as to the weather to come.

"When the wind is in the east, 'tis neither good for man nor beast" is often true, particularly in East Anglia, which in Winter catches the first blast of icy easterlies from the Continent and sometimes from as far away as Siberia. In the Summer, hot dry easterlies increase the fire risk in the countryside. East winds do not usually bring rain, but when they do "When the rain is from the east, four-and-twenty hours at least" is often true, again particularly in East Anglia and the southern half of the country. The cause is usually a depression moving along the English Channel, a situation which gives easterlies and often continuous rain; but

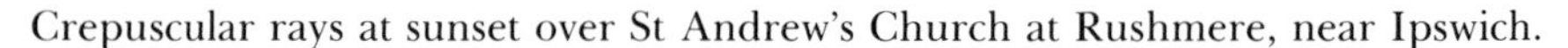

Crepuscular rays at sunset over St Andrew's Church at Rushmere, near Ipswich.

an old East Anglian saying "Rain in the east, three days at least" is, I think, an exaggeration.

Sunrise and sunset figure largely in our weather sayings, the most popular of all, with many variations, being:

Red in the morning, shepherd's warning;
Red at night, shepherd's delight.

This saying is also attributed to sailors, travellers in Scotland, pilgrims in Italy and hosts of believers in Germany. Henry Blogg's version was:

Evening grey and morning red
Makes the fisherman shake his head.

Evening red and morning grey
Is the sure sign of a very fine day.

I have little faith in the sayings concerning sunrise and sunset colourings, for the colours depend on a complication of factors, including the various wavelengths of the colours, the splitting of the spectrum by dust or droplets of moisture, the positioning of the clouds and so on. Red skies are often associated with the clouds of frontal systems and investigations have suggested that a red sunrise precedes rain within twenty-four hours seven times out of ten and that a red sunset is, seven times out of ten, followed by twenty-four hours of dry weather. Such tests need neither instruments nor scientific knowledge; simply jot down in a notebook the occurrence of each red sunrise and sunset and then make a note of what happens. Your own observations will reveal the truth or otherwise of the sayings.

What I have noticed — and I know of no scientific explanation — is that a green sky at sunset (a very rare event) is almost invariably followed by rain.

The sun's rising and setting often provide spectacular effects. There are the quite frequent "crepuscular rays", shafts of light broadening upwards through breaks in the clouds or gaps in a mountain range. Despite their name they are not exclusive to sunrise and sunset, occurring less frequently in full daylight when the downward rays piercing the clouds are referred to as the sun "drawing water" — which is incorrect. Far less frequent is a "sun pillar", a beam of light usually but not always of uniform width, above the sun, caused by the reflection of the sun (or moon) on ice particles — just as the sun or moon reflects a pillar of light on an almost calm sea. Sun pillars are usually visible over a wide area; an exceptionally wide sighting occurred on 13th March, 1924, when a sunset pillar was seen all over the southern part of England from Cornwall to Norfolk. A sun pillar has no significant forecasting value.

One of the most spectacular sunsets ever seen in East Anglia occurred on 27th November, 1979, when after a dull and gloomy day, with thick mist and fog, the whole sky at sunset became alight with a fiery pinkish-purple — an effect made more bizarre by the brightest light coming from the east, which, being the wrong direction for sunset, caused an eerie feeling of disorientation. Within minutes the telephone switchboards at local newspaper offices and the local radio and meteorological stations were jammed by calls from curious and anxious inquirers. I made a quick appraisal (which later proved to be a fair diagnosis) and immediately went on the air on Radio Orwell to assure listeners that the end of the world was not nigh, nor was there anything to worry about.

The explanation was, in part, simple. A very large area of low pressure covered almost the entire Atlantic, and just before the sunset spectacular a warm front had crossed the East Anglian coast on its way over the North Sea. Associated with it was a cover of alto-cumulus clouds (the "mackerel sky") at a fairly normal height of about 10,000 feet. The sunset coloration of the clouds themselves would not have attracted more attention than usual, but on this occasion a thin layer of misty stratus cloud, only about 500 feet up, lay across East Anglia, and it was this thin misty film which, obscuring the higher clouds, diffused and distorted the sunset colourings.

That was not all. It was later reported that, between 28th and 30th November, red dust and coloured rain had fallen in parts of northern England, Scotland and Eire — and on the 29th red dust fell over many parts of Europe, Berlin reporting that shortly before sunset there was a brief but impressive change of colour as the sky turned dark blue and then lilac. All this was apparently due to the huge Atlantic low pressure area drawing in air from so far south as to contain particles of red Sahara dust in the upper layers. So although the sunset of November was made bizarre in East Anglia with "back to front" lighting effects, it was apparently dust from the Sahara which added the Arabian Nights touch of magical effect.

The arrival in this country of desert dust is not uncommon; in November, 1984, the upper layers of a deep southerly airflow brought dust from Sahara sandstorms, falling in reddish rain over East Anglia and parts of southern England during the night of the 9th–10th. Another spectacular "invasion" occurred in August, 1987.

Dust in the upper atmosphere can have odd effects. About midday on 29th September, 1950, a "blue" sun was visible through a thin layer of cloud over the whole of East Anglia and many other places. The blue coloration was due to great quantities of ash blowing in at a height of about 40,000 feet from vast forest fires which had devastated parts of Canada a little while before.

Of all the signs in the sky, a halo round the sun or moon is by far the most reliable, but only if one keeps an eye on the barometer. A halo is rarely formed other than in the ice-crystals of cirro-stratus clouds at a height of about 20,000 to 40,000 feet in advance of a warm front, usually associated with the fair weather area in front of a depression and well in advance of the rain. It is supposed to be a sure sign of rain within twelve to twenty-four hours and is, in fact, correct about seven times out of ten.

But how are we to distinguish the seven times right from the three times wrong? The answer is fairly simple. If the depression is advancing towards us the barometer will fall, the wind freshen and the clouds thicken — and rain will usually follow. That happens about seven times out of ten. But if the depression is stationary — indicated by a steady barometer — we will remain in the fair weather area. That explains the three times out of ten when rain does not follow.

My interpretation of a halo is: if accompanied by a falling barometer, expect rain; if the barometer is steady or rising, expect the fair weather to continue. In the latter case, it is as well to remember that the absence of thickening cloud means that a "fair weather" halo will persist longer than a "wet weather" one. The sooner a halo disappears the more the likelihood of rain. It very often happens that a stationary depression on the Atlantic is giving wet weather in the west while East Anglia is enjoying a spell of fine weather — with a halo visible every day! A halo at Clacton-on-Sea may well mean that it is raining in Clovelly.

Because of the weakness of moonlight, lunar haloes are far less frequent than those around the sun. Solar haloes are visible far more often than is generally supposed and I think that hardly a week goes by without at least part of one being visible somewhere in East Anglia. Complete haloes are rather rare; small portions are quite frequent — the secret is to know where to look. Haloes almost always occur on a 22-degree radius round the sun (or moon). Having established the presence of high filmy cloud, extend your hand at arm's length; place your thumb over the sun and with fingers outspread your little finger should be just about on the 22-degree radius. Look carefully all around the radius and, even if there is not a complete halo, you will probably find a small section of one.

I have often been asked whether, as a wet weather indicator, a complete or unusually bright halo means worse weather than an incomplete or faint one. The answer is no. If you have foolishly parked your car on a double yellow line and return to find a traffic warden standing beside it, that is a fairly sure sign of trouble to come; whether you can see all or only part of the warden, clearly or indistinctly, is of no consequence.

Considering our inheritance of a wealth of old weather sayings, it seems a pity that we do not create a few modern ones. As a start I suggest:

When vapour trails adorn the sky,
A falling glass means rain is nigh;
But steady glass and trails that stay
Mean another pleasant day.

When the upper air is dry enough, vapour trails (the contrails left behind by high-flying aircraft) usually disappear quickly; sometimes they are not produced at all. But if the air is moist they can be very persistent, occasionally developing into recognisable cloud formations. The growth and persistence of vapour trails often occurs in or near the warm sector of a depression; thus, they have much in common with a halo. So if the frontal cirro-stratus clouds are too thick or too thin to produce a halo, watch out for a convenient vapour trail. If it persists or develops it may very well serve as a halo substitute — and, in conjunction with the barometer, the same rules apply.

The behaviour of wild life as a means of forecasting the weather has always been an obsessive and debatable subject. Some old sayings declare that when the scarlet pimpernel (the "poor man's weather glass") closes its petals it is a sure sign of rain. That is not true. The fact is that when the relative humidity of the air rises to about 80 per cent or more the scarlet pimpernel, disliking the dampness, puts up its shutters. So do many other plants and flowers, including the chickweed and daisy (I have noticed that cold and dull conditions can have a similar effect). But rising humidity is not in itself a certain sign of rain. Even in fine weather, humidity almost always rises towards evening; hence the nightly closing of many flowers. A daytime rise in humidity is often more likely to accompany rain than to precede it.

An amusingly irrelevant theory to emerge in the late nineteenth century was that the cricket's chirp varied according to the temperature of the air. Apparently, a cricket chirps seventy-two times a minute at a temperature of 60 degrees F. For every four extra chirps a minute one should add one degree. For every four chirps less, deduct one. I have never tested this method of taking a temperature; nor, I hope, will my doctor.

The fact that wild life responds to an immediate situation is obvious. A solitary blackbird, spilling his alarm notes along a hedgerow, can trigger off a whole chorus of anxiety from his startled companions. But he is only reacting to some immediate danger, and the resultant clamour is no indication whatsoever of trouble two or three days hence.

The arrival in this country of large numbers of northern birds is generally reckoned to be a sign of a severe Winter ahead. In November, 1974, an unusually large number of Little Auk visited the Yorkshire coast and parts of Norfolk and Suffolk; the bird had not been seen in Suffolk for many years. Redwings and fieldfares arrived earlier than usual that year and there was quite an invasion of waxwings. But after the arrival of all these "hard weather" birds, the 1974/75 Winter turned out to be a very mild one. Similarly, many "hard weather" birds were reported during the 1976/77 Winter, but it remained a mild one. Rather than indicating a hard Winter ahead for this country, it seems more likely that the birds are reacting to a current spell of cold weather farther north, which is no reason for assuming that the cold weather will necessarily spread south.

I do not think that rooks nesting high and moorhens low has been scientifically proved as an indication of a fine Summer to come (though both occurred before the historic drought of 1976); nor do I think that either bird is capable of knowing the weather expectations for weeks ahead. But, of course, it could be that they are reacting to some immediate "A" factor (p. 15) which, as yet unknown to the scientists, has some effect on our future weather. Even so, the prognostications seem unreliable.

I wish there were more exclusively East Anglian weather sayings, because there is a great sense of poetry in the idiom of rural East Anglia. I do not mean lilting rhythms such as the Welsh and the Irish, I am thinking of the brief, simple phrases which carry such a rich sense of evocation. The late Dick Bagnall-Oakley, an expert in local dialects, agreed with me on this (Dick was born in Norwich, grew up on the Broads and, during his long academic career, played hockey for Cambridge University and represented Norfolk in five different sports). He told me how, when talking to a Norfolk countryman late one October afternoon shortly after the clocks had been put back, his companion cocked an eye to the sky and said: "Ah, thass gittin' late early now." In that simple poetic phrase, one can almost feel the time ticking away.

Once I was enjoying a ploughman's lunch in a Suffolk pub. After a bright dawn start, by midday it was raining steadily. It was Monday and I said to the landlady: "Not a good day for the Monday washing?", to which she replied "Ah well, my daughter has had it all out and dried by now." "So early?" I inquired. "Of course," she replied, "we always get our washing out before the weather begins." And there's more than a grain of sense in that, considering the development of convectional clouds and the general stirring up of the atmosphere when the sun has got going. How often do we wake up to a bright, sunny morning, only to have to dodge showers later in the day?

The most cryptic remark I ever overheard about the weather was in an Ipswich restaurant. After weeks of hot, tiring Summer drought a violent early-morning thunderstorm left us with a pouring wet day. It was sheer delight to have to wear a raincoat and to smell the unaccustomed freshness of the air. As two men passed my table on their

"A Land of Win

THE strong Continental influence on our weather encourages both the cultivation of vineyards and lavender fields, about a third of the national vineyard acreage being in East Anglia. Basil Ambrose, owner of the Cavendish Manor Vineyards, says that the advantages of East Anglia are the low rainfall and predominantly alkaline soils (a vine will not grow on sour soil nor in poorly drained positions). Vines like hard Winters and warm Summers but a disadvantage is the tendency in Suffolk for late Spring frosts and the occasional very severe Winter. At the 500-year old Manor House at Cavendish harvest is in late October and the actual processing takes about six months.

way out one of them, glancing out of the window, said "Just look at that — still pouring down," to which his companion replied, seriously and with some tetchiness: "Yes — and a damn nuisance too. I was hoping to water the garden tonight."

nd Fragrant Airs..."

Of the famous 100-acre lavender fields at Heacham, Norfolk, Henry Head, managing director of Norfolk Lavender Ltd., says that the weather from the end of September to the end of May is not all that crucial, although lavender can be damaged by a very strong wind-frost, particularly during February and March if it is just beginning to "green up". Snow does no harm at all. From the end of May to the end of August hot sunny weather is needed to help the plants create the oil contained in a small sac at the base of each plant. Cold, wet weather during that period reduces the oil yield; showery weather (particularly if thundery) knocks the florets off the stem, leaving no flowers to harvest.

Opposite: Nestling in the Stour Valley, Cavendish presents a typical rural scene except that the fields in the background are not cornfields but vineyards.
Haverhill Echo

Right: Drawing off lavender oil in the distillery.
Norfolk Lavender Ltd

Cumulo-nimbus. *Keith Watson, L.R.P.S.*

CHAPTER THREE

East Anglian Weather

MUCH as I love East Anglia, I would not describe its climate as gentle. Yet it is by no means harsh. Although the northerly and easterly winds may sometimes blow most keenly, one of the virtues of East Anglian weather is its general freshness and the crisp, invigorating character of the air. White's *History of Suffolk*, 1844, says of the county that "the climate is unquestionably one of the driest in the kingdom; but the frosts are severe and the north-east winds, in Spring, are sharp and prevalent. It appears to be highly salubrious.

In contrast to the invigoration of its climate there is in East Anglia a relaxing feeling of tranquillity and space. Because of its generally low horizons there seems always to be a predominance of sky. Climb a thousand feet in Wales and Scotland and your view may be obscured by even higher mountains; in East Anglia a mere hundred feet or so in altitude can give a splendid view.

The preponderance of sky in East Anglia was well known to the late L. C. W. Bonacina, whom I had the privilege of knowing. Bonacina was not only one of this century's most respected scientists, with a great width and depth of wisdom and scientific knowledge; he was also a sensitive and humble lover of nature, his lovely style of prose bringing life and warmth to many an otherwise dry theory. In a contribution to the *Meteorological Magazine* he wrote:

> Once while on holiday in Norfolk I was told of a visitor to that county who, on asking a native countryman if he did not sometimes feel the urge to leave the plains and see the mountains, received the reply "No, sir, we have them in the sky!" And they certainly have, for in no part of England may the massive cumuliform clouds be observed to better advantage than in the wide open spaces of East Anglia.

An East Anglian proverb, attributed to the Peterborough region, says:

> When mountains and cliffs in the clouds appear,
> some sudden and violent showers are near.

That vividly describes those occasion when cumulo-nimbus clouds dramatically build up to the certainty of torrential showers in the near vicinity — and, very likely, thunderstorms.

One of East Anglia's most famous artists, John Constable, took an active interest in meteorology. His paintings portray with remarkable accuracy the various cloud forms, of which he made preliminary sketches and kept detailed technical notes including wind direction and other factors concerned with the formation and development of clouds. During the present century Edward Seago, too, proved himself a master in capturing the characteristics of the East Anglian sky.

East Anglia's peninsula-like bulge towards the Continent is a geographic feature which affects and complicates the East Anglian climate to a considerable degree and accentuates its island characteristics. The climate of an island anywhere in the world is modified by the surrounding sea, and the British Isles are no exception. The latitude of East Anglia is approximately 52 degrees North and one might reasonably expect that all other places on the same latitude and sharing the same distance between the cold North Pole and the hot Equator would experience similar temperatures. But that is not so. The climatic difference between a comparatively small island and a large continent is enormous, particularly as regards the range of temperature.

Cambridgeshire is one of the most inland parts of East Anglia (on a latitude of 52°12′N) but a comparison of its climate with that of Orenburg (Chklov) in Russia (51°45′N) demonstrates the enormous climatic difference between an island and a continental situation, even when the same latitude is shared.

At Cambridge, the average daily maximum screen temperature in January is 43 degrees F. At Orenburg it is 14 degrees F. The average January nightly minimum at Cambridge is 33 degrees F. At Orenburg it is 0 degrees F. falling to minus 2 degrees F. in February. The averages for Cambridge are for the period 1931–1960; for Orenburg, 1962–1969. The short period covered by the Orenburg figures and the differing dates do not invalidate the comparison. The lowest screen temperatures ever registered during these two periods were: Cambridge 1 degree F. (in February); Orenburg, 46 degrees F. below zero (in January). A longer period of readings at Orenburg would most likely have produced an even lower figure.

In Summer the differences are considerable, though less dramatic. Average daily maxima in July are: Cambridge 72 degrees F.; Orenburg 83 degrees F. The highest readings were: Cambridge 96 degrees F. (in August); Orenburg 103 degrees F. (in June).

Both Cambridge and Orenburg have this in common; January/February and July/August are usually their coldest and warmest months respectively. On account of its continental situation, Orenburg has a lower relative humidity and rainfall, and enjoys considerably more sunshine.

Tables giving detailed figures for Orenburg and Cambridge, as well as coastal holiday resorts in East Anglia, are to be found in the appendix. For reasons of comparison, tables are also included for Birmingham (in central England on approximately the same latitude as Cambridge); the holiday resort of Bournemouth; and — in complete coastal contrast to East Anglia — Ilfracombe.

Apart from Great Britain being an island, there is another significant climatic factor. We have never really had a climate all our own, for we are at the crossroads of four conflicting air masses, each of which can bring completely different types of weather which really belong to someone else. Westerly winds usually bring moist and temperate Atlantic weather; the northerlies can bring varying degrees of Arctic cold; southerlies often provide a touch of almost equatorial warmth, while the easterlies bring us air off the Continent — usually dry at all times but likely to be very cold in Winter and hot in Summer.

These conflicting winds can affect different parts of the British Isles in different ways. The characteristics of the westerlies are most pronounced (and often accentuated) on the west coast of Britain. Rain, snow and sleet is caused by rising air, usually due to the natural process of convection, the precipitation taking place because the air expands and cools as it rises. When already moist Atlantic westerlies are faced with the mountains of Wales and Scotland, they are forced to climb over the high ground (often at some speed and at a steep angle) and the same process of precipitation occurs — but due entirely to geographic features. This type of precipitation is called "orographic" and our western coasts get a good deal of it. But by the time the westerlies have reached East Anglia they have shed much of their moisture, the drying-out process being one of the reasons why East Anglia is so dry. Orographic rain occurs in East Anglia, but owing to the lack of any great heights its effect is comparatively slight.

The continental easterlies provide an entirely different situation, the pronounced bulge of East Anglia towards the Continent distinguishing its weather from that of the rest of the country. The easterlies are usually dry at all times but (as indicated by the Orenburg temperatures) can bring great heat in Summer and severe cold in Winter.

An additional factor, causing significant and sometimes complex variations in East Anglian weather, is the journey of the easterlies across the North Sea. Although the journey is far shorter than that which the Atlantic westerlies often travel, the brief contact with the sea can modify the air to a quite significant extent. Often, during a spell of hot easterly weather in the Summer, the air is cooled and picks up moisture from the sea, condensing into low cloud, fog or drizzle along the East Anglian coast, sometimes extending several miles inland. Quite a large part of East Anglia can be dull and cool while the rest of the country is sweltering in a heatwave. As the sheets of cloud, fog, mist or drizzle drift inland it is worth remembering that this is a mainly coastal condition. Holiday-makers unused to this unpleasant invasion from the North Sea might do well to telephone the Norwich Weather Centre (listed in the telephone directory) and ask the duty forecaster how far inland the dull weather extends. The duty weathermen are most helpful and a timely call could make the difference between a pleasant picnic in warm sunshine inland and a shiver by the sea.

In Winter the originally dry easterlies frequently pick up sufficient moisture from the North Sea to cause snow flurries along the East Anglian coast. When there is a good deal of north in the wind direction, the effect of the comparatively high ground of North Norfolk can also cause orographic precipitation, sometimes in the form of snow. With northerly winds, Norfolk is more vulnerable to heavy localised snowfalls than the rest of East Anglia. As the northerlies sweep southwards they tend to dry out but the process is often repeated on the north coast of Kent. In severe weather, some of the worst drifting of snow south-east of the Wash is often in Norfolk and Kent.

Brendan Behan once said "I wish I'd been born a mixed infant." There is much that is mixed in the climate of the British Isles — to which East Anglia adds its own local peculiarities, some of which I describe in the following pages.

Banks of snow line the road at Blyford as a result of the snow drifting
East Anglian Daily Times

Rainfall

Comparison of a contour map of the British Isles with a map of average annual rainfall immediately reveals a very closely related pattern, the high ground shown on the contour map being almost identical with the wetter areas on the rainfall map. The low-lying land of the eastern half of the country, from Essex in the south to Lincolnshire and parts of Yorkshire farther north, is matched by a corresponding area of low rainfall.

The fact that the eastern half of the country is the dry side is not surprising. A good deal of our rain — though by no means all — is brought in by depressions from the Atlantic. As they and their

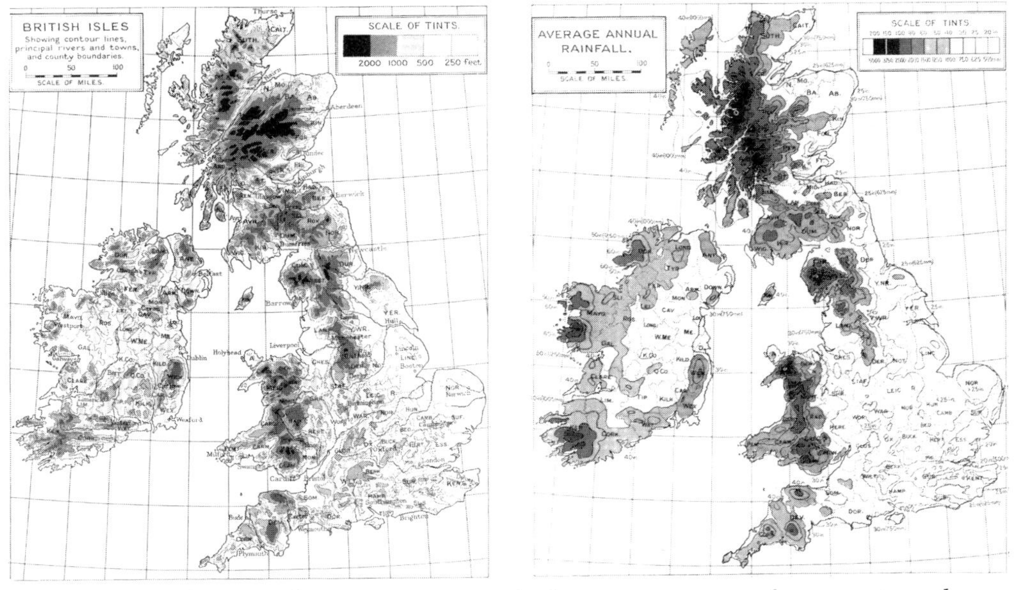

accompanying south-west to west winds sweep across the country, the rain has often dried out to a considerable degree by the time it reaches the East Coast.

Annual rainfall totals near the Fens and, notably, in the low estuary-land of south-east Essex are very small indeed. Essex has the distinction of containing the driest area in the whole of the British Isles. Before we examine East Anglian rainfall as a whole, this notably dry area of Essex deserves special mention.

Mr R. A. Robson, a professional meteorologist living in Wickham

Bishops, where he maintains his own weather station, is able to give both a professional and personal view of the climate of Essex. Mr Robson makes these comments:

> Essex is not exposed to any sea areas except to the east or south-east — and winds from this direction are usually dry, coming from Europe and unable to pick up much moisture from the short sea track over the North Sea. From Suffolk northwards, easterly winds have a much longer sea track after leaving the continent and are, therefore, sufficiently moist and often able to produce showers in Winter months. Only with north or north-east winds does the air contain sufficient moisture to sometimes produce showers over the county in Winter or Spring. Even then they occur only in cold air masses which really are unable to contain large quantities of moisture and do not contribute very greatly to the annual rainfall.
>
> Not only is Essex well sheltered from all the main rain-bearing winds from the south, through west to north-west, but nearly all of the county is low lying and what hills there are are too low to produce any significant orographic rainfall. In particular, Essex is relatively high in the west and, because it slopes steadily down to sea level, the east and south-east of the county tends to be drier than the west.
>
> The number of days when rain falls in Essex is not greatly below that in other parts of the country but the actual amount of rain produced is generally less. In general, the rainfall shows similar characteristics to much of the rest of lowland Britain, i.e., the late Summer and Autumn period is considerably wetter than the late Winter and Spring period.

In the context of the wetter Autumn period, Mr Robson points out a marked spell of much drier Octobers around the 1970s. This is a striking, if probably temporary, feature of the present British climate.

East Anglia as a whole has an annual rainfall ranging, according to location, from about 20 to 28 inches a year, with an overall average of something like 23 inches per annum.

As a guide, the following is a fair approximation of the general distribution of average annual rainfall throughout the British Isles:

APPROXIMATE AVERAGE ANNUAL RAINFALL

(inches)

British Isles	*England*	*Wales*	*Scotland*	*East Anglia*
42	33	52	52	23

The Meteorological Office's "Monthly and Average Rainfall Totals for 1970 for the UK" included averages for the 35-year period 1916–1950 which indicated that Wills Ayley Farm in the Blackwater catchment area of Essex had the lowest rainfall in the whole of the British Isles, with an annual average of only 19.80 inches. Bottisham Lock, near Cambridge, appeared to be the second driest spot in the country with an annual total of 20.16 inches. In the south-east corner of Essex, Maldon was another very dry spot with only 20.70 inches.

Of particular interest to holidaymakers, the same set of Met Office figures showed the following places as the driest coastal spots in East Anglia:

PLACES WITH LOWEST RAINFALL
East Anglian Coast

	Inches annually
Essex:	
Shoeburyness	20.28
Mersea Island	21.30
Walton-on-the-Naze and Clacton-on-Sea	21.50
Suffolk:	
Felixstowe (Landguard Point)	21.30
Hollesley	22.91
Lowestoft	23.62
Norfolk:	
Holme-next-the-Sea	22.17
Brancaster and Wells	23.46
Great Yarmouth and Bacton	24.02

(For comparison, the 1931–1960 Met Office averages show Bournemouth with 31.50 inches and Ilfracombe 40.25 inches).

The dry side of England, as seen by Reg Carter in one of his "Sorrows of Southwold" postcards. *Suffolk Record Office*

These very low East Anglian figures indicate the serious vulnerability of the East Anglian farmer in times of drought. A dry spell with rainfall over the whole country running at, say, 25 per cent of the average gives the East Anglian farmer a far smaller total than that of his Welsh counterpart. An additional factor — appreciably so in East Anglia — is the serious aggravation of any drought by the evaporation factor. During a conversation on the subject, someone once said to me "Ah, yes — but the Welsh farmer will lose more by evaporation because his land has that much more water to lose." That, however, is a fallacy. The amount of water available for evaporation has nothing to do with the case.

In general, humidities are usually lower in the eastern half of the country than in the western counties, with the result that evaporation in East Anglia is that much more rapid. A few light showers during a dry spell will, with a brisk drying wind, leave precious little water — if any — for the farms and gardens.

It is usual in Great Britain for rainfall to be well in excess of evaporation from about October to February, so we normally expect to start off the Spring with soil at "field capacity" — meaning any further rain would either have to run off the surface or find some underground outlet. Following what was in many areas the unprecedented drought of 1976, it was not until the very end of November that (despite a very wet Autumn) some parts of East Anglia could report "field capacity", whereas in most other parts of the country the land recovered by the end of September.

Although East Anglia is on the dry side of Britain it has, rather surprisingly, been the scene of some of the heaviest short-term falls of rain anywhere in the country.

To complete the comparison of the very low East Anglian rainfall with some other parts of the British Isles, the following figures (extracted from the Met Office averages 1916–1950) make interesting reading:

PLACES WITH AVERAGE HIGHEST RAINFALL

	Inches annually
East Anglia — Foulsham, Norfolk	28
Aylsham, Norfolk	27½
Melton Constable, Norfolk	27½
Swaffham (Mulsey), Norfolk	27½
Brandon, Suffolk	26¼
England — Derwent (Styhead Tarn)	173
Wales — Glaslyn (Crib Goch)	171½
Scotland — Garry (Ness) Coire Nan Gall	165

Nowhere in East Anglia does the average annual total exceed 30 inches.

Duration of rainfall

A friend of mine, Gilbert Whyatt of Ipswich, told me he once heard it said of the East Anglian climate that "it's not so much the number of fine days we get, it's the number of days when it looks like rain but doesn't." This probably refers as much as anything to those numerous occasions when the weather is in a "dry mood" (page 44), but certainly the duration of rainfall in East Anglia is very low compared with most of the rest of the country.

The following figures, reproduced by kind permission of the Meteorological Office from *British Rainfall 1951–60*, show the mean monthly and annual duration of rainfall (throughout the twenty-four hours) during the ten years 1951–1960. From the *British Rainfall* tables I have for purposes of comparison selected three East Anglian stations, with two coastal and one inland stations from other parts of the country:

MEAN MONTHLY AND ANNUAL HOURS OF RAINFALL
1951–1960

	Jan	Feb	Mar	Apr	May	Jun	Jul	Aug	Sep	Oct	Nov	Dec	Year
Ipswich	44	39	35	24	24	27	26	30	29	39	43	47	407
Peterborough	52	45	41	26	30	30	21	28	28	35	41	40	417
Marham, Norfolk	61	57	47	33	32	32	29	39	35	46	50	52	513
Folkestone	66	59	42	30	29	29	31	35	35	49	57	65	527
Elmdon, Birmingham	59	47	56	35	38	40	34	45	41	47	62	61	565
Plymouth	75	53	58	37	41	33	36	42	47	52	69	73	616

"Oh to be in England . . ." Motorists encounter unexpected problems on the Beccles–Norwich road as a result of heavy rain. *Eastern Daily Press*

In a leaflet prepared by the late Michael Hunt for the East Anglia Tourist Board, he discussed East Anglian weather particularly in relation to holidaymakers — and I am grateful for permission to quote the following:

> Rainfall which occurs at night is not very important to holidaymakers and the average TOTAL number of hours of wet weather which occur between breakfast and teatime for each month of the year is surprisingly small. The figures for one inland city and one coastal resort are reasonably representative of the area as a whole.

HOURS OF WET WEATHER BY DAY

	Jan	Feb	Mar	Apr	May	Jun	Jul	Aug	Sep	Oct	Nov	Dec
Great Yarmouth	17	15	9	9	12	12	15	15	13	18	14	21
Cambridge	13	12	7	6	10	10	15	13	11	14	11	18

> Thus it can be seen that, on average, there is less than a half hour of wet weather by day during all the Spring and Summer months . . .
>
> Monthly rainfall totals on the north coast of Spain are greater than those for all parts of East Anglia for most parts of the year. Summer rainfall over the mountain regions of Europe far exceeds that of East Anglia; for example at Lugano and Lucerne in Switzerland, monthly totals of 4 to 8 inches (100–200 mm.) are common.

Falls of 1 inch or more in 24 hours

An essential requirement of a well-run weather station is that regular daily observations should be made at precisely 0900 hrs GMT, the rainfall measured each day being the total for the preceding twenty-four hours. Even the most enthusiastic weather watcher cannot be expected to take additional readings on the stroke of midnight. So, as the period of time covered by the 0900 hrs reading belongs mostly to the previous day, the standard practice is to "throw back" the 0900 hrs reading to the day before.

This expedient works fairly well but it occasionally creates misleading discrepancies. If, for example, a fall of rain (or snow) occurred during the early hours of New Year's Day, it would be entered into the Old Year. Similarly, if we were just ending a completely rainless September (a most unusual but not unprecedented occurrence) and, say, an inch of rain fell in a thunderstorm in the early hours of 1st October, then September would not go down in the records as a rainless month.

Although similar if less dramatic irregularities frequently occur, the official procedure reflects in the long run a reasonably accurate picture — and it is from these basic twenty-four hour observations that we build up our statistical patterns of daily, monthly and annual totals.

In the wetter parts of the British Isles, particularly in mountainous districts, falls of an inch or more in twenty-four hours are quite a common occurrence. Probably one of the heaviest short-term falls ever to occur in the British Isles was 11 inches which fell in the space of fifteen hours at Martinsdown, Dorset, on 18th July, 1955. (That fifteen-hour fall produced more than half the average annual total of some of the drier parts of East Anglia.)

East Anglian twenty-four-hour "inchers" are not so common and are mostly due to two causes. The first, the less frequent of the two, is the result of a rain-bearing depression moving very slowly eastwards along the English Channel. This gives East Anglia an easterly wind during which — even if there is no great fall in the barometer (which often remains almost unchanged throughout) — rain can fall continuously for a whole day and night. But the most common cause of an East Anglian "incher" is a thunderstorm. So-called heat thunderstorms, due to excessive heating of the lower layers of air, occur most frequently inland.

The average monthly incidence of twenty-four-hour falls of an inch or more at Rushmere St Andrew, near Ipswich, is as follows. Rushmere St Andrew, being about ten miles from the sea, is reasonably representative of East Anglia as a whole.

Number of falls of 1 inch or more in 24 hours duirng the 50 years 1930 to 1979
Rushmere St Andrew, near Ipswich, Suffolk

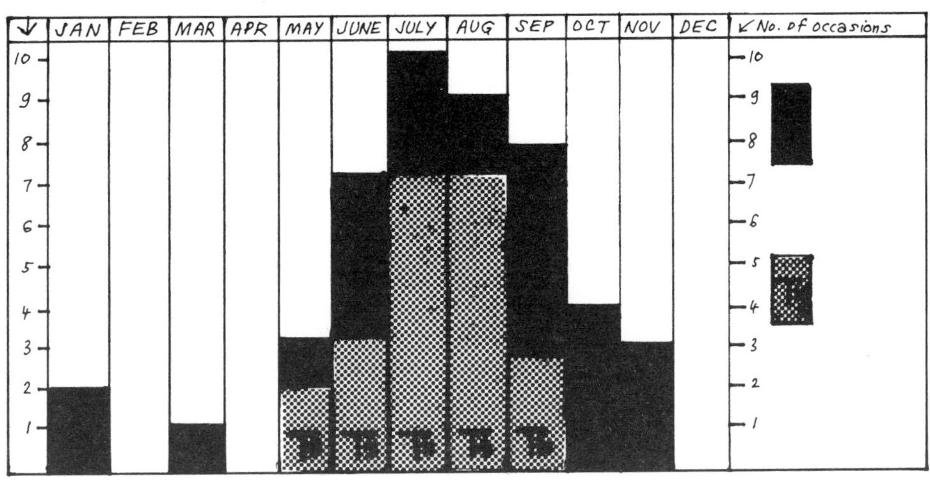

Although the above table shows that, in fifty years, falls of an inch or more occurred forty-seven times we should not assume that such falls can be expected every year. During the fifty years reviewed, fifteen years were entirely without falls of an inch or more, and twelve years each produced two falls of an inch — and in 1958 and 1969 there were three such falls. The heaviest twenty-four-hour rainfall recorded at Rushmere St Andrew was 2.35 inches in a thunderstorm during the early hours of 24th June, 1960. An analysis of the five years immediately following the above table shows a continuation of the curious absence of any "inchers" in February and December.

The table, by shading and use of the symbol ⚡ (the international meteorological symbol for a thunderstorm), shows the number of occasions on which the rainfall was due to a thunderstorm. It clearly shows the high occurrence of heavy thundery rains in the two hottest months of the year, July and August. The effect of this is shown in the fact that at Rushmere St Andrew (in common with many parts of East Anglia) July is second only to November as the wettest month of the year (in parts of East Anglia it is actually the wettest month). But that does not necessarily represent the character of the month. In any otherwise hot and dry month, a couple of torrential downpours — each of only a few hours' duration — could easily produce an above-average figure and that often happens in July.

The effect of the heavy rainfalls of thundery Summer showers, as distinct from Winter weather which includes many damp, drizzly days with comparatively low rainfall, was a point made by Mr G. W. Rolfe in *The Journal of Meteorology*, January 1979, Vol IV, No 34; pp 6–7 and can be clearly seen in the following figures resulting from an analysis by him of 1,000 rain days at Ely from 23rd March, 1971, to 7th April, 1977:

YIELDS OF RAIN DAYS BY MONTH
Ely, Cambs.

	Average fall (inches)
January	0.09
February	0.09
March	0.09
April	0.09
May	0.12
June	0.18
July	0.15
August	0.16
September	0.15
October	0.13
November	0.14
December	0.09

The bridge over the River Deben at Wickham Market collapsed in 1912 while being repaired following the August floods. *Suffolk Record Office*

In the famous 'Norfolk Rainstorm' of 25–26th August, 1912 (caused by a small depression off Cromer), over 8 inches of rain fell in parts of Norfolk, and Norwich became 'a miniature Venice'. All of East Anglia suffered, to a lesser degree, and the bridge at Wickham Market (Suffolk) was damaged by flood. During later repairs the bridge collapsed.

Heavy rain in the interior of Norfolk on 25th–26th August, 1912, caused severe flooding in Norwich, where some people had to be rescued by boat from their waterlogged homes. *Robert Malster*

Exceptional rainfalls over short periods

At most weather stations the rainfall is measured only once every twenty-four hours, thus giving no indication of the timing and intensity of short-period deluges during that period. Fortunately, many stations have an observer in constant attendance — and, better still, several have self-recording rain gauges which provide a continuous record of the rate of fall similar to the ink-line which shows changes in barometric pressure on the drum of the more familiar barograph.

From these better-equipped stations we can diagnose the vulnerability of East Anglia to short-term downpours. But we must remember that information is limited to those places where a suitable rain gauge is properly sited. Many falls of severe, and very local, intensity have escaped the network of observation — they are "the ones which got away". This underlines the value of amateurs who maintain reliable weather stations, augmenting the records of professional observers. The more information the amateurs provide, the more data is made available for research.

Although East Anglia includes the driest spots in the entire country, it is by no mean immune from extraordinary downpours. In an article in *Weather*, February 1974, Vol. XXIX, No 2, M. C. Jackson of the Meteorological Office, Bracknell, dealing with abnormally heavy falls of rain in the British Isles, produced a table showing the fifty heaviest falls in a period of two hours ever recorded during the present century. Considering that this survey included the mountainous regions it is surprising to find that one-tenth of those exceptional falls occurred in or on the threshold of dry East Anglia. They were as follows:

HEAVY RAINFALLS IN A PERIOD OF TWO HOURS

	Inches	Date
Cranwell, Lincs.	4.96	11th July, 1932
Horncastle, Lincs.	(4.60)	7th Oct, 1960
Costessey, Norfolk	(4.50)	1st Aug, 1972
Louth, Lincs.	4.10	29th May, 1920
March, Cambs	4.05	15th July, 1949
Boston, Lincs.	(4.00)	8th Aug, 1931
Writtle, Essex	3.90	26th July, 1941
Wisbech, Cambs.	3.60	28th Jun, 1970
Fingringhoe, Essex	3.41	11th Sep, 1901
Ipswich, Suffolk	3.36	1st July, 1902

The figures in brackets indicate that in a fall of more than two hours, the two-hour value has been estimated. Because of the scientific care taken in compiling figures of this nature, I think we may take the estimated figures as reasonably accurate.

As an addendum to the above heavy downpours, there were some astonishingly heavy falls during June, 1982, one of the most thundery months of the century. On the 5th, 4.51 inches fell at West Bradenham, Norfolk, in about 100 minutes, contributing to a June total of 9.01 inches and making it, as far as I can ascertain, by far the wettest month ever recorded anywhere in East Anglia, Summer or Winter.

Sometimes during a severe storm a sudden intensification will produce a few minutes of rain of extreme ferocity, often referred to as a "cloudburst" — an inaccurate phrase frowned upon by meteorologists. Such localised downpours are often due to the sudden collapse of a vigorous up-current of air within the storm, allowing a deluge to fall abruptly on the unfortunates below, rather like the bottom having fallen out of a shopping bag — and to describe the bag as having burst would not be all that amiss. At any rate, "cloudburst" is a fine evocative word — and anyone unlucky enough to be caught in one is usually more concerned with his or her discomfort than any scientific reasons for the drenching. To quote Mole again: "It don't matter what done it . . . !"

In one of his interesting leaflets Michael Hunt quoted three Norfolk examples of heavy rainfall in much shorter periods, which many would call cloudbursts:

HEAVY RAINFALLS WITHIN FIVE MINUTES

	Inches	Time (minutes)	Rate of fall per hour (inches)
July, 1917 — Norwich	0.47	2½	11.28
June, 1924 — Eaton (Norwich)	0.52	5	6.24
July, 1946 — Marlingford	0.64	5	7.68

East Anglian falls such as these usually occur only in the very disturbed conditions of a severe thunderstorm in which the violent uprushes (and occasional collapse) of columns of air result in headlines referring to "freak storm". Severe, yes; but nothing freakish. The cause is natural and well understood. Often, too, a "freak" storm is not all that intense — simply slow moving. A commonplace thunderstorm travelling at a fairly normal speed might well produce, say, half an inch of rain at all places in its track. If it is drifting along at only a quarter its normal speed, then places in its track will receive four times the usual amount.

A typical example of a very slow-moving storm occurred at Ipswich on 8th August, 1977, and had in effect an interesting similarity to the fall at Ipswich on 1st July, 1902, cited in the foregoing table of ten heavy East Anglian falls. In the 1977 storm the barometric gradient over the whole country was slack, with very few isobars on the weather maps. Consequently, winds were light and the clouds slow-moving. There was a high-pressure system over Scandinavia; some rather lazy low-pressure systems lay to the north-east of Iceland and over the North Atlantic; and, in between the Azores and Scandinavian anti-cyclones, there were shallow low-pressure areas over the Low Countries, the Bay of Biscay and Spain. The entire weather picture was one of indolent inactivity with no appreciable conflict between the opposing weather systems and very little wind.

At my routine 0900 hrs GMT observations at Rushmere St Andrew on 8th August I registered an unremarkable air temperature of 64 degrees F., a steady barometer and a light Force 1 west-north-west wind, with 7/8ths cloud cover of strato-cumulus and a slight surface mist, and not the slightest hint of impending drama in nearby Ipswich. Towards midday, stormclouds had gathered to the north of Ipswich and my personal assessment was that places in the track of the storm would probably get something like half an inch of rain.

I was wrong; although the storm might be loosely described as a "half-incher" it drifted so slowly across Ipswich that it produced one of the heaviest rainfalls of the century. It was quite a small storm and its track was narrow. Arriving at Ipswich from the north, it passed over the centre of the town and, making its exit towards nearby Woolverstone, finally crossed the coast somewhere near Clacton.

Despite some spectacular flashes of lightning and cracks of thunder there was nothing particularly violent — it was simply a very slow-moving storm which was taking its time to discharge water. So narrow was the track of the storm that at my weather station at Rushmere St Andrew, only two miles north-east of Ipswich, I registered a mere 0.02 inch. A mile away only 0.16 inch was recorded, and most places on the town outskirts measured less than a quarter of an inch. But in central Ipswich falls of nearly one and a half inches were recorded.

The next day the local press reported that branches of trees were found in Lower Brook Street, having apparently been washed down from Christchurch Park, half a mile away. It is this which provided the historical link with the previous severe rainfall in Ipswich on 1st July, 1902 (when 2.89 inches were reported to have fallen in forty minutes in what was described as the heaviest fall ever known in Ipswich). Shortly after I had been talking on Radio Orwell about the 1977 storm, an elderly listener telephoned to tell me that he clearly remembered the 1902 storm, the results of which he described as almost identical. He said it occurred between 1 p.m. and 2 p.m.; Ipswich was severely flooded; a newsagent's shop, standing where Bethesda Chapel was later built, was washed away; branches of trees from Christchurch Park were found in Lower Brook Street — and he recalled that, with other small boys (he was twelve) he rushed into Hewitt's grocery shop in Upper Brook Street begging for empty jam jars for the collection of goldfish which had been washed down from the Wilderness Pond in Christchurch Park.

More than 1½ inches of rain fell at Copdock on 27th August, 1919, and on the 30th this traffic rescue operation had to be carried out at Nayland. *Suffolk Record Office*

Droughts and spells of rainy weather

Much as we may grumble about our climate, long spells of dry weather are more frequent in East Anglia than wet ones. We call a long spell of dry weather a drought — and its often serious effects on farming, vegetation and water supplies are very apparent, so it is important that reliable and comprehensive records should be kept of the occurrence of droughts. Yet, frustratingly, an "official" definition of a drought has never been satisfactorily achieved and the arbitrary methods which have to be used have serious flaws.

Over the years, three separate and generally accepted designations of varying degrees of drought have been used, an absolute drought being defined as a period of at least fifteen days without any measurable rain, (0.01 inch is the criterion of measurable rain and a fall of 0.01 inch or more in the twenty-four hours ended 0900 hrs GMT constitutes an "official" rain-day). A partial drought is defined as a period of at least twenty-nine consecutive days, the mean daily rainfall of which does not exceed 0.01 inch, and a dry spell as a period of at least fifteen consecutive days on none of which 0.04 inch or more fell.

From this rather complicated combination of designations, the absolute drought of fifteen or more consecutive rainless days is the one in popular current use. The finer definitions tend to confuse. Indeed, even the apparently simple definition of an absolute drought is not entirely satisfactory. A more practical definition would need to be qualitative rather than quantitative. The longest drought ever recorded officially in Great Britain was in 1893 when, in the London area, there were seventy-three consecutive rainless days from 4th March to 15th May — and there was no ambiguity about that.

If, for example, we have fifteen consecutive rainless days sandwiched between two prolonged wet spells the records would show an "absolute drought" even though, because of its context, it would hardly be likely to cause any serious problems. On the other hand, we could easily have three distinct spells each of fourteen rainless days each separated from another by one single day on which only 0.01 inch of rain fell. Yet this protracted six-week spell of dry weather would not reach the record books as an "absolute drought", though its effects might be severe.

A so-called "rain-day" of 0.01 inch sometimes results from nothing more than a wet fog or heavy dew. An example of this was reported from Costessey, near Norwich, during a most unusual sequence of weather in 1865.

A notable incident occurred at Rushmere St Andrew and other places in 1959. Not a drop of rain had fallen during the thirty-eight consecutive days from 14th August to 20th September inclusive, then on 21st September a few drops of rain fell at Rushmere St Andrew, all within a half-hour and amounting to a mere 0.01 inch; there followed eighteen consecutive dry days from 22nd September to 9th October inclusive. Had it not been for those few quite inconsequential drops of rain on 21st September, which almost certainly evaporated immediately off the dry soil, we would have had an unbroken sequence of fifty-seven rainless days, making it one of the longest spells of dry weather ever recorded in East Anglia. One small swallow does not quench a thirst!

An extensive survey published in 1953 by the Ministry of Agriculture and Fisheries National Agricultural Advisory Service of dry spells in Eastern England during the twenty-five years 1921–1946 provided some comprehensive and very detailed information on the incidence of dry weather in East Anglia. The fact that the data refer to conditions fifty years or so ago by no means invalidates the usefulness of the statistics, as there is no reason to suppose that the climate has altered significantly.

The survey was intended primarily to attempt a numerical estimation of the relative suitability for haymaking of different months in different places, but the fact that the period also included the whole of the holiday season makes the figures of interest to holidaymakers seeking dry weather. The following is an abbreviated summary of the East Anglian situation:

SPELLS OF 15 OR MORE CONSECUTIVE RAINLESS DAYS
1921-1946

	April	May	June	July	August	September	Total Apr–Sept
Boston, Lincs.	3	3	4	5	3	1	19
St Ives, Hunts.	2	2	4	2	3	4	17
Peterborough, Northants.	2	3	6	2	1	2	16
Cambridge	3	2	6	3	4	4	22
Wisbech, Cambs.	2	1	8	3	3	2	19
Thetford, Norfolk	1	2	4	2	2	1	12
Hunstanton, Norfolk	1	1	3	4	1	2	12
Cromer, Norfolk	1	2	—	3	2	1	9
Norwich (Sprowston), Norfolk	1	2	3	2	2	2	12
Lowestoft, Suffolk	1	4	1	2	2	2	12
Bury St Edmunds, Suffolk	1	3	4	4	5	1	18
Campsea Ashe, Suffolk	1	4	9	4	2	2	22
Hadleigh, Suffolk	1	5	7	4	3	2	22
Bedford	3	2	8	1	3	3	20
Bradwell Bay, Essex	6	5	10	4	5	3	33
Ingatestone, Essex	2	3	7	3	2	1	18
Halstead, Essex	2	1	9	4	3	2	21
Average total of monthly occasions in 25 years	2	2½	5½	3	2¾	2	17¾

With a few exceptions (notably Cromer, which has one of the highest average annual rainfall totals on the East Anglian coast), the above survey clearly indicates, in spite of some recent wet examples, June is the month most likely to provide an absolute drought, the chances of a fifteen-day dry spell in June being more than double that of most other months. The higher frequency of drought at Bradwell Bay confirms the existence of an exceptionally dry area near the Essex coastline.

Absolute droughts do, of course, occur at other times of the year. In September, 1972, after about half an inch of rain had fallen during the first fortnight, there was a thunderstorm on the 18th and I registered just over 1.25 inches of rain — well over half the September average (and a bonus to gardeners in view of the drought to follow). Then followed one of those lovely golden Autumns; days for late picnics, lazing and picking apples in the orchard, with forty consecutive completely rainless days — the longest drought in the Rushmere St Andrew records. The drought ended at last with some light rain on 29th October — the day following the ending of British Summer Time. The planners could not have arranged it better, the 1.25 inches of rain immediately preceding the drought being particularly timely.

To augment the East Anglian table of droughts and for the interest of those seeking signs of any apparent changes in climate, a table in the Appendix shows the monthly occurrence of absolute drought in each decade from 1902 to 1979 at Belstead and Copdock. The high incidence of drought in the 1970s is an interesting feature, though probably of little significance in terms of climatic change.

How often in East Anglia has an entire calendar month been completely rainless? Droughts of more than about thirty days are so rare that the precise coincidence of such a drought with the beginning and end of a calendar month would be an accidental curiosity rather than an event of any meteorological significance. The question is worth asking, but with so many hundreds of rain gauges over hundreds of years (and, alas, so many of the very early records have not been preserved) it is quite impossible to make anything like a comprehensive reply. Judging by the various records I have inspected, I would like to think that — however rare the event — almost everywhere in East Anglia has at some time or another experienced at least one completely rainless calendar month.

Mr Richard Wilson's Belstead/Copdock records from 1902 to 1981 show no such occurrence. Orlando Whistlecraft's records at Thwaite show that from 1840 to 1882 the onlv completely dry calendar month was September, 1865, while the recoras of Francis Dix in South Norfolk (nearly thirty-six years at Dickleburgh and fourteen years at Norwich) show three completely rainless months — April, 1855 (Thwaite had 0.38 inch that month); February, 1857 (Thwaite had 0.14 inch) and September, 1865 (also experienced at Thwaite).

In fact, because of the rainy context in which it occurred that rainless September of 1865 was surely the most bizarre drought ever recorded. July and August had both been exceptionally wet, and torrential rains in October made it one of the wettest Octobers ever known. The following records of two East Anglian stations tell their own story of this quite fantastic meteorological contrast:

MONTHLY RAINFALL TOTALS, 1865

	July	August	September	October
			Inches	
Dickleburgh, Norfolk	3.55	4.23	nil	6.67
Thwaite, Suffolk	5.40	5.67	nil	8.20

This remarkable episode of topsy-turvy rainfall was not confined to East Anglia. With the exception of parts of Scotland, the whole of the British Isles experienced an abnormally dry September (not entirely rainless everywhere) sandwiched into an abnormally wet pattern of weather. The whole affair was so unusual that I think it worth while having a close look at the East Anglian scene.

During the preceding and succeeding wet months, there were some particularly heavy twenty-four-hour falls, including the following:

HEAVY TWENTY-FOUR-HOUR RAINFALLS, 1865

			Inches
JULY	7th	Wisbech, Cambs.	1.65
	17th	Bury St Edmunds	2.46
	22nd	Acle, Norfolk	1.42
	,,	Diss, Norfolk	1.62
AUGUST	23rd	Fulbourn, Cambs.	1.03
	,,	Gisleham, Suffolk	3.29
	,,	Colchester	2.90
	24th	Billericay, Essex	1.36
	,,	Aldham, Suffolk	2.32
OCTOBER	9th	Grundisburgh, Suffolk	1.70
	,,	Thurston, Suffolk	2.13
	,,	Hunstanton, Norfolk	1.03
	24th	Dunmow, Essex	1.83

Observers' reports in G. J. Symonds' *British Rainfall, 1865* speak of violent thunderstorms and heavy rain at Swaffham on 7th July and 25th

A relic of the university town's early water supply system, the fountain at Trinity College was still operating in 1865 when Cambridge had its wettest October since 1843.

August. The observer at Grundisburgh reported that the whole of that year had an extraordinary character:

> It has been a remarkable year of extremes; a wet cold month of March, dry and warm April; May more of an average; June more rain than usual (2.05) but all fell on the 1st and 2nd and 29th and 30th days; 26 consecutive days without any rain. July wet and warm; 22nd 4 a.m. to 8 p.m. 1.59. August wet and cool. September hot and dry; one thunder shower between 4 and 5 a.m on the 9th, 0.05; no more until the 8th October, 41 days, with only this shower. On the night of October the 9th we had the heaviest rain, for the time, I think I ever recollect; I never heard rain make such a noise; 1.70 fell in a very short time, not more than five or six hours, if so long. October was a very wet month, though no rain fell in the first week. From the 8th to 11th inclusive, I registered 2.31, 16th to 19th inclusive 2.61, from the 21st to 27th inclusive 1.57. November must be considered upon the whole a fine month; no heavy rains, but December still finer; no heavy rain till the last night of the month.

On the subject of a mere 0.01 inch sometimes breaking a dry spell, it is interesting to note that the observer at Costessey reported "not a drop of rain in September, but two mornings the dew was so copious, that I collected 0.02 and 0.01". Cambridge University reported "September fine and warm throughout. The wettest October in Cambridge since

1843, when the fall was 5.923 inches". The Wisbech observer commented that "the wetness of July is remarkable, but such a wet month as October has not occurred here for many years. The heavy fall on the 10th October, 1.56, all fell after 10 p.m.".

What was the reason for that 1865 upset of the rainfall pattern? The synoptic charts show that during July the weather of the British Isles was disturbed by low-pressure systems of high rainfall content; August, in particular, had more than its fair share of low pressure (the heavy falls on the 23rd and 24th apparently coincided with easterly winds); then about the 25th anticyclonic conditions took over and continued almost without interruption until 8th October. Then back to low-pressure systems — and the onset of the October downpours. So much for the cause of the weather upset. But the reason behind the cause has never, I think, been made entirely clear. Just as in the famous drought of 1976, the overall motivation of these strange weather deviations remains something of a mystery.

So much for "absolute droughts" or spells of fifteen rainless days. Despite the pessimists, the incidence of fifteen or more consecutive "rain days" (0.01 inch or more) is far less frequent. The longest spell of consecutive "rain days" at Rushmere St Andrew was nineteen days, from 3rd to 21st February, 1951. This long period of rain was heralded by a very low barometer (28.25 inches) on the 4th — and a gale.

There was a near-miss at Rushmere St Andrew of a St Swithin-type forty-day spell of rain in 1975. Measurable rain fell on fourteen successive days 2nd to 15th March inclusive; on the 16th there was a trace of rain, too slight to measure; then, after measurable rain on the seven successive days 17th to 23rd, the 24th was dry; then seventeen consecutive rain days from 25th March to 10th April; then two days, one with too little rain to measure and the other completely dry; then five successive rain days from 13th to 18th April inclusive; a remarkable spell of forty-three days during which only two days were completely dry — yet the records show that only seventeen consecutive rain days actually occurred. This example underlines the difficulty of making useful comparisons when restricted by rigid definitions.

In the Appendix is a table showing the number of occasions when spells of fifteen or more consecutive rain days have occurred in the 1902–1980 Belstead/Copdock records. Comparing this table with the one showing the occurrences of fifteen or more consecutive dry days, it is interesting to note that, although dry spells are generally far more frequent than rainy ones, the long-standing Belstead/Copdock records show that more rain spells than droughts have occurred in February, November and December.

The occurrence of monthly rainfall in 'dry/wet blocks'

Taking into consideration local variations in the average annual rainfall throughout East Anglia (ranging from about 20 inches to 28 inches), the composite average for the entire region can be fairly reliably rounded off to about 23 inches a year. Of this total, about forty-three per cent falls on average in the first six months.

Despite the reputed unreliability of our climate, this tendency follows a fairly regular six-monthly pattern during the calendar year (give or take a month either way) throughout most of the British Isles. The following figures, compiled from numerous observations taken over long and varying periods of time, provide a fair composite picture:

AVERAGE ANNUAL RAINFALL

	Jan–June	July–Dec	Year
		Inches	
British Isles	18	24	42
Scotland	23	29	52
Wales	23	29	52
England	14	19	33
East Anglia	10	13	23

So consistent is this pattern that the South Norfolk records kept by Francis Dix between 1839 and 1888 show that during all those fifty years the first half of the year was wetter than the second half on only three occasions, in 1860, 1864 and 1873. Of those three occasions the difference between the first and second halves of the year in 1864 and 1873 was only a fraction of an inch (1864 was a real headline-hitter — only 7.5 inches from January to June; 6.75 inches from July to December, giving the lowest annual total in Francis Dix's records (14.25 inches). The pattern was equally consistent at Thwaite, where Orlando Whistlecraft's forty-two-year records of 1840 to 1881 show that the first half of the year was the wettest in only two years, 1860 and 1871.

It is interesting to note that at Belstead/Copdock (less than twenty miles south of Thwaite) the pattern has, at first sight, been less consistent during the present century. During the years 1902 to 1984 the January–June period was wetter than the second half of the year on eighteen occasions — but as in eight of those years the difference was only a fraction of an inch it would be most unwise to infer from these limited comparisons any actual change in the climatic pattern.

Indeed, rather than any fading of the pattern, the intensity (as distinct from the frequency of occurrence) has certainly not declined during the present century, as will be seen by the following summaries.

Taking some of the Rushmere St Andrew records and those of Belstead/Copdock (there is usually very little difference between readings at the two localities) and examining some of the nineteenth-century records available, I give below the years (and places) when the usual seasonal pattern was particularly intense. (For comparative purposes, the approximate average annual totals at Rushmere St Andrew and Belstead/Copdock are 23 inches — both present century averages; Thwaite 26 inches (1840–1881 average) and South Norfolk 24.50 inches (1839–1888 average). With additional local information, the following summaries cover a continuous period from 1839 to 1981:

ANNUAL RAINFALL IN EXCEPTIONAL "DRY/WET BLOCKS"
(Totals in inches)

Rushmere St Andrew
(Average annual rainfall [1930–1980] 23½ inches)

1976	Jan	Feb	Mar	Apr	May	Jun	Jul	Aug	Sep	Oct	Nov	Dec	Year
	1¼	0¾	0½	0½	1	0¼	2¼	2½	4¼	4¼	2½	1¾	
	4¼						17½						21¾
1974	Jan	Feb	Mar	Apr	May	Jun	Jul	Aug	Sep	Oct	Nov	Dec	Year
	1¼	2	0¾	0½	0¾	1¼	1½	2½	4	3	4½	0¾	
	8							14¾					22¾
1960	Jan	Feb	Mar	Apr	May	Jun	Jul	Aug	Sep	Oct	Nov	Dec	Year
	2¾	1½	1½	0½	0¾	3	3	3¼	3¾	5¾	3	3¼	
	7					25							32

Belstead/Copdock
(Average annual rainfall [1912–1971] 23¾ inches)

1944	Jan	Feb	Mar	Apr	May	Jun	Jul	Aug	Sep	Oct	Nov	Dec	Year
	1½	1¼	0¼	1½	0¼	1½	1¾	2¼	3¼	4½	3½	1¾	
	7							16¼					23¼
1940	Jan	Feb	Mar	Apr	May	June	July	Aug	Sep	Oct	Nov	Dec	Year
	1½	1¼	2¾	1½	0½	0¼	3	0¼	1	2½	6½	2	
	7¾						18½						27¾
1930	Jan	Feb	Mar	Apr	May	Jun	Jul	Aug	Sep	Oct	Nov	Dec	Year
	2	0½	1½	2	2½	0¾	4¾	2¾	4¾	0¾	3¼	2¼	
	9¼						18½						27¾
1929	Jan	Feb	Mar	Apr	May	Jun	Jul	Aug	Sep	Oct	Nov	Dec	Year
	1¾	0½	<0¼	1¾	1½	0¾	3¼	1	1½	2¾	4	4¼	
	6¼						16¾						23

South Norfolk (Dickleburgh and Norwich)
(Average annual rainfall [1839–1888] 24¼ inches)

	Jan	Feb	Mar	Apr	May	Jun	Jul	Aug	Sep	Oct	Nov	Dec	Year
1886	2¾	0¼	1½	1¼	2½	0½	3¾	2	1¾	3	2¾	4	
			8¾						17¼				26
1884	1½	0½	1¼	1¾	0¾	0½	2½	1	3	3	2	2½	
			6¼						14				20¼
1880	<0¼	2	1	1½	0½	2¾	4¾	2½	2¼	4¾	2¼	2¼	
			5						21½				26½
1875	2	1¼	0½	0¾	1½	1½	6	0¾	2¾	4	6¾	2¼	
			7½						22½				30
1870	1	0½	1½	0½	0½	1	1¾	2¾	1½	3	0¾	4¼	
			5						19				24
1858	0¼	0½	0½	1½	2	1	4¼	2½	0¾	2¾	1	1½	
			5¾						12¾				18½
1857	1¾	0	0¾	1¾	0¾	2	2	2½	3¾	4¾	1¼	1¼	
			5						17½				22½

Thwaite
(Average annual rainfall [1840–1882] 26 inches)

	Jan	Feb	Mar	Apr	May	Jun	Jul	Aug	Sep	Oct	Nov	Dec	Year
1841	0¾	1	1¼	1¼	1½	1½	3¾	2½	3¾	5	2½	2½	
			7¼						20				27¼

The following table is a composite analysis of various thirty-year periods compiled from a number of East Anglian locations covering a period of 140 years from 1840 to 1979, showing the average number of times in each thirty-year period (some of which overlap) when the individual months were, in varying degrees, either dry or wet. Anywhere in the British Isles, a month with only an inch of rain or less must be reckoned as dry. In dry East Anglia, a month of 4 inches or more must be considered wet (in some parts of the British Isles, in the west and north-west, the normal rainfall for every month of the year is over 4 inches).

Taking 1 inch (or less) and 4 inches (or more) respectively as the criterion of a dry or wet month in East Anglia, I have developed this definition in column one of the table. Very approximately, the average monthly rainfall in East Anglia is about 2 inches and — bearing in mind the geographic and seasonal factors — the number of occurrences should not be taken on a strictly quantitive basis but rather as an indication of seasonal trends.

The pattern is an interesting one. In the records I have examined I could find no instance in all the 140 years of any very wet months ever occurring from February to May, *nor of a single instance of a very dry November*. The table clearly shows the tendency for the first half of the year to be drier than the second half. The high figure for the midsummer month of July reflects the frequency of thundery downpours in that month.

My examination showed that the extreme monthly totals in various parts of East Anglia ranged from no rainfall at all in April, 1855, February, 1857, and September, 1865, to over 8 inches in November, 1878, October, 1865, and December, 1939 (the quite spectacular contrast between September and October, 1865, is looked at in detail on p 47). In September, 1959, parts of East Anglia missed a completely rainless month by a mere hundredth of an inch or so.

DRY AND WET MONTHS IN EAST ANGLIA

	Dry months Average number in various thirty-year periods, 1840–1979											
Monthly Total	Jan	Feb	Mar	Apr	May	Jun	Jul	Aug	Sep	Oct	Nov	Dec
0½ to 1 inch (dry)	3	9	6	5	5	5	3	4½	3½	3	2	3
Less than ½ inch (very dry)	9¾	2	3½	3	1	2	2	0½	1	2	none	1½

	Wet months Average number in various thirty-year periods, 1840–1979											
Monthly Total	Jan	Feb	Mar	Apr	May	Jun	Jul	Aug	Sep	Oct	Nov	Dec
4 to 5 inches (wet)	0¾	0¼	0½	0½	0¾	1	2	1	2	3	2½	2
Over 5 inches (very wet)	0½	—	—	—	—	0¼	0¾	0¾	0½	1½	1	0½

Since the above table was compiled, we have had several successive wet Octobers, which adds interest to the following survey of October rainfall.

Any reduction of summer rainfall that might have occurred in recent years has been small comfort to the holidaymaker, as this photograph of Felixstowe in June shows.
East Anglian Daily Times

A few years ago Richard Wilson, of Belstead Hall, near Ipswich, provided Anglia Television with some very interesting figures in which he calculated the Belstead/Copdock average monthly rainfall for the 1970s as compared with the seventy-year (1902-1971) average. The figures showed an overall reduction in the 1970s of over an inch in the average annual total — and, although the pattern of the first six months of the year being drier than the last six months was well maintained, all that reduction was confined to the latter six months of the year.

Within this overall reduction, the most striking differences between the 1970s decade and the previous seventy years were a dramatic reduction of October rainfall; a quite substantial increase in the September average (largely due to a remarkable spell of four successive years 1973–1976 when 4 inches or more fell in each September); and a "drying out" of the three Summer months, June, July and August.

AVERAGE MONTHLY AND ANNUAL RAINFALL TOTALS

Belstead/Copdock

	Jan	Feb	Mar	Apr	May	Jun	Jul	Aug	Sep	Oct	Nov	Dec	Year	Average per month
1902–1970	**2.07**	1.55	1.62	1.68	1.59	1.82	**2.25**	**2.23**	1.91	**2.30**	**2.48**	**2.29**	23.79	1.98
			10.33							13.46				
1970–1979	**2.22**	1.67	1.76	1.53	1.62	1.55	1.67	1.86	**2.42**	1.47	**2.79**	**2.05**	22.61	1.88
			10.35							12.26				

As will be seen, the average monthly fall (for what it is worth) is a little under 2 inches. In each set of averages I have indicated by underlining all months with an average rainfall of over 2 inches. The shift of pattern is noteworthy. Particularly interesting is the fact that by the 1970s October had become the driest month of the year after a seventy-year average showing it to be the second wettest month. This had been a gradual process, a set of averages for 1941–1970 showing October (2.08 inches) to be the fourth wettest month.

The following more detailed analysis is revealing. It will be seen that the pattern is neither regular nor clearly defined but it is worth noting that in the 1970s the number of rain days in October was not only less than the previous average; there was also a striking reduction in the actual amount of rain which fell on each rain day.

OCTOBER RAINFALL — BELSTEAD/COPDOCK

Average rainfall each decade 1902–1979

Decade	Total (inches)	Number of rain days	Average rain (inches) per rain day	Number of Octobers of below 1 inch
1902–1909 (8 years)	2.67	20	0.13	1
1910–1919	2.09	16	0.13	—
1920–1929	2.29	13	0.18	3
1930–1939	2.83	16	0.18	2
1940–1949	2.35	13	0.18	1
1950–1959	1.78	14	0.13	2
1960–1969	2.29	16	0.14	1
1970–1979	1.47	13	0.11	5

The traditional assessment of October being a wet month is supported by the 1831–1849 average at Swaffham Bulbeck, Cambridgeshire, of 2.57 inches and the 1839-1888 South Norfolk average of 2.95 inches, both of which ranked October as the wettest month of the whole year (greatly so in the case of South Norfolk). In the interim period, the Norwich records kept by the late John H. Willis (1913–1942) show October's 2.58 inches as second only to December, and the Belstead/Copdock trend is matched to some extent by the 1936–1977 records at the Meteorological Office, R.A.F. Honington/Mildenhall, which show October (1.85 inches) as being, with January, the sixth wettest month of the year.

This undeniable swing towards drier Octobers was by no means exclusive to East Anglia, but because past records show that deviations from accepted patterns have often lasted for quite long periods and have then disappeared we should certainly not assume that the October change has any degree of permanence or progression.

In fact, the five successive Octobers 1980–1984 were all wet. October, 1982 (with a total of 4.5 inches at Rushmere St Andrew, over 5 inches at Belstead and 5.75 inches elsewhere in Suffolk; over 5.75 inches in parts of Essex; 5.5 inches in parts of Norfolk and over 4.75 inches in Cambridgeshire) was generally the wettest October for twenty-two years

The Queen receiving an autographic rain gauge when opening the Royal Meteorological Society's new headquarters at Bracknell, Berkshire, in 1978.

Corinne Cockrell and Weather

and the third wettest of the present century. But October, 1985 — following a very dry September — was generally the driest since 1978, most places in East Anglia reporting less than half an inch. So what sort of pattern is this?

The "Royal rains"

In 1978, the Royal Meteorological Society (whose patron is HM The Queen) moved into new headquarters at James Glaisher House, in Grenville Place, Bracknell, Berkshire (James Glaisher was a famous nineteenth-century meteorologist, a pioneer balloonist and a president of the Royal Meteorological Society). When on 14th July, 1978, the Queen formally opened the new headquarters she was presented with an autographic rain gauge, an instrument which like a barograph traces its record on a slowly revolving drum, thus keeping a constant scrutiny of rainfall and making possible the accurate measurement of intense falls over a short period.

A sunshine recorder might have seemed a happier choice, but, with a schedule containing so many outdoor ceremonials, Royalty has every right to show concern regarding rainfall. The Queen's presentation rain gauge was installed at the climatological station at Balmoral, the wettest of all the weather stations which have been in operation at Royal establishments for many years.

How does the rainfall at Sandringham, in Norfolk, compare with that at the other Royal residences? Not too well, considering East Anglia's reputation for low rainfall. I am indebted to Dr G. T. Meaden for permission to use the following table, first published in *The Journal of Meteorology* (October, 1975, Vol. I, No 1):

RAINFALL AT ROYAL RESIDENCES

	Windsor Royal Gardens, Berks.	Sandringham House, Norfolk	Balmoral Castle, Aberdeen	Buckingham Palace, London	Kensington Palace, London
First complete year of record	1876	1903	1903	1906	1919
			(Inches)		
Average rainfall (1919–1950)	25.8	27.7	33.3	24.4	25.1
Driest year (1921)	13.7	16.8	21.9	12.6	14.4
Wettest year	35.2 (1915)	37.1 (1912)	42.2 (1916)	32.1 (1951 and 1915)	32.7 (1960)

Lucky for some?

Among cricket enthusiasts, the very mention of a Test match conjures up visions of sodden pitches, bad light and the dismal drip of water from pavilion eaves. Opening matches of a new football season are often fought under the sweltering sun of an Autumn heatwave. Marcelene Cox, writing in the *Ladies' Journal* of April, 1949, remarked that one way to help the weather make up its mind is to hang out a line of washing.

Spindryers and launderettes have greatly soothed the housewives' traditional Monday morning anxieties. Vast armadas of billowing sheets have dwindled to single lines of battle, but, for those still operationally concerned, there remains a built-in apprehension that Monday may be wet.

Mr G. W. Rolfe, of Ely, in an interesting contribution to *The Journal of Meteorology* (April, 1978, Vol. III, No 38, pp 113–115), analysed the distribution of dry weather at Ely (Cambridgeshire) throughout the days of the week. Apparently, Mrs Rolfe had once suggested that Market Day (Thursday) and Monday washday were the wettest days of the week at Ely, so Mr Rolfe prepared the following table based on observations at his own weather station at Ely, commencing on 23rd March, 1971 (which was a wet day). 2,397 days later, on 13th October, 1977, he recorded his 1,000th dry day (technically, a day with less than 0.01 inches in the gauge). He then analysed all those 1,000 dry days, with the following result:

DISTRIBUTION OF 1000 DRY DAYS BY WEEKDAY AT ELY

	Dry days	Possible total	% dry days
Sunday	134	342	39.2
Monday	150	342	43.9
Tuesday	141	343	41.1
Wednesday	143	343	41.7
Thursday	152	343	44.3
Friday	139	342	40.6
Saturday	141	342	41.7
	1000	2397	41.7

Mrs Rolfe seems to have under-estimated the Clerk of the Weather's benevolence. Too much statistical reliance should not be placed on a survey covering only about seven years; nonetheless, Mr Rolfe's analysis is a fascinating one. There was an interesting letter in *Weather* (May,

1975, Vol. XXX, No 5, p. 168) in which Mr G. Carrea, of the Clarendon Laboratory, Oxford, provided figures showing that at his weather station at Irchester, Northants (on the threshold of East Anglia), an analysis of the Winter months (October to March) from 1969 to 1973 showed Thursday to be very markedly the driest day of the week in terms of total rainfall. Monday was the fourth driest and Tuesday and Sunday easily the wettest. Some similarities between the Irchester and Ely figures are worth noting.

The idea that individual days of the week could have differing weather tendencies may not be as frivolous as at first appears. St Augustine, in the context of neither market days nor washdays, wisely said "Do not presume" — a salutary warning to those who would dismiss as fanciful what might in reality be a clue to something of scientific or social value. The weather related to days of the week has long been the subject of serious discussion, with quite a spate of scientific argument in the 1960s.

Human behaviour, industrial activity and possibly increased pollution on working days are factors it would be foolish to ignore completely. During the 1960s discussions, evidence was produced (contrary to the Ely and Irchester findings) that in some parts of the London area there was a tendency for wet Thursdays during the Summer months. Critical analysis at the time suggested that such a tendency should not be lightly dismissed. There might have been some cause, however local or temporary, with probably a more marked effect in urban districts than in rural areas of East Anglia.

Prior to Mr Rolfe's Ely investigation, Mr T. R. Norgate, of Lyng, Norfolk, had already (*Weather*, May, 1974 Vol. XXIX, No 5, p. 197) provided the following data, based on his own observations at Taverham, Norfolk, for some twenty years or so, which confirmed an East Anglian tendency towards dry Thursdays:

YEARLY MEANS (BY WEEKDAY)
Taverham, Norfolk

	Rainfall, inches	Number of rain days
Sunday	3.72	23
Monday	3.69	24
Tuesday	3.45	23½
Wednesday	3.35	24½
Thursday	3.06	24
Friday	3.47	23½
Saturday	3.56	24

The fact that twenty years of observations provides over a thousand individual readings for each day of the week should very largely smooth out any exceptional happenings, and for that reason I think the above figures are worth more than a casual glance. Note, for example, the large difference in total rainfall (not the number of rain days) of Sundays and Thursdays. Mr Norgate commented at the time that "there is a noticeable

The quay at Beccles is flooded as the River Waveney is swollen by a heavy storm in April, 1981. *Beccles and Bungay Journal*

drop in the mean total of rainfall for Thursday while it also appears that Thursdays had a definite lack of heavy rainfalls".

On the other hand, Monday washday does not present such a promising prospect for Norfolk housewives as it does for those in Ely!

"Oh, to be in England . . . "

In 1981, April (usually one of East Anglia's driest months) gave Norfolk and parts of north Suffolk one of the worst downpours since the famous floods of August, 1912. The heavy rain caused the Waveney Valley's most serious flooding since September, 1968, and, with a total April rainfall of three times the normal, Norfolk was the wettest spot in the whole country.

Very little rain had fallen during the first half of the month. At Rushmere St Andrew I registered less than a quarter of an inch during the entire first three weeks — and this was the general East Anglian pattern. Clear skies made the night of 23rd–24th one of the coldest April nights of the century in many parts of East Anglia; at Rushmere St Andrew I registered a grass minimum of only 17 degrees F.

Then a quite small but intensely active depression suddenly developed over the southern half of the country, bringing cold gale-force east to north-east winds with heavy snow and considerable drifting over most of the country, including the Midlands. East Anglia escaped heavy snow but was deluged with torrential rain, Norfolk and parts of north Suffolk bearing the brunt. Richard Wilson, at Belstead near Ipswich, reported 1.75 inches during the three days 23rd–25th; a few miles to the north-east 2 inches fell at Rushmere St Andrew; farther north, at Pulham St Mary, Reg Snowling registered 3.25 inches; Stephen Bartholomew reported 4.25 inches at Beccles, Suffolk; and, in a downpour which lasted with almost unceasing ferocity from about midday on the 24th until the early hours of the 26th, Dr C. E. Briscoe's rain gauge at Buxton, Norfolk, caught over 5.25 inches.

At the time, Stephen Bartholomew remarked that his 4.25 inches was more than he had ever registered during the entire month of April since his records began in 1968. Mr T. E. Norgate, chief of the Norfolk Rainfall Organisation, commented that "whole villages were cut off; low-lying meadows of the Waveney Valley were flooded to a depth of five feet and higher ground had to be found for some of the marooned cattle."

All this started with an east wind — proving how often true is the saying: "When the rain is from the east, it is four-and-twenty hours at least".

Temperature

The climate of the British Isles is temperate, largely due to the prevailing south-west to west winds bringing generally mild air off the Atlantic; to some extent due to the warming influence of the Gulf Stream; and, more significantly, because we are an island. In daytime during the Summer the sea is generally cooler than the land and in Winter it is usually warmer at all times, thus having a modifying effect throughout the year.

MEAN AIR AND SEA TEMPERATURES COMPARED

	Air over land (E. Anglia generally)	Sea (5 miles off Felixstowe)
	Degrees F.	*Degrees F.*
January	39	42
February	39	42
March	42	45
April	48	48
May	53	52
June	59	58
July	62	62
August	62	62
September	58	61
October	52	55
November	45	48
December	41	44
Average for year	50	52

The "mean" temperature is the average between the daily maximum and the nightly minimum. The air temperature varies considerably between night and day (see East Anglian Calender p. 203); the sea, very little.)

During the Summer the days are warmer inland than on the coast. The nights are generally cooler inland at all times of the year. The chance of an air frost as far inland as, say, Cambridge is usually more than double that of any part of the East Anglian coast.

The following table shows the seasonal variations of pattern:

COMPOSITE EAST ANGLIAN DAY AND NIGHT TEMPERATURES

Average 24-hour maximum and minimum readings in screen

	Inland areas			Coastal resorts		
	Degrees °F.			*Degrees °F.*		
	Average maximum	Average minimum	Average 24-hour range	Average maximum	Average minimum	Average 24-hour range
January	43	33	10	43	35	8
February	45	33	12	43	35	8
March	51	35	16	47	37	10
April	57	39	18	53	41	12
May	63	44	19	58	46	12
June	69	49	20	65	52	13
July	71	53	18	69	56	13
August	71	53	18	68	56	12
September	67	49	18	65	53	12
October	59	44	15	57	47	10
November	49	39	10	50	41	9
December	45	35	10	45	37	8
Year	57	42	15	55	45	10

The moderating effect of the sea is usually greatest on the south-west and west coasts of the British Isles, the prevailing westerlies — frequently

When there is a warm south-westerly airstream flowing across the country in Summer, the North Norfolk coast is sometimes the hottest area in Britain.

mild and moist — often having had an Atlantic crossing of a thousand miles or more. The temperate characteristics of the westerlies diminish the farther inland they travel. Birmingham, almost in the centre of England, has a smaller seasonal range of temperature than Cambridge, East Anglia's most inland city. In the Summer, when there is a warm south-westerly airstream flowing across the country, the North Norfolk coast is often the hottest spot in the whole of the British Isles.

This, combined with the even stronger and more frequent effect of the Continental characteristics of East Anglia, makes the region a frequent "hot spot" in the Summer. A survey of over a hundred years shows that some East Anglian location was the hottest recorded place anywhere in the British Isles in one year out of four. Here, with acknowledgements to Jonathan D. C. Webb (*Journal of Meteorology*, January and March, 1984), are the details:

DATES WHEN EAST ANGLIAN LOCATIONS WERE THE HOTTEST IN THE BRITISH ISLES

Year	Hottest day temperature		Location	Date
	Degrees F.	*Degrees C.*		
1875	86	30	Hillington, Norfolk	16th August
1876	95	35	Cambridge	14th August
1879	80	27	Hillington, Norfolk	28th July
1884	95	35	Hillington, Norfolk	11th August
1887	89	32	Cambridge	3rd July
1888	88	31	Cambridge	25th June
1892	85	29	Cambridge	3rd July
1893	95	35	Wryde, Cambs	18th August
1897	90	32	Cambridge	5th August
1903	88	31	Wryde, Cambs	10th July
1915	90	32	Norwich & Cromer, Norfolk	8th June
1917	93	34	Little Massingham, Norfolk	17th June
1921	94	34	Halstead, Essex	11th July
1925	92	33	Hunstanton, Norfolk	22nd July
1932	97	36	Halstead, Essex	19th August
1933	94	34	Cambridge	27th July
1942	93	34	Sprowston, Norfolk	27th August
1945	90	32	Norwich	15th July
1946	87	31	Maldon, Essex	24th July
1951	86	30	Southend, Essex	28th July
1960	87	31	Wyton, Cambs	18th June
1962	82	28	Writtle, Essex	3rd September
1964	91	33	Cromer, Norfolk	26th August
1982	87	31	Morley St Joseph, Norfolk	3rd August
1983	91	33	East Bergholt, Suffolk	15th July

In marked contrast, the coldest night each year is almost invariably in Scotland, northern England or a few inland English locations. The solitary exception was in 1906, when the lowest temperature anywhere was 2 degrees F. (−17 degrees C.) at Woodbridge, Suffolk, on 30th December.

East Anglia has a fascinating complex of climatological factors. Its pronounced bulge and long coastline emphasises the island characteristics, and the eastwards bulge and the narrowness of the North Sea can also give quite a Continental flavour to East Anglia's weather. In contrast to the prevailing westerly winds and their often lengthy Atlantic passage, the far less frequent easterlies off the Continent have a North Sea journey of less than a couple of hundred miles, yet winds off the North Sea, which is generally cooler than the Atlantic and is particularly cold in Spring and early Summer, can have considerable local effects. Air from the Continent can be very hot in Summer and extremely cold in Winter; a hot "Continental" day in East Anglia, with blistering heat inland, can bring low stratus clouds, sea fog and a chilly wind to the coastal zone, due to the hot Continental air being chilled to saturation point by the cold North Sea, the air "drying out" as it travels inland. From Spring to Autumn, the west coast of Britain generally experiences more sea fogs and mists than does the coast of East Anglia, but the west coast fogs do not usually have such a chilling effect.

The temperature tables on pp. 231–235 show the temperature profile of East Anglia as compared with other places.

Despite the long coastline, the range of temperature in parts of East Anglia is probably greater than in any comparably sized region in the country. Large temperature changes often occur within the space of twenty-four hours or less, the greatest extremes of temperature being most likely to occur in Spring and early Summer and, to a lesser degree, in the Autumn. In Spring and Autumn we are apt to experience, respectively, a combination of late or early Winter cold and early or late Summer warmth. The clear skies of Spring, early Summer and Autumn are also conducive to severe radiation frosts at night. The ground is colder in Spring and early Summer than in the Autumn so the out-of-season frost risk and the overall temperature range is usually at its maximum during March, April and May. Dry continental air, in contrast to the moister conditions of the west coast, is associated with heat or cold (according to season), and it is this combination of factors which gives East Anglia such a wide range of temperature.

At Rushmere St Andrew 18th March, 1972, was a warm day with a maximum temperature of 65 degrees F., but during the following night the screen temperature fell to 35 degrees F. (equal to an average

The Stevenson screen contains thermometers giving readings of the temperature above the ground. Under some conditions readings at ground level can be quite different.
Casella (London) Ltd

December night), rising next day to a maximum of 66 degrees F. (similar to a late May or early June day) — a range of 31 degrees F. within less than twenty-four hours.

Another example of severe radiation loss during March occurred in 1975. At Rushmere St Andrew the screen temperature during the night of Good Friday and Easter Saturday (28th–29th March) fell to 32 degrees F., which was not in itself cold enough to do any damage — but clear skies allowed the grass temperature to fall as low as 18 degrees F., resulting in a severe and very harmful ground frost.

As for Autumn temperature variations, there was a notably large one on 29th August, 1936, when at Rushmere St Andrew the range was 35 degrees F. (from a screen minimum of 46 degrees F. to a maximum of 81 degrees F.). On the same day Rickmansworth in Hertfordshire (famous for its "frost hollow") established an English record for temperature range when the screen thermometer shot up from 34 degrees F. to 85 degrees F. in the space of nine hours, a range of 51 degrees F.

Although temperature variations are usually less during the Winter than at any other time of the year, I have known some very remarkable exceptions. During the early hours of 13th January, 1968, I recorded at

Rushmere St Andrew an exceptionally low screen minimum of 14 degrees F. (with a grass minimum of only 8 degrees F.). Later that day, with a shift of wind out of the east to south-west, the screen temperature rose to 54 degrees F. (equal to an average late March or early April midday), giving an astonishing midwinter twenty-four hour range of 40 degrees F.

Generally speaking we expect much smaller ranges of temperature during the Winter months. For example, on 10th December, 1968, the night and day temperature at Rushmere St Andrew remained completely unchanged at 37 degrees F.

Even in the Spring, when wider variations are to be expected, unusual things can happen. In March, 1981, during a dull and miserable spell of wet weather, the maximum and minimum temperatures on the 9th at Rushmere St Andrew varied by only 2 degrees F. (52 degrees F. and 50 degrees F. respectively). Sky conditions are usually the governing factor. Cloudy weather moderates the temperature, whereas clear skies (especially with warm Mediterranean air by day) can bring sharp night frosts in the Spring.

The overall annual range of temperature can be summarised as follows. The first column shows the difference between the normal warmest day and coldest night of the year; the second column shows the difference between the warmest day and coldest night ever registered during the period under review:

ANNUAL TEMPERATURE RANGES
30 years 1931–1960

	Average range	Absolute range
	Degrees °F.	
Cromer	62	78
Gorleston	57	72
Felixstowe	57	75
Clacton-on-Sea	58	70
Cambridge	70	95
Bournemouth	64	81
Ilfracombe	53	67
Birmingham	62	80
Orenburg (Russia) eight-year average 1962–1969	128	149

The sharing of continental weather is more common in East Anglia and South-east England than anywhere else in the British Isles. Usually it is in a modified and generally unspectacular form, but on Monday, 13th

June, 1977, there was a brief but quite dramatic overspill of continental heat giving East Anglia an almost exclusive mini-heatwave ("mini" both in duration and area). On Sunday, 12th June, an easterly wind was flowing across the country between high pressure over Scandinavia and low pressure mainly over France and Spain. The maximum temperature at Rushmere St Andrew was a pleasant and unassuming 70 degrees F. With heat building up over the Continent, a slight shift of wind to the South-east on the 13th brought in a patch of very hot air, and the temperature at Rushmere St Andrew soared to 82 degrees F. This overspill of continental heat was strictly confined to East Anglia and parts of Kent and Sussex; and, as far as I can ascertain, Rushmere St Andrew was one of the hottest spots in the country.

During the following night the very warm air came into collision with a cold front moving up from the South; a meteorological battle broke out over the southern North Sea and in an early morning thunderstorm on the 14th I registered half an inch of rain. This was followed by a cool, misty day with a maximum temperature of only 61 degrees F. On the following day the maximum was only 58°F., and that in turn was followed by several dull and gloomy days of even cooler weather.

A thunderstorm building up over Rushmere St Andrew, near Ipswich.

That brief but torrid involvement with the Continent was a most unusual affair, but the continental influence in East Anglia is an ever-present factor. Continental climates are noted for their low rainfall and wide extremes of temperature — a feature recognisable to a limited but very apparent degree in the climate of East Anglia.

The following table shows average monthly mean temperatures at various places over varying periods of time. The "mean" temperature is arrived at by simply adding together the average maximum and minimum temperatures and dividing by two. It does not, therefore, give any clues to the monthly and annual range of temperature but is widely accepted and used in climatology as a general indication of the midway temperature between the daily maxima and nightly minima. In other words, it is a fair approximation of the average temperature of a normal day and night :

AVERAGE MONTHLY MEAN TEMPERATURES

	Swaffham Bulbeck (Cambs) 1831–1849	Thwaite (Suffolk) 1840–1882	Belstead/Copdock (Suffolk) 1902–1971	R.A.F. Honington/ Mildenhall 1936–1977
	Degrees F.	*Degrees F.*	*Degrees F.*	*Degrees F.*
January	36.9	37.5	38.1	38.3
February	38.3	39.3	38.8	39.2
March	41.7	42.2	42.3	43.0
April	45.9	48.4	46.7	47.5
May	53.1	54.4	53.0	53.2
June	59.3	60.6	58.3	58.8
July	62.2	63.6	61.9	62.1
August	61.7	63.4	61.5	61.9
September	56.9	58.7	57.6	57.9
October	50.2	51.2	51.0	51.4
November	42.7	43.1	43.4	44.1
December	39.2	38.9	39.5	39.9
Year	49.1	50.2	49.3	49.8

The Belstead/Copdock and Honington/Mildenhall instruments are accurate and correctly exposed according to strict Meteorological Office specifications. I cannot vouch for the Swaffham Bulbeck and Thwaite records. The Rev J. L. Jenyns, who kept the Swaffham Bulbeck records, says of the self-registering thermometer, "it was fixed to a board, having a hood, projecting a short distance from the north side of a house and about 10 feet from the ground. The sun never shone on it, nor upon any near object from which a direct line could be drawn to the bulb of the instrument". I have no information as to the exposure of Orlando Whistlecraft's thermometers at Thwaite. The height of the Swaffham Bulbeck thermometer is not acceptable by current standards and I have a feeling that the Thwaite instruments were exposed in such a way as to give some rather high summer values. Both sets of records were before the standard adoption of the Stevenson screen, but both Jenyns and Whistlecraft were highly respected, conscientious and dedicated observers and, apart maybe from some of the Summer readings at Thwaite, I think their averages can be fairly compared with the strictly appointed stations at Belstead and Honington.

Hot Summers

Although we can optimistically hope for an occasional spell of pleasant Summer warmth as early as May (as the character in *The Arcadians* chirpily sang: "Eighty in the shade they say; very, very warm for May"), such dispensations are rather unusual and it is not until June that we can reasonably expect any summerlike weather settled enough to plan relaxing days on the beaches.

There are two basic reasons. Firstly, it is not until June that the Arctic ice off Greenland (a frequent menace to our weather) has sufficiently dispersed; and, secondly, around 21st June the sun is at its highest so that, although daytime solar heating and the temperature of the soil may not have yet reached their maxima, the sun's rays have their shortest journey of the year through the earth's protective atmosphere — and, the burning power of the ultra-violet rays is often at its most potent.

Some of our best Summers are caused by the kindly influence of a north-easterly extension of the benevolent Azores anticyclone which, in conjunction with comparatively low barometric pressure over the North Atlantic, can provide us with settled periods of warm south-westerly winds which will most likely have dried out by the time they reach East Anglia, giving long dry spells of warm sunshine.

Less ideally for East Anglia, a similarly persistent anticyclone centred over Scandinavia or the northern Continent and extending its influence over the British Isles can give dry, sunny conditions over most of the country but can at the same time plague the East Coast with cool north-easterly winds which, having picked up moisture from the North Sea, frequently cause prolonged spells of shivery, cloudy weather. In East Anglia the difference between warm, sunny weather and a monotonous spell of cloudy chill is often simply whether we are on the right or wrong side of an anticyclone. The reading of our barometer is no guide: it simply tells us that atmospheric pressure is high, irrespective of the actual position of the high-pressure area. Buys Ballots Law gives a clue; if the wind is north-easterly, it indicates that pressure is lower over the Continent — and we are on the wrong side of the anticyclone, whereas with the wind a light south-westerly, all could be well for East Anglia.

International co-operation between the weather systems was notably good during the famous hot Summer of 1976, when a friendly and long-lasting link was established between the Azores and the Scandinavian high-pressure systems which, joining hands, created (in barometric terms) a hard shoulder of high pressure which for months on end formed an effective barrier to all attempted invasions by the Atlantic depressions. Only in Northern Ireland and the North-west of Scotland did the depressions manage to establish any sort of bridgehead — and it was only those north-westerly regions which escaped the resulting drought. That Summer of 1976 was quite exceptional but, like many meteorological happenings commonly referred to as "freaks", it was by no means unprecedented.

Meanwhile, rather than attempt an examination of the occurrence and pattern of "good" Summers I have, for reasons of clarity, limited my comparisons to the simple occurrence of "hot" Summers; a definitive identification of a "good" Summer has never, in my opinion, been satisfactorily achieved. The ingredients of a good Summer are obvious, high temperatures, low rainfall and plenty of sunshine, but variable combinations and interpretation of these factors tend to confuse the issue. A couple of severe "heat" thunderstorms can easily give an otherwise completely rainless month an above-average rainfall so that it goes down in the records as a wet month, whereas a dull, cool and damp month with frequent rain in very small quantities can appear in the records as a dry month.

The glorious Summer of 1911 was undoubtedly one of the best of the present century, yet only in July and August did the mean temperature exceed 60 degrees F. (which it normally does in those months), whereas in a great number of far less spectacular Summers the mean temperature exceeded 60 degrees F. during at least three months. Those years (only three of which could really be described as "hot") were 1905, 1917, 1926, 1929, 1930, 1933, 1934, 1938, 1939, 1940, 1950, 1959, 1961, 1970 and 1976. The 60 degrees F.-plus measuring rod is not in itself a sufficiently reliable indicator of "goodness".

Attempts have been made to find some arithmetical definition of a "good" Summer, a scale of points being awarded to varying degrees of the relevant factors. I do not think, however, that any of these methods has so far provided an entirely satisfactory formula.

Bearing in mind that in East Anglia it is not at all uncommon for a prolonged spell of dry Summer weather to be associated with dull and cool conditions, I have restricted my comparisons simply to what I would diagnose as "hot" Summers, for which I have chosen as the sole criterion the occurrence of shade temperatures of 80 degrees F. or more on fifteen or more days during the year. Using this formula and applying it to the Copdock/Belstead records only eight Summers qualified as "hot" during the years 1902 to 1982 inclusive. Details of these qualifying years are given below. For historical reasons I have also quoted similar figures from the records of Orlando Whistlecraft at Thwaite, near Eye, in Suffolk for the famous year about which he wrote his book *The Magnificent and Very Hot Summer of 1846*. Whatever doubts we may have as to the accuracy of his records (his tendency to show higher Summer temperatures than at Copdock/Belstead could be due largely to the more inland situation of Thwaite), I think his figures are very near to the truth and there seems little doubt that the June of 1846 was quite outstanding not only for the intensity of the heat but also for the long duration of this hot spell.

ANALYSIS OF HOT SUMMERS
Copdock/Belstead, 1902–1987

Criterion for inclusion in this summary is 15 days or more with maximum shade temperatures of 80°F. and over

		May	June	July	Aug	Sept	Year	Longest consecutive spell of 80° or over
1911	Days of 90°F. or over	—	—	2	3	1	6	8 days
	Days of 80°–89°F.	—	2	11	10	5	28	
	Hottest day, °F.	77	82	91	90	88	91	
	Mean monthly temp.	55.4	59.0	65.6	67.0	59.8	—	
1923	Days of 90°F. or over	—	—	3	—	—	3	6 days
	Days of 80°–89°F.	1	—	7	6	—	14	
	Hottest day, °F.	80	79	93	89	75	93	
	Mean monthly temp.	50.8	54.2	65.5	61.2	55.8	—	
1933	Days of 90°F. or over	—	—	1	—	—	1	6 days
	Days of 80°–89°F.	—	3	6	9	—	18	
	Hottest day, °F.	78	83	91	88	78	91	
	Mean monthly temp.	53.7	59.0	64.8	65.4	60.3	—	
1935	Days of 90°F. or over	—	—	—	—	—	—	5 days
	Days of 80°–89°F.	—	3	9	8	—	20	
	Hottest day, °F.	74	84	84	84	73	84	
	Mean monthly temp.	50.3	59.9	64.3	63.8	58.0	—	
1947	Days of 90°F. or over	—	—	—	1	—	1	5 days
	Days of 80°–89°F.	1	8	6	7	3	25	
	Hottest day, °F.	83	88	85	90	84	90	
	Mean monthly temp.	56.9	62.0	64.8	66.2	61.1	—	
1949	Days of 90°F. or over	—	—	—	—	1	1	3 days
	Days of 80°–89°F.	—	2	9	6	1	18	
	Hottest day, °F.	67	86	86	87	90	90	
	Mean monthly temp.	51.0	58.3	63.8	63.5	64.3	—	
1959	Days of 90°F. or over	—	—	—	—	—	—	5 days
	Days of 80°–89°F.	—	3	7	5	2	17	
	Hottest day, °F.	73	82	86	85	84	86	
	Mean monthly temp.	53.1	59.7	64.2	64.6	60.0	—	
1975	Days of 90°F. or over	—	—	—	—	—	—	6 days
	Days of 80°–89°F.	—	—	5	10	—	15	
	Hottest day, °F.	65	78	82	88	75	88	
	Mean monthly temp.	50.0	57.1	63.2	66.1	58.0	—	
1976	Days of 90°F. or over	—	1	—	—	—	1	10 days (would have been 17 days but for interruption of 79° on 29th June)
	Days of 80°–89°F.	—	7	12	1	—	20	
	Hottest day, °F.	79	91	88	83	73	91	
	Mean monthly temp.	55.0	63.6	65.3	62.9	57.2	—	
	70-year average (1902–1971) of mean monthly temperature	53.0	58.3	61.9	61.5	57.6	—	—

For comparison: Orlando Whistlecraft's figures for 1846

	May	June	July	Aug	Sept	Year	Longest consecutive spell of 80° or over
90°F. or over	—	—	1	1	—	2	
80°–89°F.	1	18	10	5	2	36	10 days
Hottest day, °F.	81	89	93	91	85	93	(11th–20th June)
Mean monthly temp.	57.3	67.5	67.9	67.5	63.5	—	
43-year average of mean monthly temperature	54.4	60.6	63.6	63.4	58.7	—	

In the foregoing table, the maximum temperature of 80 degrees F. in May, 1923, was a record-breaker insofar as it occurred as early as the 4th (the May maximum of 83 degrees F. in 1947 did not occur until the middle of the month).

Every good Summer has its own individual characteristics. The variety is considerable, 1947 being particularly notable for the quite remarkable speed with which we were whisked in the space of a few weeks from a Winter of extreme discomfort into a Summer of very considerable content. After more than seven weeks of snowbound countryside, the ground at Rushmere St Andrew was not clear of snow until as late as 14th March. Eleven moderate-to-sharp ground frosts occurred during April, but on 7th May the shade temperature reached 70 degrees and, after exceeding 80 degrees on several days, reached 88 degrees at Rushmere St Andrew on 30th May, one of the hottest May days ever known.

Memorable as it was for a prolonged spell of glorious weather, 1983 failed to qualify for the preceding table. With only thirteen days of 80 degrees F. or more, it was generous for its quality rather than its quantity. After the coldest, wettest Spring ever known (blamed by some climatologists on unusual volcanic activity with consequent pollution of the upper air), June, 1983, was pleasant, dry but unremarkable, and July was the warmest calendar month ever known; a compact, neatly packaged mini-Summer starting on the 2nd and lasting until the 31st. At Belstead, near Ipswich, there were eleven days of 80 degrees F. or over (including 91 degrees F. on the 15th) with only two in August and none in June. On the 16th 93 degrees F. was reached at Chelmsford, Cambridge and Bury St Edmunds, among others.

Whatever methods of comparision are used, I find a most striking similarity between Orlando Whistlecraft's *Magnificent and Very Hot Summer of 1846* and the Summer of 1976. Apart from their excessive heat, they were both Summers of exceptional drought; factors other than temperature and rainfall were remarkably similar, and for that reason I have included a detailed comparison of 1976 with 1846.

I wish I had space to quote more fully from Whistlecraft's marvellously descriptive account. Here are a few extracts, reproduced by kind permission of the Suffolk Record Office:

JUNE, 1846

1846	Wind	Force	Out-door Thermometer		Rain	Evaporation	Notes
June 1	SE	2	53	75		.31	Very fine and clear.
2	SE	1	46	81		.29	Excessively hot and clear.
3	SE	1	45	84		.30	
4	ESE	1	49	84		.30	Blue haze & excessive heat.
5	E	1	55	84		.27	Excessive heat and no cloud.
6	SE	0	51	88		.19	Most excessive heat and neither wind nor cloud.
Su. 7	SE	0	56	89½!		.18	
8	WSW	2	63	83		—	Distant thunder on 8th.
9	SW	2	58½	79½		.57	Fair and moderate heat.
10	SW	2	57	73		—	
11	W	1	62½	81		—	From this day to the 22nd inclusive, an unbroken continuance of cloudless skies, and most excessive heat, beyond any instance on record in England, and the sun-beams were quite overpowering to persons peculiarly exposed to them. A few distant shows for tempest on 20th day, but more on the 22nd, and much electric display that night.
12	SE	0	56	81		—	
13	E	1	55	83		.82	
Su. 14	E	1	55	82½		—	
15	E	0	52	86		.44	
16	E	1	55	83½		.24	
17	SE	1	53	86½		.30	
18	E	2	54	84		—	
19	SE	1	54	89½!		—	
20	N	3	57	85		—	
Su. 21	NE	3	59	78½		—	
22	SE	2	56	88!		1.27	
23	NW & SW	4	67!	71	.41	—	Showery
24	SW	2	52½	69	.09	—	
25	SW & W	4	52½	64	.06	—	
26	SW	2	47	68	.12	—	
27	SW	1	58	75		—	Chiefly close and sultry.
Su. 28	SSW	3	55	72		—	
29	SW	3	61	78		—	
30	SW	3	55	75		1.14	
				Totals	0.68	6.62!	

From the 1st to the 22nd inclusive, was constant sun-shine, and excessive heat in such unbroken continuance, as cannot be found on any record for a century past, or since true registrations of Thermometer have been kept! . . . The 8th day produced thunder in many parts of the Suffolk and Norfolk borders, near the Waveney during the evening. From the 11th to the 20th, the sun rose and set in its highest lustre, amid golden skies! The daily heat now most uniform . . . The remainder of the month was close and sultry, with breezes from S.W. Hay harvests generally over by the 20th this year, and all the common garden fruits very early in ripening.

Rivulets, ponds, &c., dried up in most situations, yet the flower-gardens were very beautiful, in spite of the great heat, but the blossoms were short-lived.

JULY, 1846

1846	Wind	Force	Out-door Thermometer		Rain	Evaporation	Notes
July 1	SW	3	52	73		—	Fair and close, rain at night.
2	SW	3	60	74½	.15	—	Fair and close.
3	W	2	62	81		.68	Very fine, clear, and hot.
4	SE	1	55	89!		—	Clear and excessively hot.
Su. 5	SE	3	62	93!!		.65	Most excessively hot & clear.
6	SW	4	57	74	.15	—	Showers.
7	W	4	56	68		—	Cloudy.
8	S	1	55	66	.07	—	
9	SSE	1	59	71	.01	—	Showery.
10	SW & NE	1	59	72	.55	—	Heavy thunder showers.
11	NW	3	50	72		—	Fair.
Su. 12	W	2	53	78		—	Very fine and hot
13	W & SE	1	60	82		1.17	
14	S	3	61	88!	.04	—	Extremely hot. Thunder at eve.
15	W	3	59	78		—	Fair and very hot.
16	SW	3	60	72	.14	.67	Close, and rain at 9 p.m.
17	W	4	58	72		—	Fair.
18	SW	5	53	73½	.06	—	Sultry and stormy.
Su. 19	SW	3	54	73	.22	—	Very fine and pleasant.
20	W	1	58	79		.75	Very fine and very hot.
21	SW	5	56	74½	.02	—	Rather showery.
22	W	3	59	75	.10	—	
23	S	4	58	82		—	Extremely hot and fine.
24	S & NW	2	61	82	.22	—	Extreme heat: rain p.m.
25	W	2	56	77	.06	—	Hot, with electric showers.
Su. 26	W	2	54	77		—	Very fine and hot.
27	SW	1	59	77		—	
28	SSW	0	66	81		1.63	Excessive heat night and day, and lightning on 31st night.
29	SE	1	59	84		—	
30	E	3	64	86		—	
31	E	2	63½	87		.95	
				Totals	1.79	6.50!	

From the 2nd day, a return of West Indian heat occurred, and on the 3rd and 4th, most splendid sun-sets . . . Sunday the 5th will be remembered long by all observing and reflecting men. On this day the heat surpassed all others, and here we had no clouds till after 1 p.m., but a S.E. breeze increased as the day advanced. The wind also was literally hot as from a furnace at a short distance, and the oppressive state of the air which prevailed cannot be well described . . . At this time groups of thunder-clouds came on at S.W., and a gale sprang up from the same quarter, causing a great change. Some large drops fell, and several distant claps of thunder were heard. This was the hottest day that has been known in Suffolk for 38 years, and the long continuance of the heat now surpassed all on record . . . On the 13th, the heat again increased, and on the 14th still more so . . . Dark thunder-clouds came on at 5 p.m., and thunder-storms glided round us all the evening. A house near Bury St. Edmund's was struck . . . On the 26th, beautiful electric mixtures of sky scenery. Very oppressive sultriness on this day, and to the end of the month, both by night and day. A splendid orange sun-set on the 30th . . . The action of the liver in many persons was greatly affected during the heat, and violent disease was the consequence, and sudden death with some in the close of July. Others were unable to work in the harvest during the middle of the day, owing to the awful heat: and many bilious disorders of less importance prevailed from the same cause.

AUGUST, 1846

1846	Wind	Force	Out-door Thermometer Lowest	Highest	Rain	Evaporation	Notes
Aug 1	E	3	64½	91!	.40	—	Clear and excessive heat.
Su. 2	SE	2	66	83		—	Extremely sultry, but fair.
3	SE & S	3	60	81	.01	—	Chiefly fair and very hot.
4	SW & S	1	62	77	.05	—	Rain a.m. Fine p.m.
5	E	1	63½	72½	.73	.82	Heavy thunder storms.
6	NE	1	64	84½		—	
7	W	1	66	82		—	
8	SW	3	66	78½		—	Exceedingly fine and ex-
Su. 9	SW	3	60	74		—	tremely hot on most days,
10	SW	2	61	75		—	to the 12th.
11	W	2	58½	75		—	
12	NW & SE	1	59	78		—	
13	S & W	4	59	72½	.33	—	Hasty showers.
14	NW	0	55	74		—	Very fine and hot.
15	SSE	3	56	82		—	Extremely hot and fine.
Su. 16	W	1	57	74½		1.70	Very fine and sultry.
17	SW	1	59	74		—	
18	S	3	63	73	.14	—	Rain a.m. Fine p.m.
19	W	4	58	70	.61	—	Heavy storms and thunder.
20	NW	1	58	66	.36	—	Fine a.m. Wet p.m.
21	N	3	59	73		—	
22	N	2	60	69		—	Fine and close.
Su. 23	N	0	55	70		.57	
24	NE	2	60	67	.02	—	Cloudy with showers.
25	NE	2	54	69	.10		
26	NE	2	57	70		—	
27	NE	3	58	76		—	Very fine and hot.
28	E	3	60	77		—	
29	NE	2	63	74	.20	—	Hot with heavy showers.
Su. 30	NE	0	58	76		—	Very fine and hot.
31	SE	0	54	76		.75	
				Totals	2.95	3.84	

The dreadful storm of August 1st will be remembered by many, as well as the excessive heat of the day:—by 10 a.m. the Thermometer was 86 degrees, before noon it was 90 degrees, and at 1 p.m. 91 degrees! . . . It held out clear till evening, with an East wind: but a bank of thunder-cloud lay very distant in the South, most of the afternoon. The awful storm which commenced in Cumberland three days before, and had gone round the West and South of England on the two following days, now came on in these Eastern parts . . . It abated its severity as it came on over Essex into Suffolk, but here it was awful, and the lightning continual from 8 till 11 p.m. In Norfolk it again increased by midnight with great hail . . . The flashes of lightning were of many colours, and at first a deep purple and rose tint, then blue. Some trees were shattered

Eastward of this place at 9 p.m. . . . On the 5th also a series of awful thunder-storms. The steeple of Dedham Church, Essex was struck and much injured; a stable also at Horkesley in that County, and three horses killed: and a tree split, and a pony struck dead at Aspal, Suffolk, at 12 noon . . .

All three months, June, July, and August, gave a mean nearly alike, and from 5 to 7 degrees above the usual mean! . . . This high temperature had a sad effect upon butcher's meat, butter, candles, lard, sealing wax, and honey, this last was by most persons secured early, to prevent it being lost in dripping from the hives, and it was very abundant and good. Wasps dreadfully fierce and annoying by their vast numbers and strength this season, and flies and other insects extremely troublesome to horses and cattle, and most so on the approach of the storms. It may be noted here that although we had rain this month, the surface was never wet, as it fell like throwing water on bricks and cinders!

The temptation to compare hot (or merely very good) Summers of the present century with those of the past is almost irresistible. Do they nowadays occur with greater or less frequency or intensity? A major snag is the difficulty of comparing records taken at different geographic locations, the actual siting of the instruments and the relative over- or under-exposure of some of the early weather stations. From the various notes, diaries and other records available, I find no convincing evidence of any changes of the last few hundred years, either in the pattern or intensity of exceptionally good Summers.

To what extent is it possible to predict an exceptionally hot Summer? In my opinion it is quite impossible to do so. Scientific investigation has so far failed to provide any reliable clues, a fact which does not deter the occasional over-enthusiastic amateur from announcing to the press that the next Summer will be this, that or the other. The same naive assurance is also shown in predicting the next Winter. The success rate is pathetically low, though failures are usually ignored while any lucky success is acclaimed by prominent headlines announcing the emergence of a weather wizard.

An amateur meteorologist of the nineteenth century much respected by modern meteorologists, the Rev Leonard Jenyns, one-time vicar of Swaffham Bulbeck, Cambridgeshire, observed that the unusually hot Summer of 1846 was preceded by a very mild Winter. He also reported that the warm Summers of 1834 and 1835 were followed by mild Winters. Francis Bacon wrote that "a warm and open Winter portends a hot and dry Summer".

If a hot Summer were always preceded and succeeded by a mild Winter forecasting would be easy in a long chain of endless succession, but there are many exceptions to the theories. How do things work out in practice? Taking eight hot Summers (as defined by the formula of more than fifteen days of 80 degrees F. or over), the table below, using Copdock/Belstead records, shows the relationship between those exceptional Summers and the preceding and succeeding Winters in which, unless there is some subtle rhythm which has escaped my notice, one sees no sign of any regular pattern.

ANALYSIS OF HOT SUMMERS & ADJACENT WINTERS
Copdock/Belstead, 1902–1980

Preceding winter	*Hot summer*	*Succeeding winter*
Average to mild	1911	Average to mild
Mild	1923	Generally cold, particularly December
Average (chilly January)	1933	Severely cold December; average January & February
Mild, abnormally so, in December	1935	Cold December; mild January; cold February
Exceptionally cold, severe & snowy. February intensely cold	1947	Very mild
Mild	1949	Very mild
December mild; January cold; February average	1959	Mild December; average January; Average January & February
Exceptionally mild	1975	Average December & February; very mild January
December average; January very mild; February average	1976	Very cold December; cold January; mild February
	Thwaite, near Eye	
Mild	1846	Very cold

Some rather interesting facts emerge from the foregoing analysis of the nine "hot" Summers of the present century. The Summers of 1923, 1935, 1949 and 1975 were each preceded by an unusually cold May, which in every case was preceded by a mild or very mild Winter. On only one other occasion was an unusually cold May preceded by a mild Winter; that was in 1957, in which only a very ordinary Summer occurred. Out of the five occasions during the present century when a mild or very mild Winter was followed by an unusually cold May, four of those years gave us a "hot" Summer. Anyone looking for some pattern on which to base a long-term Summer prediction might well wonder whether there is some "A" factor (p. 15) at work here. I doubt it.

Another interesting fact is that, apart from 1923 (and to a lesser degree 1976), every hot Summer extended into a warmer than usual September. In contrast, the Summer of 1975 was to some extent comparable with that of 1923 insofar as the heat, although intense, was confined to July and August. In some of the other great Summers (strikingly so in 1947) the heat was prolonged from May to September.

It is obvious from the foregoing that the analysis of a single factor — temperature — makes it difficult to compare any one hot Summer with another accurately and definitely. Add to that comparison the equally significant factors of sunshine and rainfall and one begins to realise the complexity of rating all our good Summers in some sort of league table. But for prolonged intensity of heat, abundant sunshine and very low rainfall the famous Summer of 1976 deserves special mention.

The famous Summer of 1976

It all started with a hurricane. On New Year's Day, 1976, a large anticyclone was sitting possessively over Spain while a harmless-looking depression lay to the North-west of the British Isles. Suddenly the depression started to deepen rapidly. By 2nd January it had become extremely intense and vigorous; the anticyclone, stubbornly maintaining its pressure, refused to give way, compelling the depression, still deepening ominously, to head across Scotland towards Denmark.

The ensuing argument created a very steep barometric gradient (shown by closely-packed isobars on the weather maps) between the two conflicting systems and by 2100 hrs GMT on the 2nd, the brisk westerly wind had increased to gale force. By midnight, winds of hurricane force were howling over a wide area.

Designed in the mid-nineteenth century by Thomas Stevenson, the father of Robert Louis Stevenson, the Stevenson screen is the standard housing for the maximum, minimum and wet and dry-bulb thermometers. It stands at a height of four feet over short grass.
Casella (London) Ltd

During the last week of January, it turned very cold and I registered two "ice-days" (maximum temperature 32 degrees F. or less) at Rushmere St Andrew. Following a dry October and December, January was deficient in rainfall, thus laying the foundations which were to make more serious the drought during the hot, dry Summer ahead. Earlier deficiencies of rainfall in 1975 made the water situation in Britain even more precarious.

From then on, despite threats from several deep depressions out over the Atlantic, there was a developing tendency for the establishment of stable high pressure systems to the South and South-west of the British Isles (on 6th April I noted in my daily register that "the Azores anticyclone seems to be building itself for a possessive take-over"). By the end of the month the Azores anticyclone had extended right across the country and the associated clear skies allowed intense radiation at night. During the early hours of the 29th I registered a grass minimum of only

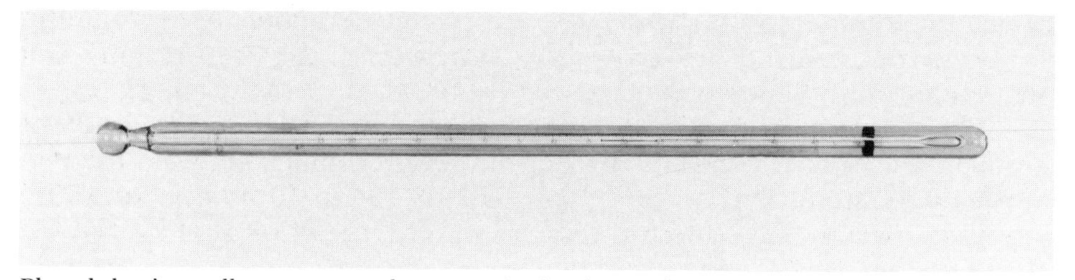

Placed horizontally on pegs about an inch above short grass, the grass minimum thermometer shows the temperature to which it is reduced by night radiation of warmth to the sky. *Casella (London) Ltd*

15 degrees F., but at Belstead it was as low as 11 degrees F. As observer Richard Wilson later remarked, that was the only occasion during the many years he had recorded the weather on which April provided the coldest night of the entire year.

The tendency for an anticyclonic "take-over" continued and rainfall during February, March, April and May was generally well below average. During the first week of May a ridge of high pressure lay South-west to North-east across the British Isles, comparatively weak but full of promise. This was to become the dominant feature during the hot, dry spell to come. The weather remained dry, and shade temperatures exceeded 80 degrees F. in many parts of the country including East Anglia. The 7th was generally the hottest May day since the glorious Summer of 1947. At Witham, Essex, the shade temperature reached 82 degrees F.

But there were penalties to pay and, with clear skies, sharp ground frosts occurred. At Belstead the grass minimum during the night of

13th/14th was only 26 degrees F. It can be assumed that further inland, particularly in some of the "frost hollows", much lower readings were registered.

Towards the end of May the anticyclonic build-up had developed with unshakeable determination and during the first week of June the high pressure systems finally assumed complete control, their domination continuing with little interruption until the first week in September.

The scene was set for an historic June which was to prove the hottest, sunniest, driest and most scorching in living memory, the highest temperatures occurring in East Anglia and the South-east. The long-distance forecasters were taken by surprise. The Meteorological Office statement on weather prospects for June (issued on 1st June) said:

> After a mainly dry and settled spell in most districts, rather changeable westerly type weather is expected to predominate over the month as a whole.
>
> Although a few brief warm spells are likely, temperatures and amounts of sunshine are expected to be below average in most places but near average in the Midlands, East Anglia, central southern and South-east England.
>
> Total amounts of rainfall will probably be above average in Scotland, Northern Ireland and northern parts of England and Wales and near average in the Midlands, East Anglia, southern England and South Wales.
>
> The frequency of thunder will probably be about average generally.

In fact, apart from the extreme North-west of Scotland, sunshine was well above average, rainfall scarce and thunder almost non-existent.

The failure of the long-distance forecast is not surprising. The monthly predictions (later axed for reasons, it is said, of economy) are based on analogies with weather situations of previous years, the general idea being that patterns may recur. But it is usual for the weather to be unusual.

By the middle of June, Belstead had already registered eight days of 75 degrees F. or over, without any measurable rain. Then on the 25th, with a maximum of 91 degrees F. at Belstead, began what is generally considered to be the longest continuous spell of hot weather in this country since at least the eighteenth century; it lasted well into July. The average mean temperature at Belstead for the whole of June (63.6 degrees F.) broke all June records going back to 1902 and this story was repeated throughout most of the rest of the country. Temperatures of 90 degrees F. and over were commonplace in East Anglia, a few places reporting 95 degrees F. or over. But the clear skies allowed great radiation losses at night and on the 21st a ground frost was reported at King's Lynn.

During that blazing hot spell I was frequently asked "why, with all this heat, aren't we getting any thunderstorms?" In the "COL" monthly report for June, the only two East Anglian stations to report thunder were Old Costessey, Norfolk, and Elmswell, Suffolk, each on one day only. The answer lay largely in the fact that heat thunderstorms are caused by violent uprushes of surface air due to excessive heating. As the air rises it expands and cools and the moisture content is condensed, first into clouds and then into rain and often hail. A striking feature of that heatwave in 1976 was the acute dryness of the air; if there is insufficient moisture in the air condensation cannot take place, In 1976 we had all the machinery for the creation of thunderstorms but not the raw material.

The unusual dryness of the air in June had other side-effects. Towards midday on 30th June I could hardly believe the reading of my wet and dry bulb hygrometer, which showed a relative humidity of only 12 per cent. Very occasionally the humidity falls to as low as 20 per cent but this was ridiculous. However, a telephone call to the Meterological Office at R.A.F. Honington confirmed that the humidity further away from the sea was even lower, a mere 8 per cent.

I immediately went on Radio Orwell to broadcast hourly warnings to sunbathers that there was practically no protective moisture between us and the sun, added to which the light easterly wind blowing in from the sea was almost free of any protective dust content, and the burning powers of the ultra-violet rays were probably the greatest ever known. We are well accustomed to gale, frost and fog warnings, but this was the first and only time I had ever issued a sunburn warning.

So clear was the air that a pilot from a military airbase in Suffolk, flying at a height of 30,000 feet, could clearly see Liverpool Bay some two hundred miles to the North-west.

By that time there was a firm link-up between the Azores anticyclone and another in the region of Scandinavia, thus creating a hard shoulder of high pressure right across the British Isles. The causes of such a "blocking" situation have interested climatologists for years but so far no effective means of forecasting a situation of this kind at long distance appears to have emerged.

In 1976 the blocking system gave blazing sunshine over almost the entire country. At one time, a 5,000-mile belt of high pressure extended from Bermuda across Britain to Eastern Europe. The hard shoulder of high pressure stubbornly resisted any invasion attempts by the Atlantic depressions which, accepting defeat, slunk away north-eastwards. As a result of this prolonged pattern, it was only in some northern parts of the British Isles that the 1976 rainfall was above the average. Over England and Wales the Summer drought was the culmination of the driest sixteen-month spell since 1727.

During June the defeated depressions acquired the weariness of frustration; the high-pressure systems relaxed and soon both the lows and the highs became less intense. Before long there were few isobars on the weather maps, and what had started much earlier as a battle between the systems became a listless stalemate, very different from the steep barometric gradients causing the violent hurricane which had heralded 1976.

Harvests were seriously affected, and by the end of June, according to the local branch of the NFU, many cereal crops on Suffolk's 500,000 acres of agricultural land were already burning up. The total rainfall at Rushmere St Andrew for the first half of the year was a paltry 4½ inches, compared with an average for the same period of 10¼ inches. Loss by evaporation, accelerated by the very dry air, created almost desert-like conditions.

By the end of the first week in July, the country generally had experienced what was reckoned to be the longest hot spell for at least 250 years and East Anglia, though not generally the hottest spot during the spell, was certainly the sunniest. During the whole of June and July over 600 hours of sunshine were registered in East Anglia, the greatest total for any two months ever registered in England, and in many parts of Norfolk and Suffolk there was an absolute drought of twenty-five days from 20th June to 15th July (St Swithin's Day). Did the saint intervene? Not by giving us forty days and forty nights of rain (he never has in East Anglia), but peculiar things did happen later.

Meanwhile, for the first time in its 132-year history the Diss Horticultural Society's mid-July Summer Show had to be cancelled because of the risk of a poor exhibition of blooms.

In the Witham region of Essex the month proved to be probably the warmest July since 1868. At many places in Essex, Cambridgeshire and Suffolk shade temperatures exceeded 91 degrees F. on the 3rd and 4th, and in Norfolk King's Lynn endured a scorching 93 degrees F.

But relief — and trouble — was on the way. By about the middle of July the long-standing partnership between the high-pressure systems was dissolved, to be resumed in modified form in August, and the prowling, long-frustrated Atlantic lows moved in to assume temporary command.

Much cooler air brought predictable thunderstorms. During an early morning storm on the 16th about three-quarters of an inch fell at Rushmere St Andrew and at neighbouring Belstead, while at Rayleigh in Essex 1¾ inches fell. Particularly severe thunderstorms on the 20th gave 1¾ inches at Colchester and, although on the same day Rushmere St Andrew received only about three-quarters of an inch, Belstead was deluged with 2.19 inches in the space of only four hours, the heaviest fall in twenty-four hours recorded at that station since 29th August, 1916.

By the end of July, cool, strong North to North-west winds were sweeping most of the country in the rear of a depression from the Atlantic, East Anglia suffering as much as anywhere. Gale force winds on the 30th caused severe blowing of topsoil in the King's Lynn area of Norfolk, reducing visibility to less than 65 yards. On the following day, Colchester managed a maximum temperature of only 58 degrees F., plunging to a goose-pimpling 51 degrees F. in a mid-afternoon hail shower.

During July, rain fell in East Anglia on only three to five days, according to locality, but the severe thunderstorms produced a near-average July total — a little above in places.

The real drama was still to come, however, in a crescendo of activity which provided one of the most sensational transformations in meteorological history. The meagre 4½ inches of rain which I had registered during the first half of the year was to be almost counterbalanced by a total of 17¾ inches during the last six months, bringing the year's total to 22¼ inches compared with an average annual fall of 23½ inches. This pattern was general in East Anglia and, indeed, in most of the country. So much for averages! Anyone, years hence, scanning annual totals in

Residents of Geldeston, close to the Norfolk–Suffolk boundary, discuss their third flooding in twelve months in April, 1981. *Eastern Daily Press*

search of unusual rainfall would assume 1976 to have been an almost normal year, whereas it gave us one of the driest Summers and wettest Autumns ever known.

August started off, unusually, with a ground frost at Witham and Belstead, but the most significant feature was the positioning of a large anticyclone right over the British Isles. There were occasional minor variations but the general pattern was of a resumption of hot, dry weather with no hint of more drama to come. The sun had lost a little of its bite but temperatures were in the mid to upper seventies on most days, soaring as late as the 25th to 86 degreees F. at Great Easton in Essex and Elmswell in Suffolk.

After a little thundery rain on the first two days, the drought continued until the 25th, by which time the water shortage had for some time caused severe deprivations. A ban on the use of hosepipes and the washing of cars had long been in force. Most rivers were very low, the River Stort being reported dry above Bishop's Stortford and the River Cam dry from the Essex border to its source. Many village ponds had completely dried up. In South Norfolk the situation was reported as "not yet critical" but in North Norfolk there was only about six to eight weeks' supply left. Supplies from the underlying chalk were at record low levels and there were contingency plans for standpipes during the next two months. Throughout most of East Anglia rainfall for the past six months had been, despite the July thunderstorms, considerably less than half the normal.

All that suddenly changed. A rain-making guru from India was persuaded to come to London to try to break the spell. There appeared on television on the evening of Wednesday, 25th August, a white-robed figure surrounded by his circle of priests, incanting for rain.

The official weather forecasters were unimpressed. So was a determined and very strong anticyclone with a central pressure as high as 30½ inches, which was, on the 27th, sitting firmly astride the British Isles with a supporting connecting link to the Azores high. With not the slightest sign of any break in the drought, the forecasters confidently predicted a continuance of fine weather over the Late Summer Bank Holiday weekend. That same night, a thundery low having developed over France, things quickly went meteorologically haywire; it seemed to me that in the confusion a pool of cold upper air which should have travelled South-west with the depression took the law into its own hands and moved instead North-west. Whatever the motivation behind this weird scene, severe thunderstorms broke out over a wide area. An inch of rain fell at Rushmere St Andrew and there was flooding in nearby Ipswich. Things rapidly got worse, the most violent storms occurring during Sunday and the early hours of Bank Holiday Monday when 1¼ inches of rain fell at Rushmere St Andrew. In Ipswich falls of about 2 inches were reported, and King's Lynn in Norfolk was deluged with 4¼ inches.

All this meteorological hullabaloo proved too much for the high-pressure systems and their regime finally collapsed during the first week of September. On 23rd September violent thunderstorms produced "freak" hailstorms in parts of North Suffolk. Worst hit was Westleton,

which was cut off by floodwater two to three feet deep. A six-foot wall was demolished and hailstones the size of marbles lay about four inches deep, with roadside drifts to about a foot high. On 25th September Scole, on the Norfolk side of the Waveney, experienced its first completely sunless day since 18th April.

The gurus had long since departed. It turned out to be one of the wettest Autumns in living memory.

Opposite: In a sweltering heat-wave, passing motorists could hardly believe their eyes.
East Anglian Daily Times

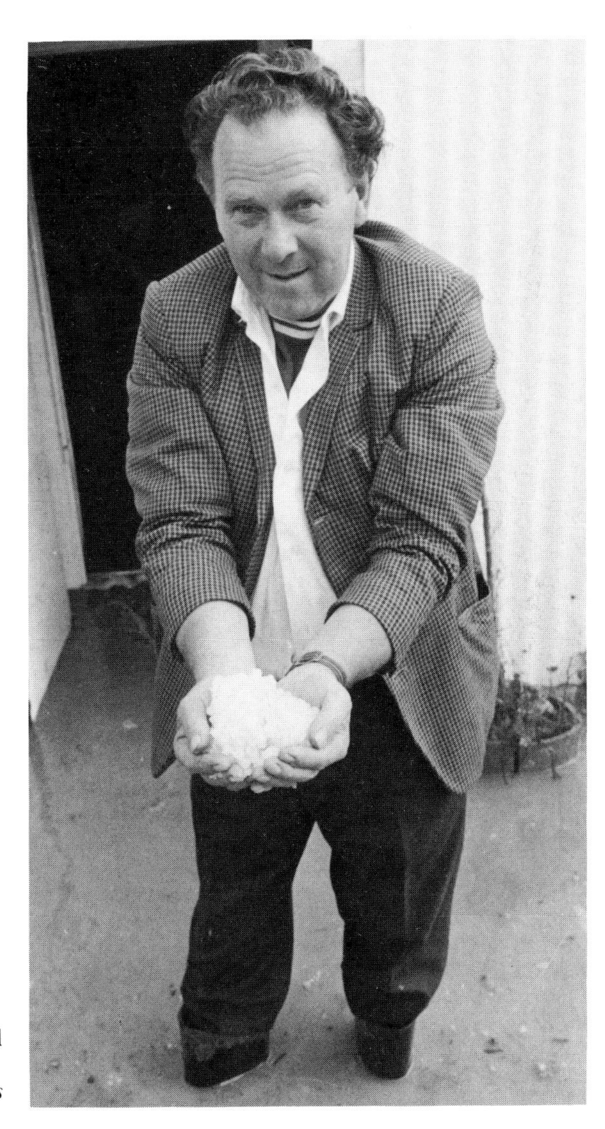

Right: Who's for a hail-ball fight?
East Anglian Daily Times

Soil temperatures during the heatwave

Farmers, horticulturalists and amateur gardeners suffered severely. The greater heating under bare soil (e.g. flower beds) is clearly shown in the accompanying table and it needs little imagination to appreciate from these morning observations the scorching heat to which soil (particularly when dry) is subjected by the blazing midday sun, with everything below the surface completely denied any cooling benefits from the wind.

HIGHEST SOIL TEMPERATURES RECORDED AT 0900 HRS G.M.T. AT LEVINGTON, 1976

	Depth under grass, inches			Depth under bare soil, inches		
	2	4	8	2	4	8
		Degrees F.			*Degrees F.*	
May	61	57	56	65	61	58
June	74	71	69	79	75	73
July	78	72	72	79	75	72
August	67	67	68	72	68	68
September	63	62	61	63	62	61

In 1976 I did not possess thermometers for very shallow readings but, better equipped, I have in later years often registered temperatures

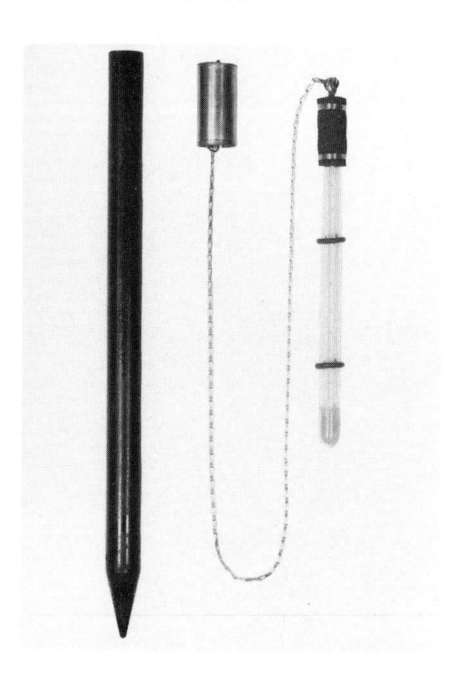

An earth thermometer is used for registering soil temperatures at depths of a foot or more. A metal tube is sunk to the depth required. *Casella (London) Ltd*

of over 100 degrees F. just below the surface when, with a fresh wind, midday shade temperatures have barely exceeded 75 degrees F. In 1976, temperatures far exceeding 100 degrees F. must have been commonplace in the first inch or so of soil.

Severe Winters

Really severe Winters in the British Isles do not occur in geographic isolation. Like hot Summers, they are major events, usually being part of an extensive cold weather system covering at least Scandinavia and large parts of the Continent; it would hardly be possible for East Anglia to have a severe Winter all to itself.

One of the most severe Winters ever known in this country was that of 1683/84. Another famous one was that of 1894/95, when the Thames was completely frozen over and there was ice to a depth of two feet in the Cambridgeshire Fens.

Severe Winters are even more difficult to define than outstandingly good Summers. A cold Winter with great amounts of snow tends to linger in the memory longer than one of lower temperatures but less snow. There are many complications in analysing and classifying severe Winters, but I give below my own selection of winters between 1875 and 1985 which could fairly be described as very severe, particularly as regards heavy snowfalls:

1875/76	1916/17
1878/79	1946/47
1885/86	1962/63
1894/95	1978/79

In many parts of the country, including East Anglia, December, 1981, was the coldest December for over a hundred years, but fairly

UNUSUALLY SNOWY WINTERS*
Rushmere St Andrew, 1939/40 to 1984/85

	No of days of snow or sleet					No of days of snow lying (0900 hrs G M T)				
	Dec	Jan	Feb	Mar	Total	Dec	Jan	Feb	Mar	Total
1939/40	2	10	10	4	26	—	16	13	4	33
1946/47	4	8	19	5	36	6	10	28	13	57
1962/63	7	19	13	1	40	3	29	27	4	63
1978/79	3	14	6	5	28	4	19	11	1	35

*Although, meteorologically, winter consists only of the months December to February, I have included March in the above Table in order to show the unusual protraction of winter snow in 1947.

UNUSUALLY COLD WINTERS
Belstead/Copdock, 1902/03 to 1984/85

	Mean monthly temperatures, degrees F. Dec	Jan	Feb	Winter mean
1916/17	36.9	34.5	33.2	34.9
1928/29	38.3	33.6	31.4	34.4
1939/40	37.3	29.6	34.4	33.8
1946/47	36.6	34.3	28.5*	33.2
1962/63	34.9	27.9*	29.7	30.8
1978/79	40.1	30.7	33.9	34.9
1981/82	32.4*	37.1	39.5	36.3
1984/85	41.4	32.2	35.3	36.3

*Indicates the coldest month of this name since the Copdock/Belstead records began in 1902.
Apart from six of the winters quoted, no winter since records began in 1902 had a mean temperature below 35°F.

normal temperatures in the following January and February disqualified the Winter of 1981/82 as a severe one. The Winter of 1962/63 is generally accepted as the snowiest of the present century but, because of the complexities of comparision, there is argument as to whether 1962/63 was in fact worse than 1946/47. The following comparative figures for the Ipswich region provide information which may help readers make their own judgment.

COMPARISON OF THE 1946/47 AND 1962/63 WINTERS

	Temperature, Belstead									Snowfall, Rushmere St Andrew	
	In screen					On grass					
	Average max. °F.	Average min. °F.	Mean temp. °F.	Lowest max. °F.	Lowest min. °F.	Lowest min. °F.	No of air frosts (32°F.)	No of ground frosts (32°F.)	No of ice-days (32°F.)	No of days snow or sleet	No of days snow lying
1946–47											
Dec	41.1	32.1	36.6	33	23	14	17	24	—	4	6
Jan	39.0	29.7	34.3	26	16	6	21	27	8	8	10
Feb	31.5	25.6	28.5	26	11	1	27	27	19†	19	28
Mar	44.3	33.3	38.8	31	16	9	15	19	1	5	13
	39.0	30.2	34.6	26	11	1	80	97	28	36	57
1962–63											
Dec	40.3	29.5	34.9	30	19	10	29	29	3	7	3
Jan	32.4	23.4	27.9	28	8*	1	29	31	15	19	29
Feb	33.9	25.4	29.7	28	16	10	27	28	8	14	27
Mar	48.4	36.4	42.4	37	25	12	8	16	—	1	4
	38.7	28.7	33.7	28	8	1	93	104	26	41	63

*Coldest night locally this century.
†Includes 14 consecutive ice-days.

I have always had the impression that the 1946/47 Winter was rather more severe than that of 1962/63, but that could be because in 1947 I was involved in frequent car journeys into snowy Norfolk. At any rate, the above table clearly indicates that in the Ipswich area 1962/63 was slightly more severe, with the exception that the very coldest days in 1947 were a little colder than in 1963; 1946/47 had two more "ice-days" than 1962/63; and in February, 1947, the average daily maximum temperature was lower than in any other month during the two winters.

Although the Winter of 1978/79 was not in total a record-breaker, the terrible road conditions in February, 1979, were unprecedented and merit special mention. I do not look at them comprehensively but simply from my own experience as a weather observer in Suffolk. December, 1978, had been a month of average temperatures, with a little snow on the first couple of days, some heavier falls just before Christmas and some really heavy snow, with drifting, on New Year's Eve. On New Year's Day I measured snow cover to a depth of five inches. For the rest of January snow lay on the ground on most days, being reinforced by further falls. Over England and Wales it was the third coldest January of the century, beaten only by 1947 and 1963.

Following a brief respite in February there was a sudden, sharp drop in temperature. Before dawn on Wednesday, 14th February, the temperature at Rushmere St Andrew was over 40 degrees F.; by midday it had dropped to 29 degrees F., turning overnight rain to snow. Severe Atlantic storms had caused flooding in Spain and Portugal, and in this country East Anglia had some of the worst blizzards. Increasingly heavy snow, lashed by relentless north-easterly gales into fierce blizzards, soon made roads impassable. Before that Wednesday was out, much public transport had been brought to a standstill; power cables, weighted by snow and lashed by the gales, were down in many places; fallen trees were blocking many roads; and Saffron Walden was reported as being completely cut off, as were dozens of other towns and villages.

Thursday the 15th was even worse. The blizzards, whipped by biting north-easterly gales from Russia, had caused drifting up to ten feet deep in many parts of East Anglia. Several local services, including Meals on Wheels, were put out of action and the RAC reported abandoned vehicles "all over the place". The Ipswich-based Radio Orwell switched to a round-the-clock emergency information service, the value of a local radio station in a crisis being made evident by the constant broadcasting of information and advice from police, motoring organisations and other public services. I kept listeners up to date with the weather prospects.

Next day East Anglia was almost buried under a thick blanket of snow and the 10 a.m. Radio Orwell newsreader described Ipswich as "a ghost town". Standing, surrounded by deep drifts, at my weather station at Rushmere St Andrew close to the normally busy main A12 road, I

Whatever the effect on traffic and on life generally, snow does have a great visual attraction, as this night-time photograph of Belstead Road, Ipswich, illustrates very well.
East Anglian Daily Times

called my wife out to listen; not a vehicle could be heard, nor the bark of a dog — there was total silence. The radio announcements went on. A Mr Fox, of Ipswich, offered snow-clearing help in his neighbourhood; performances at the Ipswich Theatre were cancelled; some firms offered tractors to help with towing; a few kindly private residents gave their addresses, offering hot drinks to stranded motorists; the Ipswich Co-operative Society announced suspension of all milk deliveries, though milk could be obtained at their shops and garages. Forty drivers were reported marooned at the *Magpie* public house at Stonham Parva on the Ipswich–Norwich road, while the local brewers announced cancellations of all deliveries; a local school of motoring thoughtfully announced that lessons were cancelled for the day. While helicopter crews were — in between the blizzards — searching for broken electricity cables, the Radio Orwell "Quick Sale" department announced that a listener wished to dispose of a tropical fish tank.

On Saturday the 17th, Ipswich Corporation buses were still out of action. The temperature remained below freezing day and night from Wednesday the 14th to Sunday the 18th, and only on Monday did a very slow thaw set in; but even up to Friday the 23rd slight night frosts were causing dangerously icy roads as the melting snow and slush were temporarily refrozen. Two days later we had the highest barometer readings for twenty-five years — 30.83 inches (1044 millibars) — in parts of East Anglia. Most of the snow on level surfaces had melted but it was not until early March that the last traces of drifts had disappeared. It was fortunate that the temperature rose slowly; a more rapid thaw could have caused disastrous flooding.

So ended a most alarming experience of gales, blizzards and drifting snow. Yet, statistically, that Winter was nothing compared to 1946/47 and 1962/63. All the chaos was created by only two days of blizzard conditions, due jointly to a depression to the South of the British Isles and an anticyclone to the North. The steep barometric pressure gradients between the opposing systems caused the north-easterly gales and freezing temperatures — and the depression which had flooded Spain and Portugal provided all the moisture needed to produce the blizzards.

That the February road conditions in 1979 were generally described as the worst in living memory was, I think, attributable to three factors. Firstly, the ferocity of the gales and the intensity of snowfall in such a short period; secondly, the greatly increased number of vehicles on the roads as compared with previous decades which greatly aggravated the dislocation of traffic; and, thirdly, the disappearance of many of the hedges which once served to protect roads from driving snow.

Just as the Winter of 1978/79 did not rank as one of the classic ones, the 1984/85 Winter was not one of the "greats", though two particularly vicious spells in January and February broke many records for low temperatures. After a mild December, the night of 7th–8th January, 1985, was the coldest ever known over many parts of the country. The coldest spot in East Anglia was apparently Loddon in Norfolk, with an air minimum of minus 4 degrees F. At Rushmere St Andrew the air minimum was 6 degrees F., beating the previous record of 8 degrees F. on 20th January, 1940.

A return of very severe weather during the second and third weeks of February was notable, because although snow depths were generally less than six inches or so, strong gale-force winds caused severe drifting and gave a dramatic wind-chill effect, adding to the miseries of a Winter that will long live in the memory.

To return to my overall comparison of severe Winters — considering only the temperature factor — the only years in Orlando Whistlecraft's records at Thwaite (from 1840 to 1882) which were equal to or colder than either 1939/40, 1946/47, 1962/63 or 1978/79 were:

MEAN TEMPERATURE, degrees F.

	Dec	Jan	Feb	Dec/Feb
1840/41	32.2	32.6	34.9	33.2
1870/71	31.7	31.9	41.2	34.9
1878/79	32.0	31.1	37.3	33.5

The Rev Leonard Jenyns, analysing his records at Swaffham Bulbeck for the years 1831–1849, commented that during that period only four Winters were particularly severe:

1837/38	1844/45
1840/41	1846/47

He observed that "none of these Winters had a mean temperature exceeding 34½ degrees F. The severest of all was that of 1840/41, the mean temperature of which was only 32.7 degrees F." The records of Orlando Whistlecraft at Thwaite agree substantially with the Swaffham Bulbeck figures, but the Thwaite temperatures are slightly higher. I do not think this necessarily means that Thwaite has milder Winters than Swaffham Bulbeck; the differences are very small and could easily be accounted for by discrepancies between the siting and exposure of the two sets of instruments.

Summing up, there are undoubtedly periods with marked tendencies towards mild or cold Winters (there was a run of generally mild Winters during most of the 1970s) but I can find no evidence of any definable pattern. Nor can I find evidence that really severe "Christmas card" Winters are becoming a thing of the past.

Ice-days

The term "ice-day" is not merely a splendidly evocative one; it is a phrase used by meteorologists to define an occasion when the screen (or air) temperature does not at any time rise above freezing point (32 degrees F.) during the twenty-four hours ended 0900 GMT. There is just one snag. The routine 9 a.m. reading is always "thrown back" and credited to the previous day — a reliable procedure at least nine times out of ten. If, for example, the temperature remained below freezing all day but a thaw set in between midnight and 0900 the following morning, then the previous day would lose its right to be called an ice-day. The effect of this small loophole is that statistics will show slightly fewer (never more) ice-days than have actually occurred during daytime. For purposes of comparision, however, the figures are useful.

The following table shows the number of ice-days recorded at Belstead/Copdock each decade since observations commenced in 1902. (No ice-days have ever been registered in the locality between April and October inclusive):

NUMBER OF ICE-DAYS IN EACH DECADE

	January, February, March	November, December	Total
1902–1911	13	11	24
1912–1921	23	3	26
1922–1931	21	7	28
1932–1941	21	6	27
1942–1951	63	5	68
1952–1961	33	—	33
1962–1971	42	16	58
1972–1981	19	2	21

"The time is out of joint"

"It is usual for the weather to be unusual": so, in East Anglia, when — and how often — can we expect heatwaves and cold snaps out of season?

July and August are normally our warmest months, with almost identical temperatures ranging from daily maxima of 67–69 degrees F. on the coast to about 72 degrees F. further inland — and we gratefully accept as a fair expectation that similar temperatures often occur in June and September. But in other "out of season" months of the year such temperatures are less common and arouse appreciative comment.

Taking an East Anglian overall daily maximum for July and August of 71 degrees F., the table shows the number of days during the twenty years 1961–1980 when, during the "out of season" months, the temperature at Rushmere St Andrew reached or exceeded the July–August average.

January February	March	April	May	October	November December
—	2	13	91	18	—

"Chilly for the time of year"

January stands alone as our coldest month, with very little variation in average temperature over the whole region. We expect — and get — similar midwinter temperatures quite frequently in December and February, but we tend to grumble if they occur earlier or later than that. Taking a maximum daily temperature of 43 degrees F. as a fair Winter average for the whole of East Anglia, the table shows the number of days during the twenty years 1961–1980 when — outside the three Winter months of December, January and February — the maximum temperature at Rushmere St Andrew did not rise above the January average:

March	April	May, June, July, August & September	October	November
221	20	—	1	112

Analysis of these tables shows that anticipation in May of Summer temperatures occurs far more frequently than does the October retrospect. March may be the gateway to Spring, but it is more frequently the backdoor of Winter — and in nine of the twenty years the cold was very prolonged. As the front door to Winter, November treats us more kindly. "Winters set in later nowadays", many people say — but my scrutiny of old records does not indicate any material change in the pattern. November has never been a Winter month.

The notorious fickleness of April is shown by the fairly even number of occasions when it has given us both midsummer and midwinter temperatures — and in each of the years 1962, 1968 and 1979 it gave us both extremes. Sometimes the April extremes occur in the wrong order. Outside the period covered by the foregoing tables, during the second and third weeks of April, 1945, temperatures soared on six days well above the July average and, following several weeks of generally mild weather, Spring growth was doing well. Orchard blossoms had been spectacular; the profusion of white blooms so obscured the leaves and branches that it looked like snow on a Christmas card. On 30th April (nine days after a temperature of 73 degrees F.) we woke, pinched ourselves to make sure we were not dreaming, and faced the shivering reality. Thick, heavy snow was falling silently in huge flakes — and the leaves and branches of the fruit trees were again obscured. Boughs drooped low with the weight of snow and motorists had to shovel snow away to get out their cars for the morning journey. For two days we suffered in below-January temperatures. Then, by the second week of May, we were basking in a heatwave of 80 degrees F.

In 1947, also outside the period under review, we have another exceptional example. From January to March we had one of the severest winters of the century, followed by one of the best and hottest Summers ever. At Rushmere St Andrew, the ground had been completely covered with snow from 23rd January to 13th March inclusive. During March the maximum temperature failed to exceed the January average on thirteen days (two of which were below freezing-point all day); three days in April failed to exceed the January average, but, in a spectacular recovery, May gave us sixteen glorious days of temperatures to be expected in July, culminating in successive maxima of 81 degrees F., 86 degrees F., and 88 degrees F. on the last three days.

Soil temperatures

Whatever heat may be generated at the earth's core, the temperature of the outer layer of soil is, to a depth of several feet, closely related to the heat of the sun's rays and the temperature of the layer of air immediately above the earth's surface. This is clearly indicated in the composite table overleaf showing a profile of the temperature pattern above and below the earth's surface, based on the records at Levington and Copdock, both in Suffolk.

Levington and Copdock are less than ten miles apart, and the fact that the averages are derived from different periods does not detract from the value of the table. Indeed, the results serve to emphasise the overall uniformity of the pattern, both in time and place.

It is interesting to note that, despite the storage of the sun's warmth by the earth in the Summer, the average annual figures at all depths below the surface are very close to the average mean air temperature (average daily maximum plus average daily minimum divided by two). For comparative purposes, I have included in the table the average grass minimum temperatures; too much importance should not, however, be attached to these. On a cloudy night the grass minimum is usually very close to (and sometimes the same as) the screen minimum; on a clear night it is usually several degrees lower. Consequently, the "radiation index" which I have inserted has no definite quantitive value but — showing the difference in degrees F. between the average screen and average grass minima — it does give some indication of the seasonal pattern of loss by radiation. The tendency for clearer skies in Summer gives a higher average loss than at other seasons — but the most severe

PROFILE OF MONTHLY TEMPERATURE VALUES ABOVE AND BELOW THE SURFACE

Compiled from observations at Levington (6 miles SE of Ipswich) and Belstead/Copdock (3 miles SW of Ipswich). All temperatures above the surface and down to 8 inches were recorded at Levington; the values at 1 foot and 4 feet at Belstead/Copdock.

No of years'		Temperatures to nearest whole degrees Fahrenheit												
average ended 1980	*Above grass-covered surface* — Levington	Jan	Feb	Mar	Apr	May	Jun	Jul	Aug	Sep	Oct	Nov	Dec	Year
25	Mean temperature in screen (4 ft above ground)	38	39	42	46	52	58	61	61	58	52	44	40	49
25	Average screen max. (4 ft above ground)	43	44	48	53	59	67	68	69	66	58	50	45	56
25	Average screen min. (4 ft above ground)	34	34	36	39	44	50	53	53	51	46	39	36	43
25	Average grass min. (exposed to sky 1 in. above ground)	30	30	32	35	39	45	48	48	45	40	34	31	38
No of years' average ended 1980	*Below grass-covered surface* — Levington													
20	Average earth temperatures at varying depths at 0900 hours G.M.T. — 2 ins below surface	38	38	40	47	55	62	65	63	58	52	44	39	50
24	4 ins below surface	37	38	41	46	54	61	63	63	58	52	44	40	50
24	8 ins below surface	38	39	41	47	53	60	63	63	59	53	45	40	50
No of years' average ended 1941	*Below grass-covered surface*—Belstead/Copdock (Average screen temperatures at Belstead/Copdock are almost identical to those at Levington)				*					*				
28	Average earth temperatures at 0900 hours GMT — 1 ft below surface	39	39	41	46	53	60	63	62	58	51	45	40	50
28	4 ft below surface	43	42	43	46	50	56	59	60	58	55	49	45	51
	Radiation index — difference between average screen and grass minima at Levington	4	4	4	4	5	5	5	5	6	6	5	5	5

*It is interesting to note the "threshold" months at the 1 ft and 4 ft depths; the transition period before the 1 ft readings become warmer than at 4 ft during the summer — and vice versa individual losses due to clear skies are most likely to occur in fine, calm weather during Spring, Autumn and Winter months. Such losses are greatest in areas of sandy soil, particularly when the soil is dry.

In studying the table it is important to bear in mind that, whereas the screen (air) temperatures cover the whole twenty-four hours, the soil temperatures refer only to the daily observations at 0900 hrs GMT. There is very little time-lag between air temperatures and temperatures down to a depth of about four inches. At about eight inches to one foot depth, temperatures are usually at their lowest about 0900 hrs. The time-lag at four feet is anything from three to four days, so that time of day is immaterial.

As a guide to the range of temperatures which can occur below the surface, the following table shows the extremes registered at Copdock/Belstead during the forty-one years 1914 to 1954. These figures refer to the 0900 hrs GMT readings when the one-foot temperature is just about at its lowest (after a hot Summer day the one-foot thermometer usually reaches its highest during early evening). Temperatures at the lower depth of four feet have no relationship to the time of day.

HIGHEST AND LOWEST EARTH TEMPERATURES
Below grass, 0900 hrs GMT at Copdock/Belstead, 1914–1954

Depth	Highest temp., °F.	Lowest temp., °F.
1 foot	71.7 13th July, 1941	32.8 13th March, 1947
4 feet	63.1 23rd August, 1932	35.9 16th March, 1947

The average figures in the preceding Levington/Copdock/Belstead table by no means tell the whole story. The overall uniformity of pattern is real enough but, as we know, averages are simply an agglomeration of variables. In the short term, very wide differentials between air and earth temperatures frequently have a marked effect on our weather, particularly in the local sense. This is generally due to the time lag between changes in the air temperature and their subsequent effect on the temperature of the earth. A commonplace example is when a sudden thaw sets in after a long wintry spell. A mild and moist airstream drifting across land which has become thoroughly chilled will, in contact with the cold ground, be cooled to saturation point, thus causing widespread fog. It takes time for the ground to warm up.

It is a relationship full of complexities. On a sunny Summer day, even with a cool, brisk wind, the soil an inch or so below the surface — fully protected from the wind but in the full glare of the sun — will very quickly rise to temperatures far higher than that of the air above it. A typical example of this very common occurrence was on Easter Saturday, 18th April, 1981, when following a ground frost (grass minimum 28 degrees F.) the previous night, an East to North-east wind kept the screen temperature down to a rather chilly 54 degrees F. But it was a sunny day and a thermometer an inch below the bare soil of our rosebed rose to 76 degrees F.; there was that night another ground frost (29 degrees F.).

Thus, young plants whose roots are encouraged by July-plus temperatures during the day can have their tender leaves nipped during

The author taking his daily readings of maximum, minimum and wet and dry-bulb thermometers in the screen. He also records minimum grass temperatures and earth temperatures at several levels from an inch to four feet beneath the surface. *Tony Ray*

the night by midwinter temperatures. Dry soil heats readily; wet soil has a dampening effect on the sun's heat.

Obviously the temperature of the soil and its relationship with that of the air is of considerable significance to gardeners and some further notes on the subject appear in chapter four.

Seeking the sun

How do the temperature patterns of East Anglia compare with some of the well-known foreign holiday resorts? The following table is not designed so much for visitors as for residents of East Anglia, particularly those who may be interested in locating holiday spots where they can enjoy East Anglian Summer temperatures at out-of-season times. These are indicated by the lines of demarcation in the table:–

EAST ANGLIAN AND FOREIGN RESORTS COMPARED

	Averages,* East Anglian daily maximum temperatures °F.	Average daily maximum temperatures, foreign holiday resorts				
		French Riviera °F.	*Rome* °F.	*Majorca* °F.	*Corfu* °F.	*Canary Islands* °F.
January	42	55	53	57	56	71
February	44	55	55	59	58	71
March	50	58	61	63	61	72
April	56	63	67	66	66	73
May	63	69	73	73	74	75
June	68	75	82	80	83	80
July	71	81	87	84	88	83
August	71	81	87	85	88	84
September	67	77	81	81	82	82
October	59	70	72	73	73	80
November	50	63	62	64	65	73
December	45	56	55	59	60	70

*The composite temperatures in column one are compiled from averages representing inland areas and places within the coastal strip. Averages for places actually on the coastline have not been included. Regarding the latter, it can be reckoned that average maximum daytime temperatures at such places as Cromer, Aldeburgh and Clacton-on-Sea are usually about the same as those inland in mid-Winter but about two or three degrees cooler in Summer.

In putting the above table to practical use, an important fact to remember is that all the figures are shade temperatures. Generally speaking, most of the localities in the table enjoy more sunshine than we do.

Sunshine

The wind "bloweth where it listeth"; rain can fall at any hour of day or night; there is no practically defined limit to the amount of rain that can fall, nor to the highest or lowest temperatures. But sunshine happens only between dawn and sunset — and its maximum possible duration is mathematically predictable.

Sunshine potentials vary over the British Isles according to latitude and the declination of the sun. Scotland has the greatest seasonal differential — a magnificent "possible" of about 18½ hours a day in June (two hours more than the East Anglian potential) and a meagre "possible" of six hours a day in December (nearly two hours less than in East Anglia).

The maximum possible daily sunshine in East Anglia is approximately as follows:

Jan	Feb	Mar	Apr	May	Jun	Jul	Aug	Sep	Oct	Nov	Dec	Possible annual total
8½	10	11¾	13¾	15¾	16½	16¼	14½	12¾	10¾	8¾	7¾	4471

The standard instrument for measuring the duration of sunshine is the Campbell-Stokes recorder, a solid glass sphere about 4 inches in diameter mounted on a post. Behind the sphere is a curved card on which the sun's rays are sharply focused, charring a line as the burning spot slowly makes its daily journey along the card. Each day's total sunshine is calculated by adding together the lengths of successive burn marks (unbroken, of course, on days of continuous sunshine). The sun does not have sufficient power to make its mark immediately after sunrise or before sunset, nor when it is hazy; hence official records refer to hours of "bright" sunshine.

In terms of actual sunshine as a percentage of the possible, the South fares better than the North — over thirty-five per cent annually in parts of southern England and only twenty-five to thirty per cent in Scotland. East Anglia averages about thirty-five per cent. Actual hours of recorded bright sunshine average between 1,000 hours and 1,200 hours annually in the North of Scotland and about 1,800 hours along the south coast, Generally speaking, the sunniest parts of the British Isles lie in a narrow belt from Great Yarmouth in Norfolk, southwards down the East

Anglian coast and thence — mostly in a wider strip — along the south coast to Devon and Cornwall.

In October, 1920, Felixstowe, Suffolk, was the sunniest spot in the entire country, with a total of 207 hours during the month. On average East Anglia generally has only about sixty-six completely sunless days per annum — about ten days a year better than parts of Central England and the west coast.

The inland parts of East Anglia have an average of something like 1,500 to 1,550 hours a year. Along the coast annual totals vary between

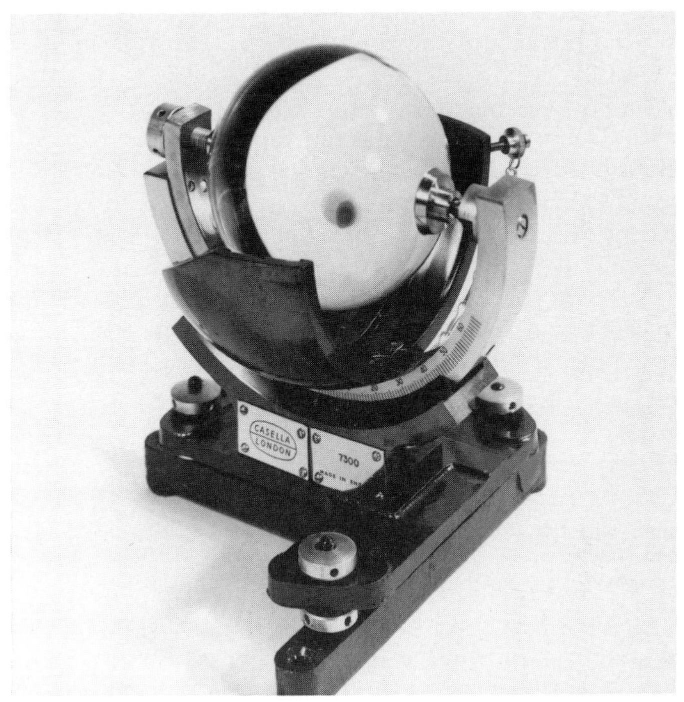

A Campbell-Stokes sunshine recorder.
Casella (London) Ltd

1,550 and 1,675 hours. The lower averages inland are probably mostly due to the frequent formation overland of "convection" clouds, caused by the heating of the land by the sun. Other things being equal (most inportantly, the relative humidity of the air), the hotter and more prolonged the sunshine the more likely are the convection clouds to form. The sea absorbs rather than reflects the sun's heat, so in hot weather convectional clouds develop less frequently over and very near to the sea. When and where they occur they do, despite their innocent nature, cast shadows. On a fine, warm day one can often, in the coastal strip, see the coast outlined in the sky by the presence of inland convection clouds. In the Winter, with the sea a warming factor, convection clouds tend to develop over the sea, though usually less frequently and to a lesser extent.

Industrial haze can be a contributory factor to the loss of inland sunshine. In this respect, East Anglia is far better off than many other parts of the country. On the other hand, low cloud and sea fog often cut off the sun near the coast while inland it is sunny. But the effect on the annual total is not very great.

Looking further afield to the vast continents of the world, sunshine totals in the central regions can be very high indeed — largely because, being far removed from any moist sea air, the strong vertical air currents caused by the sun's heat have too low a humidity to allow the formation of clouds.

The sunniest months in East Anglia are usually May, June and July, with December the dullest month of the year. As the days lengthen, February shows a marked increase in both potential and recorded hours of sun. But there is a sting in the tail. "As the day lengthens, so the cold strengthens" says the old proverb. That is very often true. Some of our most Wintry weather often occurs in February, as in 1979.

From the weather records diligently kept by the late John H. Willis, of Norwich, the following table shows the monthly totals of bright sunshine at Norwich during the thirty years 1913 to 1942:

NORWICH SUNSHINE, 1913–1942

	Hours,	Sunniest recorded		Dullest recorded	
	average	Total hours	Year	Total hours	Year
January	50	74	1940	22	1922
February	67	120	1934	28	1940
March	122	192	1931	66	1916
April	155	252	1942	56	1937
May	214	280	1922	118	1932
June	204	260	1940	136	1916
July	194	295	1935	108	1913
August	182	234	1933	131	1920
September	152	213	1928	107	1941
October	114	184	1920	57	1918
November	66	109	1920	34	1933
December	43	67	1925	24	1934
Year	1563	1799	1921	1298	1932

There was a most remarkable sunshine bonanza in May, 1980, when from the 9th to the 19th the British Isles experienced one of the sunniest spells ever known, with East Anglia enjoying the most sunshine of all. In describing this magnificent event, I am grateful for permission to reproduce the following map and some details from an article in the *Journal of Meteorology*, April, 1981 (Vol. VI, No 58), by David G. Tout of the Department of Geography, University of Manchester.

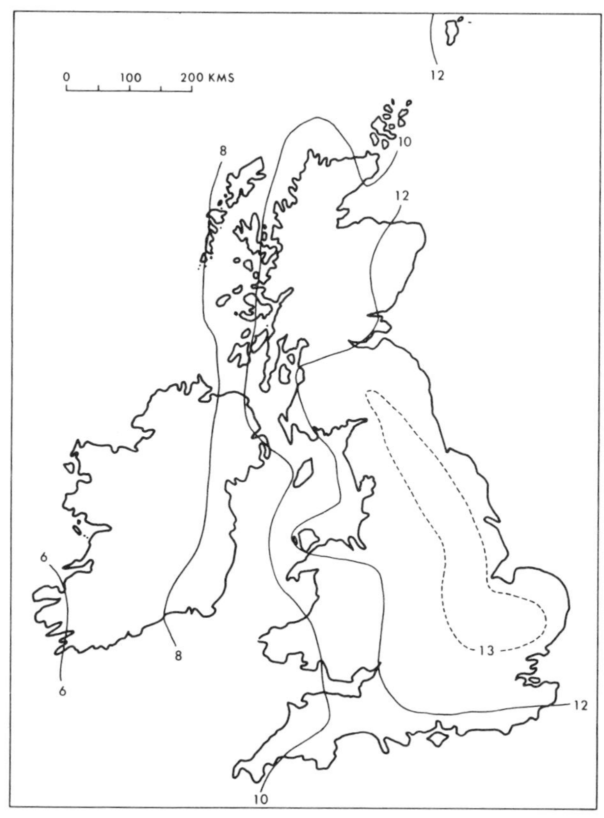

Mean daily bright sunshine (in hours) for the period 9th–19th May, 1980, based on 53 synoptic stations. The map clearly shows the inclusion of East Anglia in the sunniest area — during the whole of that eleven-day spell sunshine over a large area of Eastern England exceeded an average of 13 hours a day, with a maximum of 13.6 hours at Wittering, Cambridgeshire.

By courtesy of David G. Tout and the Journal of Meterology.

That brilliant spell was not without its drawbacks. The anticyclone which provided the blue skies also brought in some very dry south-easterly winds from the Continent, during which time I was registering some very low mid-afternoon relative humidities. On 14th and 15th May the humidity was as low as thirty-three per cent. The speed of the continental air current was brisk (Force 4 to 5) and this, combined with the drying effect of the sunshine, caused serious dehydration of some plants. At Rushmere St Andrew, tender newly-formed leaf buds on our rose bushes were shrivelled and browned just as though affected by a sharp frost. Rushmere St Andrew is only 10 miles from the coast and a high salt content in the onshore wind may have been a contributory factor in the ruination of the leaf-buds.

Barometric pressure

You do not need thermometer to tell you that the weather is hot; nor a rain gauge to tell you it is pouring with rain; but you do need a barometer to know whether the atmospheric pressure is high or low — unless you are one of those who claim they feel a tingling sensation when the barometer is very high. Some victims of multiple sclerosis suffer increased symptoms when atmospheric pressure is low and some alleviation when it is high. Recent medical research, still in the experimental stage, appears to indicate that perhaps sixty per cent of

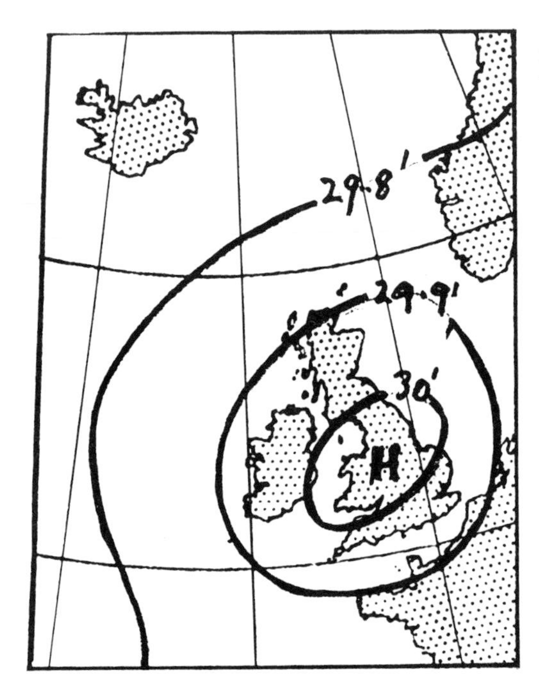

A typical synoptic chart with isobars linking places with equal pressure.

multiple sclerosis sufferers treated obtain relief from hyperbaric oxygen treatment, in which they are subjected to more than double the atmospheric pressure (33lb per square inch instead of the natural normal of about 14lb).

So far as the weather is concerned, although the barometer is probably the most important single meteorological instrument, the reading of one barometer in isolation has little value except to tell us whether pressure is rising, falling or steady. The significance, particularly for forecasting purposes, lies in the geographic distribution of pressure — a matter of relative values.

Although East Anglia has its own characteristics regarding rainfall, temperature and other factors, the readings of barometers within the region merely conform to the general pattern over the rest of the country. Any sudden (and often very local) jumps and jerks in pressure are usually associated with thunderstorms, tornadoes and the like, frequently associated with the arrival of a cold front.

Those fortunate enough to own a barograph will see these tell-tale traces clearly shown on their chart. A micro-barograph (which magnifies the variations) can produce some spectacular records.

One of the largest variations of barometric pressure over a few days occurred in 1943. At Belstead Hall the barometer was as low as 28.97 inches (981 mb) on 8th May, during a spell of strong to gale winds with rain. Less than a week later glorious sunshine was the order of the day and by the 16th the barometer had reached 30.80 inches (1043 mb), more than 14 hours of sun being recorded on each of the four successive days 16th–19th. Remarkable!

The old records of the Rev. L. Jenyns show that the average

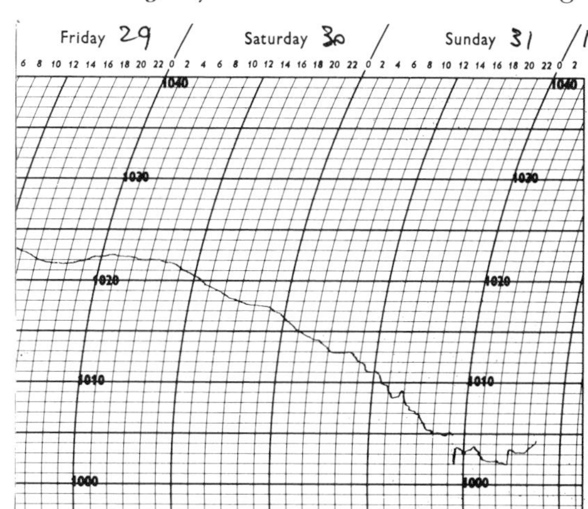

A section of a micro-barograph chart showing the barometric pressure fluctuations at Belstead, 29th July to 1st August, 1983. The unstable conditions as a thunderstorm develops after a period of great heat are clearly seen.
Richard Wilson

barometer readings at Swaffham Bulbeck, Cambridgeshire, during the nineteen years 1831–1849 was 29.89 inches. The highest and lowest readings were 30.88 inches and 28.14 inches, both in January. A survey shows that at Copdock/Belstead, Suffolk, the highest and lowest readings during the forty years 1915–1954 were 30.98 inches (1049 mb) on 26th January, 1932, and 28.53 inches (966 mb) on 9th December, 1954. It is interesting to note that the extreme readings both in Cambridgeshire and Suffolk, over different periods of time, all occurred during midwinter.

Relative humidity

The long East Anglian coastline makes humidity an important factor in the local climate. The relative humidity of the air affects us all, including the little toy men and their wives who pop in and out of their quaint weather-houses. It affects us in a variety of ways and it can be a deceiver.

Often, in hot weather, I have heard comments during the afternoon when the temperature should be beginning to fall such as "Phew! Isn't it getting hot?" Quite frequently it is the relative humidity and not the temperature which is rising. Indeed, one can experience a feeling of increasing oppression when an actual drop in temperature accompanies the arrival of moister air. This particular deception can be explained by the "Discomfort Factor". As a rule-of-thumb guide, the "70s rule" is quite useful: if the shade temperature is 70 degrees F. or more and the relative humidity 70 per cent or more, we can be pretty sure that conditions will feel close and muggy.

What is the actual definition of relative humidity? Why "relative" — and how does it affect East Anglian weather? The actual amount of moisture in the air can be measured as an absolute figure in terms of vapour pressure (the vapour being invisible until precipitation occurs in the form of cloud, rain, snow, hail, fog, mist, dew and frost). This quantitative information has scientific significance but it is the relative and not the absolute amount of moisture in the air which makes us aware of dry or damp conditions.

There are limits to the amount of moisture the air can hold. The relative humidity tells us the actual amount expressed as a percentage of the maximum possible. Thus, a relative humidity of 100 per cent does not mean a state of 100 per cent water (in which we would all drown!). It simply means that the moisture content of the atmosphere is at its maximum possible level — i.e., saturation point (or "dew-point"), which is when precipitation of some form or another usually occurs.

Temperature is all-important. Warm air can hold more moisture than cold air. When we feel the air to be either dry or humid, we are reacting not to the absolute amount of moisture (the vapour pressure) but to the combination of temperature and the amount of water vapour expressed as a percentage of possible.

If unsaturated air is cooled sufficiently, saturation can occur without any increase in the actual moisture content. Even when the absolute moisture content of the air is fairly constant (and it often is), habitual nocturnal cooling can in itself achieve saturation point, resulting in dew (hoar or rime frost when it is freezing), mist or fog. Next morning, when the sun comes out, the relative humidity will fall even though the absolute moisture content may remain the same.

These relationships cause many complex situations. East Anglian averages conform to the general pattern that the relative humidity is usually at its highest just before dawn and lowest shortly after midday — the exact reverse of the day and night temperature trends.

South-westerly winds from the Atlantic are usually associated with moist air. In East Anglia however, they have dried out considerably during their long trek from the West Coast, but they often retain a fair amount of moisture. In contrast, although easterlies from the Continent are often very dry indeed, the short journey across the North Sea usually increases their relative humidity (particularly if they are travelling slowly), though they dry out again as they continue their journey westwards.

In a hot easterly spell in late Spring or early Summer (with the North Sea not yet recovered from its Winter cold) the sharp cooling effect can quickly bring the originally dry continental air up to saturation point — and sunbathing on some East Anglian beaches can be quickly spoiled by chilly banks of mist or fog rolling in off the sea, helped along by the easterly breeze.

Sea breezes are, by their nature, almost invariably accompanied by an increase in relative humidity.

Very low relative humidities usually create conditions of unusual clarity, with exceptional visibility. A combination of strong sunshine and an extremely low relative humidity has its hazards (as many sunbathers learned in the famous heatwave of 1976).

When a dry easterly wind blowing in from the Continent is a particularly brisk one, the journey across the North Sea is too swift to allow much moisture to be picked up and the continental air which arrives in East Anglia is almost as arid as when it started, giving some very low readings of relative humidity. One unwelcome side effect is excessive dehydration, particularly affecting young plants.

Dry winds in East Anglia do not always come from the East, however. They sometimes come from the usually moist West or South-west — and when they are strong and the weather warm, they create a most uncanny feeling. A spectacular dry and warm south-westerly gale occurred on 14th August, 1979. On the previous day, the weather charts showed a depression off South-west Ireland which looked fairly harmless, even though the forecasters expected it to deepen as it moved north-east. At 0900 GMT on the 13th I registered a SSW wind, Force 3; a temperature of 67 degrees F. and a high relative humidity of 88 per cent. During the day the temperature rose to 73 degrees F. and the humidity remained high; the depression had started to turn nasty, deepening rapidly as it moved up the Irish Sea.

At 0900 GMT on the 14th I reported a SSW wind with a strength up to Force 6 — and increasing. The temperature was 65 degrees F. and the relative humidity again high — 84 per cent. The sky was half covered with alto-cumulus and strato-cumulus clouds. During the morning the depression became increasingly vicious as it continued to move up the Irish sea, deepening alarmingly. The BBC midday news reported 70

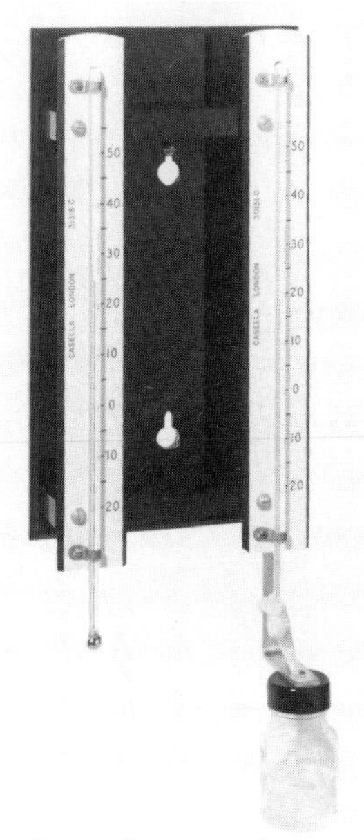

A wet and dry-bulb thermometer. *Casella (London) Ltd.*

m.p.h. gales, and caught in this rapidly worsening storm were yachts taking part in the Fastnet Race; the tragedy that resulted has become part of yachting history. Force 10 winds had also been reported and there were warnings of possible structural damage.

Fortunately, we in East Anglia were well away from the main storm (I registered only 0.02 inches of rain throughout) — and it was on that day that a most remarkable change in humidity took place. By 1000 hrs GMT the clouds had almost cleared at Rushmere St. Andrew; the wind was gusting from the South-west to Force 7 to 8 — and at 1130 GMT, with a practically cloudless sky and a temperature of 71 degrees F. the relative humidity had made a surprising and spectacular drop to only 45 per cent. The combined effect of warmth, a SW gale and an unusually low relative humidity created a most eerie "drying" feeling. Descriptive notes in my daily register were: "a warm and very dry storm".

Night-time relative humidities have their own interesting qualities. On a cold, clear Winter night, other factors being equal, a low relative humidity is far more conducive to severe frost than moist air, particularly when it is in a region of dry, sandy soil. In Summer, a high relative humidity on a very warm night is as much the cause of inability to sleep as the temperature itself.

Towards dusk, the interaction of temperature and relative humidity often causes shallow "lakes" of mist to form near the East Anglian estuaries, on marshy land, and in the Fens and the Broads. Particularly in calm weather, the lower layers of air over moist areas have so high a relative humidity that it requires very little nocturnal cooling to bring them to saturation point. Starting off like thin skeins of filmy cobweb, the condensation develops into more continuous sheets of mist, often drifting away from their source of origin and harassing motorists on nearby roads with unexpected and tricky patches only a few feet high. Although the layer of air over neighbouring dry land may be cooled to the same extent, its lower relative humidity may allow the cooling to take place without saturation point being reached.

The instrumental measurement of relative humidity is interesting. It can be achieved with a fair degree of accuracy with a hygrometer motivated by strands of human hair — or, far more accurately, with a pair of thermometers, a dry-bulb and a wet-bulb. Apart from its greater accuracy, the latter method has the advantage that the wet-bulb temperature has a very significant bearing on human comfort and discomfort and this information can be of great value.

The following is a very simple table, based on my own observations, as a rule of thumb guide to the practical values of relative humidity:

Relative humidity, %	General description
90–100	Very damp
80–90	Damp
70–80	Fairly damp
60–70	Average
50–60	Dry to average
40–50	Dry
30–40	Very dry
less than 30	Exceptionally dry

The above are outdoor values. (It is generally recommended for comfortable living conditions indoors that the relative humidity should be about 50 per cent, preferably with an indoor temperature of about 68–70 degrees F.). Out-of-doors, a very hot day with a "fairly damp" humidity would feel far more humid and oppressive than a cooler day with the same relative humidity because of the "Discomfort Factor".

Wind

The prevailing winds over the British Isles are mainly from between south-west and west — and have been for a very long time, certainly for the past six hundred years or so. East Anglia is no exception to the rule, sharing with the rest of the country a general pattern of airflow which is caused by a marked tendency for high barometric pressure near the Azores and generally low pressure over Greenland, extending to Iceland.

The differences in barometric pressure between the "high" and "low" systems are, on average, at their greatest during the Winter months (indicated by a lot of isobars on the weather maps); hence winds are usually stronger in the Winter than in the Summer. Broadly speaking, the month with the highest average wind speed in East Anglia is March, closely followed by January, February and December. July has the lowest average speeds, followed by June and September. Although the average wind speeds over East Anglia are probably lower than in any other region of the British Isles, that does not mean that winds from all quarters are generally lighter in East Anglia than elsewhere. An important factor is the natural slowing of wind speeds due to friction with the earth. Above two thousand feet or so, the effect of friction is greatly reduced. Even fairly low-lying clouds can often be seen scudding along at an obviously faster rate than that of the surface wind. Forests, profuse vegetation, uneven contours and the buildings in large towns all contribute to the slowing down of the wind. Absence of such features means that large, flat and more desolate areas like the Fenlands of Cambridgeshire and Lincolnshire suffer far more from bleak, whistling winds than many other areas.

Thus, one of the reasons for lower average wind speeds in East Anglia is logical — and open to misinterpretation. The wind over the British Isles blows more frequently from the South-west than from any other direction. Draw a line north-east from Land's End and it will reach to Great Yarmouth, more than three hundred miles, a longer SW to NE overland route than anywhere else in the country — which means that the cumulative slowing down by friction of the prevailing south-westerly winds over the land is at its maximum in East Anglia. On the contrary, easterly winds in East Anglia are subject to very little friction.

The average strength of the wind has a diurnal as well as a monthly pattern. Average speeds over South-east England generally reach their highest somewhere between 0800 hrs GMT and about 1900 hrs and are at their lowest approximately between midnight and 0600 hrs. A detailed survey of East Anglia would probably show that the highest average speeds of the year occur from about midday to 1500 hrs. GMT between late February and April.

But these are broad generalisations, and it would be foolish to assume that a gale will inevitably ease off during the night or strengthen during the day. Passing storms are no respecters of timetables. But in quieter conditions the diurnal pattern is noticeable. During fair weather the wind often drops at night, freshening next morning when the sun recommences its stimulation of the atmosphere — that is the weather machine at work. Between early Autumn and late Spring, a falling off of wind at night — if accompanied by clear skies — is a frequent indicator of a night frost. Although a fresh wind makes the air feel colder, that is a deception; a clear, calm night induces cold.

It is worth noting that the prevailing south-westerlies mean an onshore wind on our western seaboard, whereas in most of East Anglia it is an offshore wind. Navigators of light sailing craft and holidaymakers

Old trees often become the victims of strong winds, and when they fall across the road, as this one did in Paper Mill Lane, Bramford, near Ipswich, a problem is posed for the police and the highway authorities. *East Anglian Daily Times*

whose children are clamouring to use rubber dinghies and the like should heed the dangers of being carried out to sea by offshore winds.

The pattern of East Anglian prevailing winds is fairly constant over differing times and places, as follows:

PREVAILING WINDS IN EAST ANGLIA (DAYS)

	N	NE	E	SE	S	SW	W	NW
Levington (near Ipswich, Suffolk) 1960–1980	41	43	25	32	34	82	54	54
Thwaite (near Eye, Suffolk) (1840–1856)	19	47	32	48	28	83	51	57
Swaffham Bulbeck (Cambs) (1831–1849)	38	53	20	25	19	97	46	67

A graphic method of demonstrating the prevalence of the various winds over varying periods of time is by means of the "wind rose", in which the relative frequency of wind directions is indicated by the lengths of lines drawn for each point of the compass. Fisons Ltd. have very kindly

When strong winds whip the fresh snow across the fields it can lead to severe drifting, but sometimes the scenic effect can be quite spectacular, as this view at Rougham, near Bury St. Edmunds, demonstrates. *East Anglian Daily Times*

provided me with several wind roses which they have prepared from observations made at their research station at Levington, Suffolk. These figures have been used to compile the following table illustrating the average annual frequencies for the years 1960–1980:

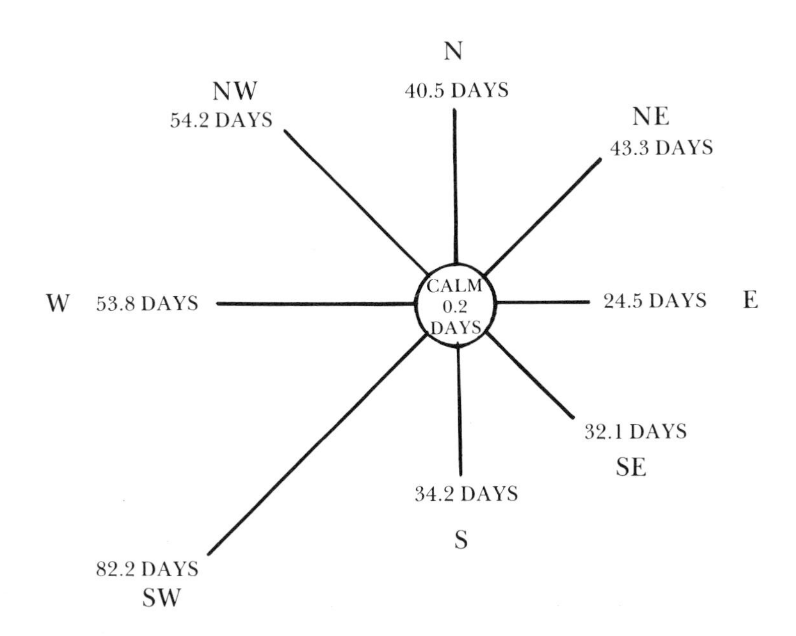

Levington is only five miles from the coast but as their observations are taken daily at 0900 hrs GMT, the effects of daytime sea breezes (or night-time land breezes) are unlikely to have any impact.

It is very unusual for an entire calendar year to show a prevailing wind other than from between south-west and west. An outstanding exception in the Belstead/Copdock records (1902–1980) was in 1915 when the prevailing wind was from the north-east — exactly opposite to the normal. Similarly, at Levington (typical of the local scene) the year 1973 showed a marked preponderance of north-westerly winds. Similar reversals of the prevailing south-westerly winds (and other variations in the pattern of wind directions) have occurred over the centuries, but there is no evidence to my knowledge of any permanent or developing deviations from the accepted norm.

Yet to accept the statistical evidence of prevailing south-westerlies is to over-simplify the situation. For instance, there is a tendency for the southerly and westerly winds to become less prevalent during the Spring and Summer, with a notable increase in northerlies and easterlies from

February onwards, reaching a peak in April and then tending to fall off in May and towards July.

East Anglia, by its geographical situation, inevitably takes the first sharp spearhead of attack from these often biting northerlies and easterlies — just as the western seaboard of the British Isles has to endure the maximum ferocity of the westerly gales. In rural East Anglia people talk of the penetrating easterly as a "lazy " wind — instead of the blast taking the trouble to go around it blows straight through.

In East Anglia the unfortunate tendency for Spring to produce unwanted cold winds is more marked than elsewhere. The following table, which I have compiled from the Levington records, shows the pattern of winds from some northerly or easterly point, graphically demonstrating the frequent onset of north-westerlies in February, merging into a north-easterly ascendancy in late Spring and early Summer. The marked tendency for north-westerly winds in December in interesting.

DOMINANT WINDS
Numbers of occasions during the 21 years 1960–1980 when the dominant winds (not necessarily prevailing) were from some N. or E. point
Levington

	NW	N	NE	E	SE
January	4	2	2	—	1
February	**7**	4	5	2	—
March	**9**	5	**8**	1	—
April	**9**	5	**11**	—	4
May	3	4	**7**	2	2
June	5	**7**	**8**	1	1
July	**9**	5	3	—	1
August	4	2	4	3	—
September	**8**	4	3	2	—
October	2	2	1	—	1
November	8	2	3	1	—
December	**10**	3	3	—	2

Bold figures indicate a dominance in one-third or more of the 21 years previously.

My use of the designation "dominant" rather than "prevailing" is simply explained. Taking, purely as an example, a hypothetical month in which there was a south-westerly wind on eleven days, a north-westerly on eight days, a northerly on seven days and a north-easterly on five days, the prevailing wind — numerically — would be south-westerly, whereas there would have been an overwhelming domination of winds from between north-west and north-east.

On 24th April, 1981 (one of the coldest and snowiest Aprils of the twentieth century over a large part of the British Isles, with East Anglia escaping the worst of the snow), the weather — with winds between north and east — was so cold that a cricket match at Fenners between Cambridge University and Essex provided the bizarre spectacle of players in woolly caps; bowlers unable to grasp the ball properly; a batsman unable to see clearly because of the joint effect of the bitter wind

and his contact lenses; and fieldsmen almost immobilised by frozen fingers. Cricketing Law 3, sub-section 14 D, was consulted:

> The umpires should suspend play only when they consider conditions are so bad that it is unreasonable or dangerous to continue.

The umpires and players conferred. It was agreed that conditions were unseasonable, unreasonable and dangerous — and play was suspended.

The late John H. Willis in his book *Weatherwise* (George Allen & Unwin, 1944) says of the bitterly cold Spring of 1936:

> . . . capricious alternations in temperature continued very largely right through the spring. In April, to the 23rd, unrelenting chill draughts through our northern and eastern doorways swept almost daily through the month, staging on the 20th, in mid-spring, astonishing scenes as of an old-fashioned Christmas with its landscapes of snow and snow-weighted branches.

In that brief paragraph, John Willis provided evidence that chilly Springs are nothing new, and that a White Christmas has always been considered a thing of the past.

The following table from the Rev. J. L. Jenyns' book *Observations in Meteorology* (1858) shows the monthly frequency of winds as recorded at his weather station at Swaffham Bulbeck, Cambridgeshire, during the years 1831 to 1841.

WIND DIRECTIONS (days)
Swaffham Bulbeck (Cambs.)

	Jan	Feb	Mar	Apr	May	Jun	Jul	Aug	Sep	Oct	Nov	Dec
N.–E.	99	109	124	147	141	79	58	60	63	72	71	99
E.–S.	69	54	60	48	57	47	40	35	43	58	68	62
S.–W.	230	188	190	144	176	241	216	147	132	237	218	245
W.–N.	137	127	184	164	114	131	178	140	117	146	106	134

The above table clearly confirms the strong tendency for northerly to easterly winds from February to May. This early nineteenth century evidence surely refutes any suggestion that there has been a recent change in climate — and it serves as a pointer to the fickleness of April.

This is amply confirmed in the following table compiled from the Belstead/Copdock records in which I have deliberately examined four decades well away from the periods already quoted, thus underlining a frequent and persistent climatic feature which, by analysis, discredits the descriptions of "unseasonable" when we are really talking about typical April weather.

APRIL WINDS
Analysis, by decade, of the pattern of prevailing April winds during the years 1902–1941
Belstead/Copdock

	NW	N	NE	E	SE	S	SW	W
1902–1911	2	1	3	—	—	2	1	1
1912–1921	2	1	4	—	—	1	1	1
1922–1931	5	1	3	1	—	—	—	—
1932–1940	4	1	2	—	1	—	1	1
Total — 40 years 1902–1940	13	4	12	1	1	3	3	3

The figures in the table indicate the number of occasions in each decade on which the various wind directions prevailed. The occasional sharing of prevalence between one or more directions produced fractions which I have rounded off to the nearest unit. This "smoothing" does not, however, detract from the general accuracy of the table — which dramatically shows the April ascendancy of NW to NE winds at the expense of the S to W winds.

It may be that our criticism of April is largely her own fault. If she did not so gaily bedeck herself with nodding daffodils and all the other romantic adornments immortalised by the poets, we might not expect so much of her. The cuckoo could help if only he would defer his first calls until May.

As it is, recognising March as the back door of Winter, we must expect residual cold draughts to be whistling around in April, despite her brave show of Spring gaiety. And we should not grumble about an imagined worsening in climate.

Gales

Over the British Isles generally, gales are usually more frequent and severe on the coasts than inland, their occurrence in coastal areas being greater in the West than in the East. The frequency of gales on our western seaboard is about double that on the East Anglian coast.

Scotland and Ireland are by far the stormiest regions. One of the strongest gusts ever recorded was 144 m.p.h. in Scotland on 6th March, 1967 — but that was at a height of over three thousand feet in the Cairngorm mountains. Less spectacular, but unusual in its locality, was a

Gales might be more frequent in the West, but their destructive effects are all too often felt in East Anglia.
East Anglian Daily Times

gust of 111 m.p.h. at Cranwell, Lincolnshire, in a severe north-westerly gale on 17th December, 1952.

Meteorological Office records for Mildenhall/Honington show that the highest gust recorded there during the period 1935 to 1977 was 98 m.p.h. on 16th March, 1947.

The frequency of gales, after an appreciable pre-Winter increase in September, is at its greatest during the five months October to February, with the back door of Winter frequently banging in the wind during March.

An almost complete immunity from gales in June is very marked. That is why the Allied Forces, in close co-operation with the Meteorological Office, chose June for the D-Day invasion of 1944 — yet in the event unusually strong north-westerly winds created unexpected and serious hazards. The only two June gales I have registered were in 1975 (accompanied by the rare occurrence of a June snowfall, when snow stopped play at a county cricket match at Colchester) and in 1980 with a thunderstorm.

In common with the rest of the country, gales in East Anglia come mostly from some westerly point between north and south. As winds blow across any stretch of country they tend to be slowed down by friction with the land, so westerly gales are usually far less severe on the East Coast than elsewhere. Easterly gales are far less frequent than those from other directions but their maximum effect is, obviously, on the East Coast.

The most dangerous gales off the East Anglian coast are from the North-west. It is these north-westerly gales which, in conjunction with low pressure over the North Sea, are the most frequent cause of coastal flooding in East Anglia.

Hurricanes

In Emlyn Williams' play *The Late Christopher Bean*, adapted from René Fauchois' comedy *Prenez Garde A La Peinture!*, Gwenny the Welsh housemaid makes the discovery that "a man can get drunk, and not be no different, only just more so". Hurricanes are no different from gales — only more violent. The Beaufort scale of wind, generally accepted as a good measuring rod, defines a gale as a wind of 39 to 46 m.p.h.; if the speed exceeds 72 m.p.h. (Force 12) then it qualifies as a hurricane — without necessarily any change in character. Gwenny would understand that.

A hurricane, like a gale, is caused by steep barometric gradients, indicated by unusual closeness of the isobars on the weather maps. The closer the isobars the steeper are the gradients — and the stronger the wind. Thermal differences in this country are insufficient to cause a hurricane.

One of the worst hurricanes ever experienced in England occurred on 26th and 27th November, 1703 (26th November is 6th December in the new calendar introduced in 1752). That was the hurricane which, shortly before midnight on the 26th, demolished the Eddystone Lighthouse (killing its designer, who was on a visit). The storm, travelling eastwards, first struck somewhere near Liverpool; although the worst-hit areas were south of a line from the Bristol Channel to the Thames. East Anglia was badly affected.

Hurricanes are not uncommon in East Anglia, a notable one occurring in the early hours of 11th January, 1974. Associated with a "line-squall" (a long line of strong winds sweeping across the country), an unofficial anemograph in the Ipswich area showed a rise in speed from a mere 4 m.p.h. to 77 m.p.h. in only three-quarters of a minute. Detailed reports were incomplete because many instruments were put out of action by the severity of the hurricane. In the Atlantic, ships reported speeds of 112 m.p.h., with their barometers showing the lowest readings of the century.

Fortunately for East Anglia, the severity of a hurricane has usually been reduced by the time it reaches the East Coast and earlier reports from further inland (assuming it is travelling from west to east) give advance warning of its severity.

The destructive hurricanes of the USA (identified by the Weather Bureau by Christian names) quite frequently cross the Atlantic, but by the time they reach the British Isles their force is mostly spent and they appear on the weather maps as ordinary-looking depressions with fairly strong winds. There are exceptions — the remains of a Caribbean hurricane reached East Anglia on 9th August, 1979, with strong winds, rainfalls of half an inch or more and thunderstorms in many places. The sharp barometric changes in East Anglia are shown in the attached record of the barograph at Rushmere St Andrew. As the barometer fell in front of the depression, there were fresh southerly winds, veering and strengthening from the north when the barometer rose in the rear of the depression. During 4/5th October, 1984, the remains of West Indies hurricane "Hortense" brought us strong winds, severe thunderstorms and torrential rain.

The dramatic effects of unusually steep barometric gradients were evident in a hurricane which struck the British Isles on the night of 2nd/3rd January, 1976 (ironically, the year of the famous drought and scorching Summer), with winds in East Anglia of over 100 m.p.h. Considered by some climatologists as comparable with the notorious

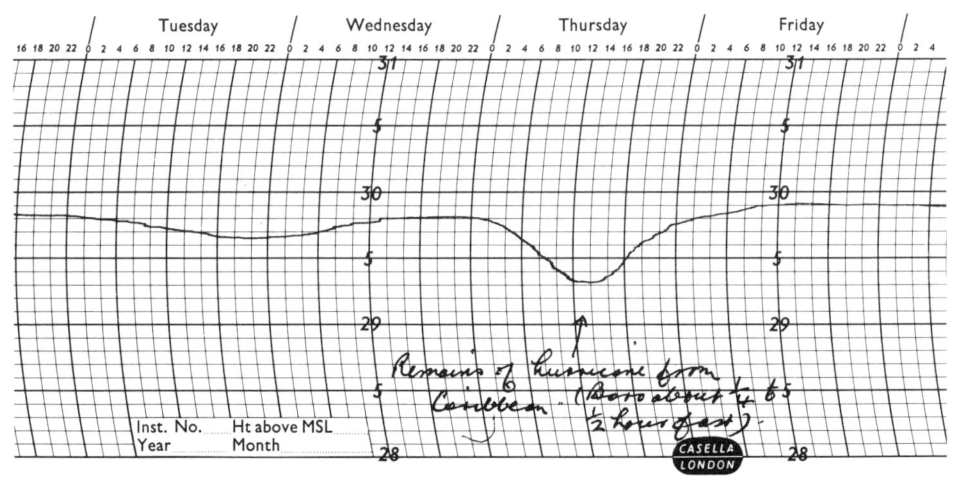

A barograph trace showing the drop in pressure marking the passing of the remains of a hurricane from the Caribbean. *Author*

1703 storm, it was caused by the all-too-familiar situation of an intense and rapidly deepening depression crossing the North Sea from Scotland to Denmark — a dangerous situation for East Anglia similar to that which was responsible for the tragedies of 1st February, 1953. Fortunately, flooding was not nearly as severe in 1976 and, largely owing to the existence of the Storm Tide Warning Service set up after the 1953 disaster, advance warnings ensured evacuation of vulnerable areas. Nonetheless, East Anglia was one of the worst affected areas and in the Thetford Forest area alone nearly a hundred trees were either blown down or seriously damaged. Gusts of 105 m.p.h. were reported at Wittering, Cambs; 104 m.p.h. at Cromer, Norfolk; 102 m.p.h. at Norwich; 89 m.p.h. at Honington, Suffolk, and 85 m.p.h. at Gorleston, Norfolk. By next morning the winds had dropped to gale force and, considering the severity of the storm and the intensity of the depression which caused it, rainfall was not generally heavy. At Rushmere St Andrew I registered a mere tenth of an inch.

Another hurricane swept East Anglia during the night of 11/12th January, 1978. It was severe and, coming from the North, again caused widespread flooding from the North Sea. Details of this damaging storm are given in chapter five, East Anglia at Risk. Only a few days earlier (3rd January), a severe tornado had struck Newmarket, Suffolk, leaving a four-mile trail of damage from Newmarket Heath (west of Newmarket) to Ashley (south-east of Newmarket). Two men died in the tornado, one blown off his motorcycle at East Runton, Norfolk, and the other drowned in a flood at Wisbech, Cambridgeshire.

Typhoons

Just as there are proverbially no snakes in Ireland, there are no typhoons in East Anglia; nor, indeed, anywhere in the British Isles. Violent winds and peculiar whirlings are frequent but use of the word "typhoon" (from the Chinese "t'ai fung", a strong wind) is commonly restricted to the fierce cyclonic hurricanes such as occur in the Pacific, the Indian Ocean and the South China Sea.

Any notable whirlings of the wind which occur in the British Isles are usually caused by "vortex" winds — of which East Anglia seems to experience rather more than its fair share. Vortex winds, as their name implies, have a spiralling motion; are often of short duration and of very local occurrence. Because they are members of a rather badly-behaved and often unpredictable family, I have given this particular group of meteorological delinquents a section all to themselves.

The vortex winds

Vortex winds are of mixed origin. They can be caused by sharp thermal differences (often due to intense and very local heating by the sun), by artificial obstructions to the main flow of wind, or by unusual discontinuities in the barometric pattern. In the latter case the circulation would most likely be anti-clockwise. In a vortex whirl arising from thermal differences the spiral can be in either direction.

A very local and insignificant vortex wind is frequently seen in whirling spirals of dust and loose paper, often in built-up areas where, particularly on windy days, structural angles disturb the general flow of the wind. A favourite rendezvous for these local dances of dust is near the entries and exits of tunnelled-out shopping precincts and they frequently occur in the gardens and paths of houses wherever there are angles and tunnel effects.

More violently, less frequently but on a larger scale, the vortex winds manifest themselves in spectacular waterspouts over the sea and dark "funnel" clouds which sometimes form round the centre of a tornado or waterspout. In this country, funnel clouds do not in themselves cause very much damage and are as nothing compared with the devastating "twisters" of the United States. But we do experience them — and East Anglia seems to be at greater risk than many other parts of the country.

Many of the earliest records and medieval diaries contain references to tornadoes, waterspouts, funnel clouds, dust devils and a host of allied phenomena, but it was not until about the middle of the nineteenth century that meteorologists began seriously to investigate the subject.

Since then, an ever-increasing amount of detailed observation and analysis has been carried out — much of it at the Climatic Research Unit at the University of East Anglia, led in the first place by Professor Hubert Lamb.

It was Dr G. T. Meaden, of Trowbridge (the founder and editor of *The Journal of Meteorology*) who, in conjunction with M. W. Rowe of Lillington, Leamington Spa, enthusiastically and painstakingly set about the task of collecting and examining reports from a wide section of the public. In 1974 Dr Meaden founded the Tornado Research Organisation (TORRO). Now known as the Tornado and Storm Research Organisation, TORRO collates, analyses and discusses the observations and sightings of a large and excellent team of experienced amateurs, whose ranks also include many professional and well-known meteorologists. I am indebted to Dr Meaden for permission to publish the following map showing tornadoes, funnel clouds and waterspouts reported in a TORRO survey covering the period from January, 1974, to mid-September, 1975. The vulnerability of East Anglia is very noticeable.

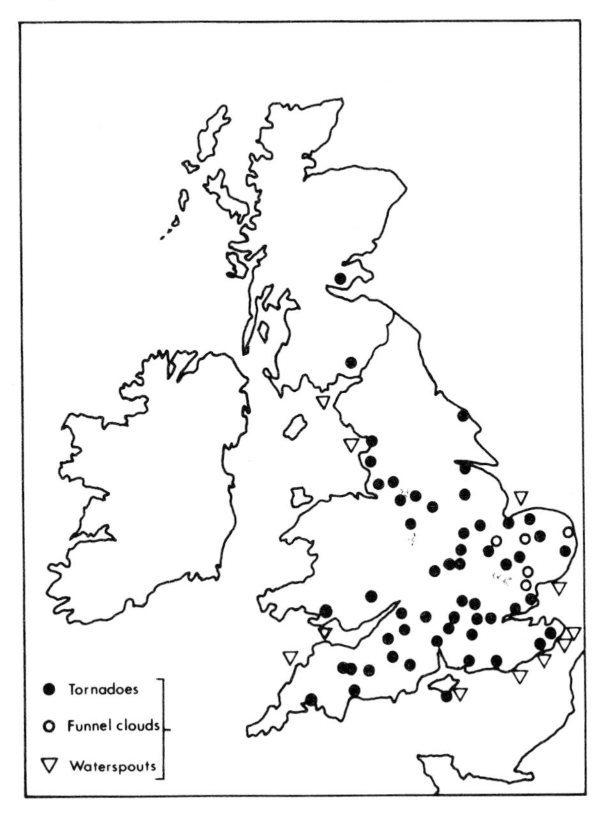

The locations of tornadoes, funnel clouds and waterspouts known to have occurred in Britain between January, 1974, and mid-September, 1975.
Journal of Metorology

Tornadoes

In its most severe form a tornado is one of nature's most disastrous occurrences, rendered even more frightening by its unpredictable and often erratic path.

The dangers of a really violent tornado are twofold. Firstly, the sheer ferocity of the wind, made more dangerous by the fact that the wind speed is often wildly erratic in a very small area, frequently having a twisting effect on objects in its path. Trees and poles can be broken or uprooted. Secondly, a tornado often has a central area of extremely low barometric pressure. Even if a building withstands the force of the wind, the higher air pressure inside cannot always adjust itself in time to avoid the building exploding into the sudden lack of pressure outside. When we hear of plate-glass windows having been shattered by the force of an East Anglian gust it may be that the damage was caused not so much by the wind as by the abrupt arrival of very low barometric pressure, causing an explosion from the interior. In that case the evidence would be of the glass having been blown outwards.

Tornadoes sometimes have a severe suction effect, resulting occasionally in the bizarre "raining" of frogs, tadpoles, caterpillars and other small creatures some distance from where they had been suddenly whirled out of their natural habitat. With wind speeds sometimes exceeding 200 m.p.h., even more ferocious things can happen. In *The Guinness Book of Weather Facts and Feats* Ingrid Holford remarks that on 26th September, 1971, a tornado moved a 90-ton engine 150 feet along a railway track near Rotherham in South Yorkshire. Ingrid Holford also notes that the longest recorded track of a single tornado in this country was a hundred miles from Great Missenden, Bucks, to Blakeney, Norfolk; it was travelling at an average speed of 25 miles an hour.

Tornadoes often cause a twisting column of cloud; the line of damage is not usually more than a hundred yards or so in width — and they "breed" most frequently in very unstable atmospheric conditions, frequently forming along the line of a cold front. Old diaries and journals abound with often lurid accounts. I mention just a few of the more recent ones.

On 18th November, 1963, at least seven separate tornadoes occurred along a line stretching from Barry Island in Wales to Orfordness in Suffolk. In a comprehensive survey in *The Journal of Meteorology* (July/August, 1980; Vol. V, No 50), Dr G. T. Meaden reported that at Barry Island a sea-front fair was wrecked at 0500 hrs GMT. The sixth tornado in the series was reported from West Hertfordshire, apparently heading towards East Anglia. Sure enough, at 0926 hrs GMT a tornado was seen approaching Orfordness across the marshes, having probably been invigorated by the proximity of humid maritime air. In his admirable survey of the day's events, Dr Meaden says of the Orfordness tornado:

> So many buildings in Quay Street were damaged that it took most of the morning to clear the debris. Three big chimney stacks at the *Jolly Sailors Inn* crashed on to the roof and into the street. A large garage, once used by an omnibus company, was destroyed. A part of its corrugated iron roof whipped itself around a precariously-leaning telegraph pole on the opposite side of the road. Chimney stacks fell from neighbouring cottages, tiles were torn off, telephone wires were brought down and 20 metres of roadside fencing were ripped away. Twelve houses had their roofs badly damaged and many garages and outhouses were wrecked. Two cars were buried under the debris. (At Boxford, Suffolk, hailstones were big enough to crack and puncture the rear window of a car being driven by a young woman.)

Tornadoes can happen at any time; meteorological disturbances that can make one's heart go bump in the night. In a joint article in *The Journal of Meteorology* (January, 1977; Vol. II, No 15) Dr C. E. Briscoe of Buxton, Norfolk, and Michael Hunt of Anglia Television gave a detailed analysis of a group of tornadoes which swept across East Anglia during the night of 1st/2nd December, 1975, causing considerable damage. Tornadoes were reported in Norfolk at Felmingham, Hindolveston, Saxlingham Nethergate, Sidestrand, Barnham Broom and Snetterton, and in Cambridgeshire at Waterbeach.

Michael Hunt and Dr Briscoe reported that all the tornadoes followed a straight course from west-south-west to east-north-east (approximately parallel to the line of a cold front) and they all occurred around 2300 hrs GMT. The most accurate timing was that of a clock at Felmingham which stopped at 2310 GMT. In its course to the outskirts of North Walsham (a distance of 3 km), the track of the Felmingham tornado was between 70 and 100 metres wide and in this track turnips were uprooted and a piggery roof blown away. Numbers of large trees were either blown down or badly damaged. On a farm on the north side of the B1145 Aylsham to North Walsham road, one corner of a newly-thatched barn roof was torn away and two adjoining buildings on the east side had their roofs almost completely removed. The north end of this range of buildings was largely levelled to the ground; all the bricks had fallen outward, suggesting a suction effect. After creating considerable havoc all along its path, the tornado crossed a field and struck the first houses in North Walsham, dislodging some tiles and knocking down a garage, but fortunately it died out before reaching the rest of the town.

The tornado which started at Hindolveston covered a distance of 6 km through Craymere Beck to Briston Common. As it passed the village street of Hindolveston it folded up the tiles on the roofs of houses

A tornado funnel-cloud at Stanford-le-Hope, Essex, on 3rd August, 1979. At the time of its occurrence East Anglia was in the track of an unstable, showery north to west air current sweeping round a depression over Scandinavia. *D. J. Walker*

like fanned packs of cards, cutting off the electricity supply and demolishing two garages and de-roofing another. One observer described how he woke up the next morning to find only a concrete pad and an oil drum where his garage had stood! A barn, directly in the path of the tornado, had its roof (which was estimated to weigh two tons) lifted and rotated anti-clockwise through 45 degrees while its walls collapsed outwards; the straw inside, however, remained comparatively undisturbed. Creating more havoc, it then crossed the old Melton Constable railway line before entering open fields where it seems to have died out.

At Saxlingham Nethergate, about 9 km south of Norwich, a tornado is reported to have passed near a private nursing home, knocking down several trees in the garden and removing some tiles from a neighbouring house before crossing a field and passing into a wood. In this tornado the characteristic roar, which was preceded by a flash of lightning, lasted for about a minute and was followed by an unnatural stillness.

The other tornadoes all caused damage of various intensities.

Another entire family of tornadoes swept Eastern England on 3rd January, 1978, the worst affected area being Newmarket. In the following brief account I gratefully acknowledge permission to use material from an article by Dr G. T. Meaden and another by P. S. J. Butler (of the Building Research Establishment, Garford, Watford) in *The Journal of Meteorology* (October 1978; Vol. III, No 32) and a paper by L. G. Chorley (at that time of the Meteorological Office, RAF Honington, Suffolk) in the *Meteorological Magazine* Vol. CVII; 1978.

The tornadoes (accompanied in many parts by thunderstorms, hail and heavy rain) were caused by a cold front (associated with a depression on its way towards Denmark) moving southwards across the country. Tornadoes developed in several parts of Eastern England and the abruptness of occurrence was due to the 45 m.p.h. speed of the cold front. The tornadoes occurred generally between about 0700 hrs and 1100 hrs GMT. One was reported from North Suffolk about 0930 – 1000 hrs, moving approximately north-north-west to south-south-east along a narrow track about 20 metres wide, starting at Ringsfield near Beccles and passing through Sotterley village and park.

But it was Newmarket which was worst hit, the southern part of the town suffering the most severe damage. Described as "coming like a corkscrew, dark with thunder and hail", the tornado wreaked havoc in a path estimated to be about 70 yards wide. Roofs were ripped off, windows smashed and a railway signal-box weighing several tons severely damaged and moved on its foundations. The main damage in Newmarket was to roofs.

Elsewhere in East Anglia, the violent weather of 3rd January, 1978, took its toll in other ways. Fortunately, no one was killed or seriously injured but there was an unusual and fatal effect on some flocks of wild geese caught in the storm. Dr G. T. Meaden, reporting the occurrence in the *Journal of Meteorology*, October, 1978, (Vol. III, No 32) commented that when a gale builds up or a squall approaches most birds seek cover or become grounded. But on this occasion the effect on several skeins of geese was different and quite disastrous. As the cold front or line squall approached with its thunderstorms and tornadoes, the wild geese feeding on the coastal marshes of the Wash either rose in alarm or were directly levitated by one of the tornadoes. Whatever the reason, it appears that they were caught up in the turbulent winds (perhaps in a tornado funnel) and carried to greater heights than those at which they normally fly. During the next hour, 136 pink-footed geese were killed in flight and dropped dead out of the clouds along a track 45 km in length, the track stretching west-north-west to east-south-east across Norfolk between Castle Acre and Swardeston.

Although tornadoes usually occur in very disturbed barometric conditions with high winds and a cold front, associated phenomena can happen in quieter weather. In an article in the *Journal of Meteorology*, October, 1975 (Vol. I, No 1) Michael Hunt of Anglia Television reported having received five accounts of a well-formed tornado funnel cloud in Suffolk around 1600 hrs GMT on 18th July, 1974, in the vicinity of Stowmarket and Framlingham — an area approximately bounded by the villages of Wilby, Worlingworth, Southolt, Bredfield and Saxtead Green. On that day a placid ridge of high pressure lay over Eastern England and the North Sea, ahead of a warm front lying over the Hebrides and Western Ireland. But trouble was brewing. A trough of cold upper air was located just to the East of the British Isles and there were reports of heavy showers in a narrow band over East Suffolk during the afternoon, but no thunder was reported. At Rushmere St Andrew it was a fine, sunny day with a light northerly wind and a maximum shade temperature of 68 degrees F. — a few degrees below the July average. Michael Hunt suggested the possibility of a minor trough line (possibly a sea-breeze front) lying north-north-east to south-south-west inland from the Norfolk, Suffolk and Essex coastlines. He commented that there was one rather vague, unconfirmed report of damage in the Suffolk area but in general it appeared that as the funnel was about to reach a potentially damaging state the processes causing its formation diminished in intensity.

Waterspouts

When a funnel-shaped tornado cloud develops over the sea, a waterspout will very likely occur.

But waterspout-spotting is about as fruitless an occupation as pacing the shores of Loch Ness seeking a glimpse of the monster. Whatever the truth of the monster, there are no doubts as to the existence of waterspouts, even though the chances of seeing one are slight — and most unlikely on a calm day of moderate temperature.

In more disturbed conditions, there is a possibility, however remote. Any rapid darkening of a portion of turbulent-looking cloud is worth watching — with a camera at the ready in case you are lucky. Having spotted a darkening patch of cloud, a roughly triangular shape might be seen descending towards the surface of the sea, accompanied by a very noticeable turbulence on the surface of the water. This combination of a writhing funnel-cloud, agitation of the surface of the sea and an attendant waterspout very likely explains some of the highly dramatic accounts (mostly from long ago) of sea-serpents having been seen leaping and twisting out of the water.

The map shows that even during the short period between January, 1974, and mid-September, 1975, several waterspouts were sighted off the East Anglian coast, though not in such great numbers as off the coasts of Kent and Sussex. The trouble with maps of this nature is the varying number of observers from area to area. Is the higher number of sightings in East Anglia, Kent and Sussex simply an indication of a larger number of interested observers than elsewhere?

The fact remains that waterspouts can be seen off the East Anglian coast — and not only over the sea. Sometimes, having developed over the

One of a sequence of photographs reproduced in *The Journal of Meteorology* in December, 1982, showing a whirlwind crossing a stubble-burnt field between Halstead and Braintree in Essex on 18th August, 1976. Weather conditions were warm and quiet, with a hazy sun and a generally light Force 2 wind. Because of the heatwave, soil temperatures were unusually high. *V. R. Williamson*

sea, they move a little way inland, occasionally causing some damage before they disintegrate.

Waterspouts are usually short lived and inland invasions are very brief and unusual — but I remember one notable occasion on 22nd August, 1975, when several waterspouts moved inland and invaded East Anglia. Damage varied from damaged roofs at Kessingland, Suffolk, to a dinghy being hurled into the air and travelling over 400 feet at West Mersea, Essex. On that day, the wind at Rushmere St Andrew was a moderate to fresh north-westerly; the synoptic chart showed that an extension of the Azores anticyclone lay to the South-west of the British Isles with a strong ridge extending to Iceland. Pressure was low over Scandinavia and the Continent, giving a broad north-westerly stream over almost all the country. On that occasion, it seems that the invading waterspouts came in against the general direction of the wind.

Dust devils and land devils

The names imply something infamous and vicious — and in hot tropical deserts they can be violent. But in the British Isles they are more gentle and usually quite harmless.

In this country, dust or land devils are usually caused by thermal differentials of a very local nature. Whereas in the hot foreign deserts they can rise to heights of several thousand feet, the East Anglian cousins (of similar, less intense, thermal origin) are docile creatures, often lasting for only a matter of seconds and rising but a few feet in the air.

They are most commonly seen in the rural areas of East Anglia. A wind of Beaufort force 3 (8-12 m.p.h.) and upwards would usually disperse any temperature differentials. But on a hot, calm day a "hot-spot" could easily develop in, for example, the corner of a dry, well-tilled field where a sun-trap might be accentuated by a sheltering hedge, causing these little dust whirls to appear suddenly, sometimes lifting loose straw and chaff to a height of several feet.

In East Anglia, these dust or land devils are sometimes called "Rogers", a name which is supposed to have a Danish origin, although I have not been able to determine this. The term "Roger's blast" or "a Sir Roger" has also been used to describe a sudden gust which blows up on a hitherto calm Summer's day. In Allan Jobson's *A Suffolk Calendar* (Robert Hale, London), p. 171, the blast is mentioned as particularly noticeable in the Broads district with the suggestion that the phenomenon was credited to Sir Roger Ascham in one of his moods — or that it might have described one of the Bigods. Whatever the origin, a peculiar gust can raise the comment: "Thar gew Roger's blast acrost ta fild a twizzlin the barley!"

Sea breezes and land breezes

Sea and land breezes are altogether more gentle in character than any of the winds we have so far dealt with. Although the main circulation of the earth's atmosphere is originated by the energy and heat injected by the sun, the day-to-day flow of the wind is determined by the barometric systems, the wind blowing obliquely from areas of high pressure to those of low pressure.

But there are other winds, usually, but not always, of a very local and minor character. "Shut that door!" complains comedian Larry Grayson, implying the existence of a cold draught blowing in from somewhere. Cold air will always rush in to replace warmer and comparatively lighter air. Hence the warmer a room becomes and the colder the air outside, the more pronounced will be the draught coming through an open door or window. What Larry Grayson is complaining about is a thermal air current, as distinct from a barometric one.

Thermal air currents of variable intensity occur in many parts of the world. One of the better-known examples is the cold and dry north-westerly to northerly mistral which blows down from the Rhone Valley in France across the Mediterranean coasts of the French Riviera and Spain. The mistral can become very strong indeed and visitors to the island of Minorca and other holiday spots may well have experienced its blasts.

In the British Isles, easily the most common thermal winds are the sea breezes by day and the land breezes at night — the former being by far the most frequent and the most noticeably active. The coastal areas experience the maximum effect of the sea breezes and counties well inland in the British Isles are rarely, if ever, affected to any appreciable degree.

Sea breezes occur most frequently and with greatest effect during the Summer in quiet, warm and sunny weather. On a hot day, the sun heats the lower layers of air over the land, which begin to rise; the much cooler (and denser) air over the sea (the North Sea can be particularly cool in early Summer) pushes in to replace the rising currents of warmer air over the land. It is one of nature's more beguiling paradoxes that the sweltering heat of the sun actually causes these refreshingly cool onshore winds. The hotter the sun the more likely is a sea breeze.

Some minor changes in barometric pressure may also occur, but these are a technical side-effect. Inequality of temperature over the land and the sea is the main feature and the one to which our bodies react.

The sea breeze is a very shallow invasion of air; generally only about five hundred or a thousand feet deep, but occasionally more. It usually penetrates quite effectively up to ten or fifteen miles inland. Further

Overdressed Edwardian holidaymakers must have welcomed the cooling sea breeze when enjoying themselves on Lowestoft beach. *R. Malster*

inland its presence becomes diminished, but under favourable conditions much deeper penetration can occur. It is by no means uncommon for sea breezes to be registered by the instruments at the Meteorological Office at RAF Honington, Suffolk, 35–40 miles inland, but they seldom reach so far inland before late afternoon, sometimes not until quite late in the evening. Even as far inland as Cambridge sea breezes are by no means unheard of. In an article by J. E. Simpson in *Weather* (January 1978, Vol. XXXIII, No 1) it was noted that on 27th June, 1976, glider pilots Chris Chapman and Duncan Cumming found a sea breeze front at a height of about 3,200 feet near Cambridge Airport. The time was 1830 GMT and the edge of the sea-air could be seen as a faint haze lying in a general north-east to south-west line.

Sea breezes do not usually exceed 10–15 m.p.h. (Force 3 to 4 on the Beaufort Scale). On a hot Summer day the sea breeze, starting off as a light drift, can become increasingly active near the coast as early as 0900 hrs GMT, often lasting well into the evening. On hot days in the Summer we have noticed, sitting in our garden at Rushmere St Andrew, that the fresh and noticeably cooler air often arrives shortly after 1500 hrs GMT (2 p.m. BST), its arrival bringing a drop of something like 5 degrees F. in temperature and a rise of 10 per cent or more in the relative humidity. Rushmere St Andrew is only about ten miles from the coast, so that, with a Force 3 sea breeze, we often enjoy invigorating air which barely an hour previously was actually over the sea. Why join the bumper to bumper queue to the seaside when, with patience, one can wait for the sea air to come to you?

I quote just one typical example of a sea breeze arriving at Rushmere St Andrew. On 13th July, 1979, during a settled spell of fine, dry and warm weather, the Azores anticyclone, already well established, thrust a ridge of high pressure north-east across the British Isles. This, combined with a shallow and harmless area of low pressure over the Continent, put the whole of East Anglia under the influence of a light northerly wind. The following table clearly shows how, during the day, the sea breeze took over from the northerly. (In this table I have converted the times of observation from GMT to British Summer Time, which I hope makes the picture a more realistic one.)

SEA BREEZE, 13th July, 1979
Rushmere St Andrew

Time of observation BST	Shade temperature °F.	Relative humidity %	Wind	
			Direction	Force on Beaufort scale
10.00 a.m.	68	71	NNE	2
noon	74	50	N	2
2.00 p.m.	77	42	NNE	1
2.15 p.m.	75	51	SSE	3
3.00 p.m.	75	53	SSE	3
4.00 p.m.	72	49	SE	3
5.00 p.m.	71	48	SE	3 to 4
6.00 p.m.	70	51	SSE	3 to 4
*7.00 p.m.	66	61	SSE	3

*The 7 o'clock drop in temperature and rise in humidity indicates a normal cooling and moistening of the air towards evening.

It will be seen that by 2 p.m., with an almost cloudless sky and hardly any wind, conditions had become very hot and dry — and the normally hottest part of the day was still to come. But at 2.15 p.m. precisely the comparatively cool and moist sea breeze duly arrived from the direction of Harwich and Felixstowe with an immediate drop in temperature and rise in humidity. Neither temperature nor humidity really recovered during the rest of the day, thus turning what would have been an afternoon of dry, scorching heat into one of more gentle warmth.

Air flow of the sea breeze type can also occur near large lakes and stretches of inland waters, such as the Norfolk Broads. Genuine sea breezes have a more marked effect in East Anglia than in western England — for two main reasons. Firstly, the prevailing winds of the British Isles being south-west to west, the difference between an isobaric prevailing wind and a sea breeze might pass unnoticed. On the other hand, over the whole country, easterly winds are far less frequent than the westerlies — and, along the East Anglian coast, they are often entirely due to a sea breeze. The second factor distinguishing the East Anglian sea breeze is that the temperature of the North Sea is usually lower than that of the Atlantic; consequently sea breezes in East Anglia are usually more refreshingly cool than those in the West Country or, indeed, along the South Coast.

The effects of a sea breeze largely depend on direction, if any, of the isobaric wind. As Dr Charles Briscoe, of Buxton in Norfolk, points out, with an easterly isobaric wind the sea breeze will merely reinforce it, while with a light south-westerly or westerly wind a sea breeze from the East or North-east will often clear the skies of cumulus clouds around 2 p.m.

This clearing of the skies is interesting and is mentioned in the following notes kindly provided by Mr R. A. Robson, a professional meteorologist, of Wickham Bishops, Essex. Referring to the occurrence of sea breezes in Essex, Mr Robson says:

> Easterly or South-easterly sea brezes are frequent enough in Essex to give a prevailing wind from this direction on the coasts in the Summer. Their penetration inland obviously depends on the overall situation on any particular day and these are far too variable to give any hard and fast rules. It is usual on several days during any year for sea breezes to penetrate right across the whole county. If one looks at a map of Essex the long, wide estuaries of the Thames, Crouch, Blackwater and Stour are immediately noticeable. Sea breezes can, therefore, penetrate quite deeply and unhindered into the county, especially in the southern half.
>
> As with other coastal areas, the stabilising effect in Essex is quite apparent. Convectional rainfall is noticeably inhibited or prevented altogether — and this factor contributes to the dryness of the Essex coastal areas. However, inland, the sea breeze can intensify or actually produce showers and thunderstorms in certain situations along the leading edge of a sea breeze front.
>
> An excellent example of a thunderstorm forming, or at least intensified, by a sea breeze pushing inland was on 10th June, 1970. The whole of the south and east of Essex was clear and sunny with a light to moderate south-easterly sea breeze. Temperatures were high inland (a maximum of 86 degrees F. at my station at Wickham Bishops). By 4 p.m. a huge cumulo-nimbus cloud was developing some fifteen to twenty miles to the north of my station. The base could not be seen because of the distance but the huge anvil top slowly spread south and east over Wickham Bishops. Earls Colne was estimated to be near the centre of the storm — 1.30 inches of rain fell there while much of the county remained dry and quite sunny. This is an extreme example of an occurrence which happens to a lesser degree rather more frequently.

My own register shows that on that day at Rushmere St Andrew, thirty miles north-east of Wickham Bishops and twenty-five miles north-east of Earls Colne, the sky at 0900 hrs GMT was completely cloudless: the wind was north-north-east Force 5. Maximum temperature during the day was 88 degrees F. (the hottest day of the year) and the weather was completely rainless — but well-defined cumulo-nimbus clouds were visible to the south-west during the day. As a matter of interest, following a spell of thirty-one days from 29th April to 29th May during which I had registered less than half an inch of rain, we were, on 10th June, in the middle of a spell of nineteen completely rainless days, with severe water restrictions having been imposed by the authorities.

Mr Robson continues:

> Arguably, there may be occasions when the sea breeze is prevented from penetrating inland, perhaps by a westerly or north-westerly wind, of just sufficient strength — but may lead to showers being intensified near or on the coast itself, thus tending to counterbalance the occasions when the sea breeze prevents rainfall.
>
> Obviously, an important factor is that coastal areas are kept cooler than further inland during Summer afternoons. Typically, while temperatures are rising into the upper 70s or 80s F. inland on a hot, Summer's afternoon they may remain fairly constant around 67 degrees F. to 71 degrees F. on the coast. Additionally, the stabilising effect of sea breezes greatly inhibits clouds of the cumulus variety and the coast often enjoys more sunshine than inland.
>
> Sometimes, during a spell of warm weather with a humid air-mass (particularly in early Summer when the sea is still relatively cold), fog forms over the sea and, as a sea breeze develops, the fog can creep unpleasantly overland in the coastal strip.
>
> On a clear Summer night temperatures inland will fall considerably lower than on the coasts (since soil cools much quicker than water and conversely). This means that, as the temperature rises during the morning, the coast has a "head start" and for a time may remain higher than inland. Such a typical day might well be summarised as follows:

Time, BST	Coastal air temperature *Degrees F.*	Inland air temperature *Degrees F.*
2 a.m.	55	50
5 a.m.	54	46
9 a.m.	61	57
12 noon	72	70
3 p.m.	68	75
6 p.m.	66	73
9 p.m.	63	64
Midnight	59	55

These notes by Mr Robson underline the fact that, although the physical causes of a sea breeze are simple enough, occurrence and effect can become very complicated. Usually, sea breezes are welcome, bringing cooling fresh winds on an otherwise stiflingly hot day; sometimes — particularly on and near the East Anglian coasts — they can bring an uncomfortable and unwelcome chill.

As for complications, it is obvious that if we have a brisk offshore isobaric wind, the sea breeze will not often operate except perhaps as a slight check on the isobaric wind. If the original offshore wind is not very strong, the sea breeze may largely cancel it out. A brisk onshore wind is likely to be increased in speed if sea breeze conditions are operating. Mr Richard Wilson of Belstead has noted that, under the influence of a sea breeze, a north wind often becomes north-easterly, and a south-westerly becomes south-easterly. But these, of course, are all generalisations. I have no personal experience of sea breezes in Norfolk but, by the curve of the Norfolk coastline, it is obvious that on a calm hot day the sea breezes between Great Yarmouth and Cromer would seem most likely to come from the North-east, while between Cromer and Hunstanton they would most probably be from the North. Once we go beyond Hunstanton down the coast of the Wash, we have a west-facing coast — and as Mr Robson has commented, things must sometimes be fairly complicated in the King's Lynn area. There is also, of course, the minor effect of the Norfolk Broads — all of which adds up to a most fascinating picture which certainly makes life interesting for anyone living or holiday-making in Norfolk.

Of course, the interest does not end in Norfolk. Taking the whole of East Anglia the sea breezes in Suffolk are most likely to come from the East from Great Yarmouth down to Orford and from the South-east from Orford down to Felixstowe. In Essex we have a generally south-easterly tendency, modified by the extent and position of the more important estuaries.

Sometimes it is altogether more simple. On 7th July, 1981, I was fortunate enough to be at home and able to log a neat and compact sea breeze, so uncomplicated as to need only a minimum of description. On that day East Anglia was under the influence of a broad, rather warm south-westerly wind. The morning was overcast but the clouds had disappeared completely by about midday, shade temperatures soon rising into the 70s F., the wind remaining steady and light from the south-west. Here is the arrival and effect of the sea breeze:

SEA BREEZE, 7th July, 1981
Rushmere St Andrew

Time BST	Screen temp. °F	Relative humidity %	Wind Direction	Wind Force	Weather
10 a.m.	62	84	SW	2–3	Overcast
3 p.m.	75	66	S.W.	2	Sunny
3.15 p.m.		Arrival of	sea-breeze	with SE	wind.
3.30 p.m.	70	77	S.E.	4–5	Sunny

Subsequently, the temperature did not recover to more than 71 degrees F. The sea breeze did not reach as far inland as the

Meteorological Office at RAF Honington (35–40 miles from the coast) where the wind remained south-westerly and the temperature rose to 77 degrees F. during the afternoon — only equalled that day at Coltishall, Norfolk, and Benson, Oxfordshire.

Soil cools (and heats) more quickly than water. Water is a greedy absorber of heat; land tends to reflect it and overheat the lower layers of air. Some people are very fortunate; they can eat as much as they like without putting on weight or disturbing their outward shape. The sea is rather like that, greedily absorbing great quantities of heat and tucking it away into its vast reservoirs, with surprisingly little change in its surface temperature. So, generally speaking, the sea is warmer than the air in Winter and cooler in Summer — particularly so in the case of the North Sea.

As Mr Robson's table indicates, on a clear Summer night the air cools rapidly (largely due to loss of heat by radiation) and we thus have a nocturnal reversal of the thermal process which originates a sea breeze. Under these night-time conditions, the inland air temperature becomes lower than that of the air over the sea. The cooler (and denser) inland air pushes out to replace the comparatively warmer air over the sea — and, thus, we have a land (or offshore) breeze. Mr Robson's computed table suggests that the temperature differential increases during the night to a maximum around dawn, and it is a fact that land breezes are usually most apparent during the early hours of the morning and towards dawn.

Nocturnal land breezes are not nearly so noticeable as the daytime sea breezes (maybe because many of us are still in bed) and they do not usually exceed a speed of about five miles an hour (Force 2 on the Beaufort Scale). They are, therefore, rarely operative other than in calm weather. But, being offshore winds, they do have their hazards — and these and the more serious dangers of the stronger offshore isobaric winds to swimmers, light sailing craft and children using rubber dinghies are dealt with in chapter four.

The "bulge" of East Anglia means that the definition of an offshore wind varies according to locality. Generally, they are any winds blowing from between South-west and North-west; along the North coast of Norfolk and near Hunstanton, offshore winds are those which come from between South and East.

I have deliberately dealt at some length with the subject of sea and land breezes, particularly the former. Rightly so, I think, because owing to its characteristic bulge into the North Sea there are very few (if any) parts of East Anglia which have never experienced a sea breeze, however slight. And in a scorching heatwave it is useful to know where, according to conditions, one might find cooler weather.

Thunderstorms

Although a commonplace occurrence, a thunderstorm is spectacular and, for some people, frightening. "Better the devil you know . . ." — and the more familiar one becomes with the nature and behaviour of the storms, the less alarming they become. But familiarity should never breed contempt. Nearby thunderstorms should always be treated with cautious respect, but, provided careless risks are not taken, they give little cause for fear.

The chance of being killed by lightning in this country has been estimated at something like five million to one, and the average number of deaths by lightning is only about ten a year — less than the daily total of traffic fatalities. Injuries by lightning in the country average about 45 per annum.

In England, about two-thirds of lightning flashes occur between two areas within the same storm cloud; some travel from one cloud to another and some — those which cause alarm and do the damage —

A thunderstorm building up over Rushmere St Andrew, near Ipswich.

strike from cloud to earth. Cloud to earth flashes usually aim at metal objects or the highest objects within reach — hence the use of metal lightning conductors on tall buildings to attract any nearby flash and steer it safely to ground.

It is a fallacy that lightning never strikes twice in the same place. Some vulnerable objects have been struck several times. St Botolph's Church at Boston, Lincolnshire, was struck four times between 1865 and 1908. The only recurrent electric shocks of which I have experience are the arrival of the quarterly electricity accounts.

Cruel mischance can cause a lightning fatality — but many deaths could have been avoided had safety precautions been observed. Personal

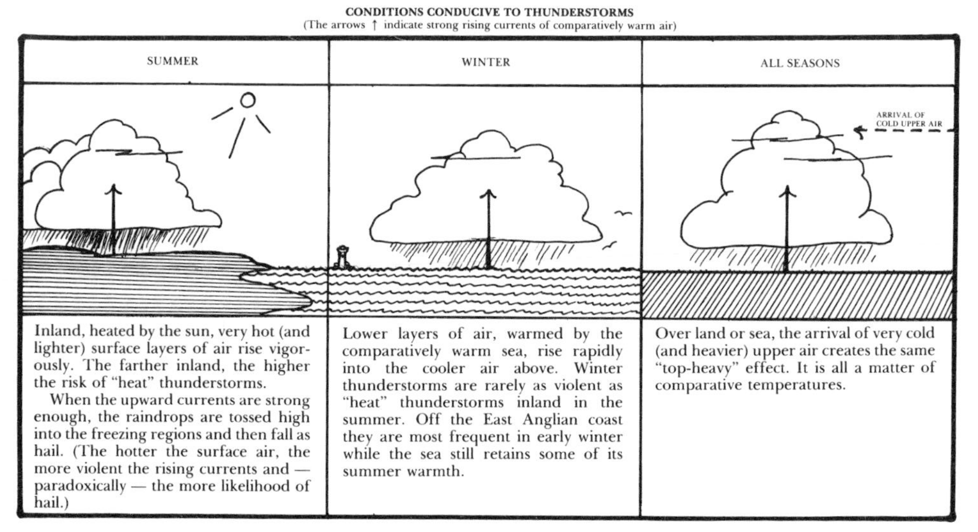

CONDITIONS CONDUCIVE TO THUNDERSTORMS
(The arrows ↑ indicate strong rising currents of comparatively warm air)

safety is increased by knowing how a thunderstorm is likely to behave, how to track its course and by the use of commonsense.

There is no difference between sheet and fork lightning. Apart from ball lightning, thunderbolts and similar mysterious happenings, all lightning is "fork". Sheet lightning is simply fork lightning which is obscured by some intervening object. A common cause of sheet lightning is when the fork is obscured by the clouds. At night it provides a dramatic effect as it suddenly, briefly and brilliantly, outlines the impressive contours of a towering cumulo-nimbus cloud in, or behind, which the flash occurs. Sheet lightning also occurs when the fork is obscured by a range of mountains or is below the horizon. Because it can be clearly seen at night when the thunder is too far away to be heard it has acquired a reputation of mystery. Often referred to as "Summer" lighting, there is an old saying that "If there be sheet lightning with a clear sky on Spring,

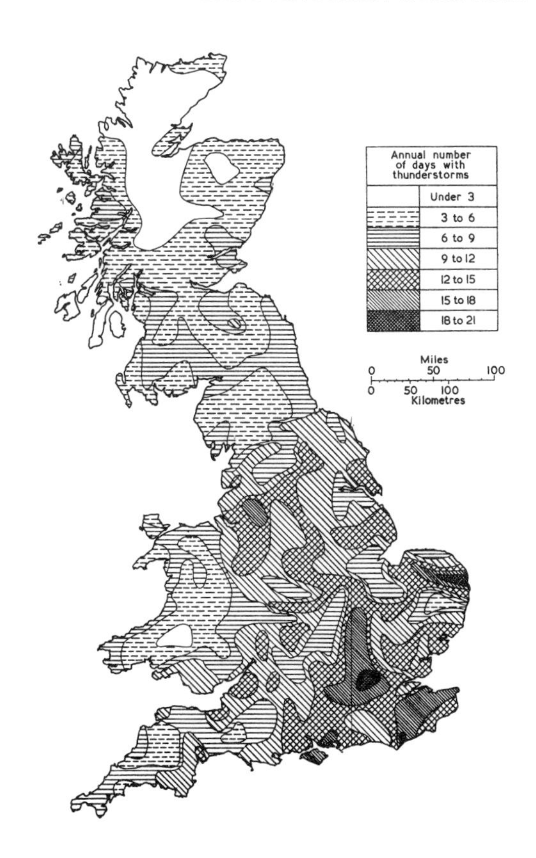

Map showing the typical annual number of thunderstorm days in England, Scotland and Wales.

Summer and Autumn evenings, expect heavy rains". With a clear sky it certainly denotes disturbed weather a long way away but that does not imply that the rain will necessarily move towards the observer.

Sheet lightning below the horizon at sea is particularly impressive. The coast of southern East Anglia is an excellent vantage point, giving a grandstand view of distant storms moving up from France. Although the storms may already have reached Kent, East Anglians can enjoy the grandeur of a continental firework display without any risk of a misdirected rocket.

Despite the notoriously stormy weather of mountainous districts, more thunderstorms occur in parts of East Anglia, the South Coast and a small area near London than anywhere else in the British Isles. Some places average as many as fifteen and even over twenty a year. Invasions by northward-bound continental storms have something to do with that.

The most likely place and time for a thunderstorm in the British Isles is Norfolk and Suffolk in July. Surface heating of the earth being one of the commonest causes of thunderstorms, the greatest risk is inland during the Summer months.

Cambridge has one of the highest Summer thunder risks in the country. When the Summer heating of the land is over, thunderstorms reach their minimum frequency. During the Winter, the comparative warmness of the sea becomes a stimulant when colder air is overhead. Thus, the position is reversed and the chances of a Winter thunderstorm are greater at Great Yarmouth than at Cambridge.

The map on page 141 shows the average annual distribution of thunderstorms over the whole of the British Isles. From observations over varying periods of time, I have calculated the approximate average monthly occurrence of thunderstorms in East Anglia as follows:

THUNDERSTORMS

	Average number, East Anglia
January	Less than 1
February	Less than 1
March	Less than 1
April	1
May	2
June	2½
July	3
August	3
September	1¼
October	Less than 1
November	Less than 1
December	Less than 1
Year	14

The above are composite averages for the whole region. The average number of thunderstorms occurring annually at places well inland and on the coast would probably be:

Inland 15–16
Coastal 12–13

In order to look more closely at the East Anglian scene, Mr R. Snowling of Pulham St Mary has kindly prepared for me the following statistics (taken from the monthly reports of the "COL" team of observers) for the ten years 1971–1980. In this summary, as in all the other statistics, the figures refer to "thunder days" — that is to say, days on which thunder is heard even though the storm may not be in the immediate vicinity.

THUNDER DAYS, 1971–1980

Year	Mean total, various locations No of days	Extremes No of days	
1971	13	16	Dunmow, Essex.
		12	Framingham Earl, Norfolk.
1972	12	16	Downham Market, Norfolk.
		7	Scole, Norfolk.
1973	17	23	Dunmow, Essex.
		12	Colchester, Essex.
1974	16	22	Dunmow, Essex.
		9	Colchester, Essex.
1975	15	20	Ely, Cambs.
		12	Elmswell, Suffolk.
1976	11	16	Epping, Essex.
		7	Royston, Herts.
1977	11	20	Epping, Essex.
		5	Buxton, Norfolk.
1978	15	20	Ely, Cambs.
		11	Royston, Herts.
1979	15	24	King's Lynn, Norfolk.
		9	Colchester and Leigh, Essex.
1980	14	21	Foulness, Essex.
		9	Buxton, Norfolk, and Royston, Herts.
Ten-year average	— 14		

Mr R. J. (Bob) Prichard of Loughton in Essex (a well-known voice on the London Weather Centre's radio forecasts), looking on the East Anglian scene generally, remarks that:

> The area around King's Lynn often comes up with the most days of thunder in the British Isles in a year, and most of East Anglia rates highly on this score, though with a marked decrease towards the East Coast. The reason for this appears to lie in a combination of relatively high inland temperatures with the (normally) storm-bearing south-west to westerly winds, the higher ground to the west and south-west of the area setting off the showers.

Thunderstorms are the most frequent cause of torrential rain and hail and severe local flooding. A spectacular onslaught of hail which occurred in a thunderstorm in the Blythburgh and Westleton area of

Suffolk on 23rd September, 1976 is referred to in detail in chapter one. White's *History of Suffolk*, 1844, records that at Blythburgh on Sunday, 4th August, 1577, "a dreadful thunder storm happened during divine service, when the lightning did great damage to the church, and struck down twenty people, of whom two were killed and others scorched. The spire and part of the steeple were thrown down and other parts of the church were rent and torn by the tempest, which took its course to Bungay, where it did much mischief".

White's *History of Suffolk* also records two other severe storms. The first was at Thetford, when

> on the 9th of August, 1843, this town, like many other places in the neighbourhood, suffered severely from a dreadful STORM of thunder, lightning, hail, rain, and wind. For about 25 minutes, between 6 and 7 in the evening, rain and hail descended in torrents, and most of the windows that faced the hurricane were broken. Many of the cellars were filled with water, and some of the warehouses and shops were inundated to a depth of 2 feet. When the coach came in from Lynn, the horses, in passing through Bridge Street, were up to their chests in water. In various parts of the town, walls were thrown down by the immense weight of water pressing against them; and in the surrounding country, the gardens and cornfields sustained great injury. Many of the hail stones, or rather pieces of ice, were upwards of 1¼ inches square, and after the storm, more than 100 sparrows were picked up dead in the gardens of W. Clarke, Esq. Similar storms happened in the preceding and in the same month, in various parts of the kingdom.

According to the records of Francis Dix (*British Rainfall*, 1880) the total rainfall for August, 1843, at Dickleburgh, Norfolk, was 5.40 inches, compared with an August average for South Norfolk of 2.25 inches.

The other violent storm recorded in White's *History of Suffolk* occurred at Hadleigh on 15th August, 1843 (within a week of the Thetford storm). It is recorded that

> Hadleigh, like many other places in the county, was visited by an *awful storm*, which commenced about 2 o'clock in the afternoon, and continued for 45 minutes, during which vivid flashes of lightning and loud crashes of thunder followed in quick succession, accompanied by deluging torrents of rain, large hailstones, and pieces of ice, which destroyed glass in many of the windows, and flooded the lower parts of the town. In some parts of High Street, the water was 18 inches deep, and a punt was seen rowing about in it (sic) for some time after the storm had abated.

On 15th June, 1987, nearely 2½ inches fell in two and a half hours at Sudbury, Suffolk, and boats were again seen in some streets.

An entire dossier of East Anglian thunderstorms and floods could be compiled from eye-witness accounts in ancient diaries and contemporary press cuttings. One thing is clear; whether expressed in dispassionate meteorological observations or in the melodramatic and turgid prose of some of the old diaries, nothing over the centuries has altered the general characteristics of such events — which today are often headlined as "freak" storms. Violent they may be, but freakish, no. Very often a so-called "freak" downpour is due to nothing more than a storm of quite normal intensity moving more slowly than usual.

One question about thunder and hail storms which engages scientific attention is whether there are some small areas where storms occur more frequently than in the surrounding district. Research continues, but there is a need for a closer network of competent observers in order to detect any patterns of behaviour (organisations like COL and TORRO perform very useful services). Many people believe that thunderstorms tend to follow the course of rivers. There may be substance in this theory; the upward currents of air require sufficient moisture to trigger off a thunderstorm. (In the famous 1976 Summer, the layers of hot surface air provided plenty of uprush but at the height of the drought there was not enough moisture to create even a few harmless "fine weather" cumulus clouds.) Rivers could provide moisture which might otherwise be absent.

The remains of the National School at Capel, near Ipswich, after being struck by lightning. From the *Illustrated London News* of 19th August, 1854. *Suffolk Record Office*

In my own experience, I have noticed that a seemingly favourite track of storms to the north of Rushmere St Andrew is along a line very roughly from the Stowmarket and Claydon area ENE towards Wickham Market. A network of observers in the area would be necessary to check my impression. Once, when I was giving a talk to the Women's Institute at Thwaite, near Eye, Suffolk, I was asked why Thwaite suffered more hailstorms than the surrounding countryside. I knew of no reason for this and I must confess I wondered if it was just one of those local sayings arising from supposition rather than fact. Later, out of curiosity, I consulted the Norwich Union Insurance Group, who were kind enough

Damage caused to the plastic roof sheeting of a nursery at Ufford, near Woodbridge, by the hailstorm of 22nd August, 1987. *East Anglian Daily Times*

to loan me documents, some of them old, showing that over the years the premiums charged to farmers for insurance against hail damage varied according to the locality.

But we should not jump to conclusions, because the higher premiums are calculated not on records of the frequency of hail storms but on the number of claims received from the various localities. Farmers with uninsured crops would not claim, so this map could conceivably do no more than indicate either those areas where farmers were more prudent or areas where they were mindful of what might be a local supposition.

Dreaming of a white Christmas . . .?

". . . just like the ones I used to know" crooned the incomparable Bing, with nostalgic fervour but climatological inaccuracy. There are no indications that the frequency of White Christmases — either in this country or in the United States — has been declining since the beginning of the present century, even though the oldest inhabitant enjoying his pint at the local may stoutly declare that in his youth they were the rule rather than the exception.

How then does the belief originate? One of Harold Pinter's characters in his play *Hard Times* muses that "sometimes we remember things that may never have happened". I do not think that is true of the old chap in the local, but I do believe that his impression of a succession of White Christmases years ago is largely due to a foreshortening in the perspective of the memory.

To regard a White Christmas as an old-fashioned one has probably been a nostalgic figure of thought for many generations. Mr T. B. Norgate, of Lyng in Norfolk, contributed to *Weather*, August, 1977 (Vol. XXXII; No 8), some fascinating notes compiled in the early seventeenth century by churchwardens at Beeston-next-Mileham, near Dereham, Norfolk, and noticed that the churchwardens, writing of "a great fall of snow and frozen ice . . . on 1st Februarie 1614", described the snow "*as there was in former times yce throughout the time of Christmas festivities*".

More than 300 years later John H. Willis of Norwich in his book *Weatherwise* (George Allen and Unwin) reported on the tremendous blizzards which swept the country at Christmas, 1927:

> By Christmas morning the returning cold was transformed into snow, which already by evening had become so bafflingly deep that by Boxing Day wide areas of the country lay isolated by vast drifts, and we were back in one of the early Victorian winters which we term seasonable, and whose absence we deplore till they come.

And Willis, commenting on some exceptionally snowy weather in April, 1936, described the scene "as of an old-fashioned Christmas, with its landscapes of snow and snow-weighted boughs". Whatever conjectures those seventeenth-century diarists and others may have had as to the reason for a White Christmas being something of the past is not known. During the 1914–18 War, gunfire in Flanders was often blamed for unusual weather — particularly heavy rain. Nowadays there is a tendency to put the blame for any suspected change of climate on nuclear explosions, atmospheric pollution (and its possible "greenhouse" effect)

Everybody's idea of a White Christmas.

or some mysterious climatic evolution leading us to warmer Winters and recessions in the central heating industry.

Michael Hunt has suggested that so far as South-east England is concerned the possibility of a White Christmas was probably greatest at the end of the eighteenth century and during the first decade or so of the nineteenth, when there was a one in four chance of snow lying on at least two of the three days of Christmas. He suggests, too, that the writings of Charles Dickens (born in 1812) were probably influenced by some very real childhood memories. Michael Hunt also made the very valid point that, prior to the reform of the calendar in 1752, Christmas fell on what is now 6th January — and, with the general tendency for Winter to strike in January rather than in December, this obviously gave somewhat increased chances of a White Christmas centuries ago.

The famous Winter of 1947 did not begin until late January. In the equally spectacular Winter of 1962–63 only a few insignificant flakes of snow fell at Christmas. The really wintry weather did not set in until 28th December. Similarly in the Winter of 1978–79, there were only a few falls of snow before Christmas — which was a particularly mild one, entirely free of frost. The blizzards did not arrive until 30th December, continuing relentlessly throughout January. There was a brief two-week respite in early February, following which East Anglia had its worst blizzards in living memory, with entire communities completely isolated by snowdrifts.

Michael Hunt suggested that the probability of a White Christmas in the present century might be about one in ten. This is confirmed by an analysis I made of the fifty-year period 1932 to 1981. Because of its scientific insignificance, there is no official designation of a White Christmas (the bookmakers' definition of as little as one flake of snow on Christmas Day on the roof of the London Weather Centre is daft beyond belief). For the purposes of my analysis of meteorological observations at Rushmere St Andrew I adopted the simple rule-of-thumb criterion that for any Christmas to qualify as "White" there must be snow actually lying on the ground on at least one of the three days, Christmas Eve, Christmas Day or Boxing Day (for this purpose I used the routine logging of "snow lying" at the 9 a.m. observation).

During the whole of that fifty-year period a White Christmas occurred on only five occasions — with two very near misses — as follows:

1981 During the coldest December for over 100 years, snow fell and lay on the ground as early as the 8th, reaching depths of five inches with considerable drifting. These conditions lasted over the entire Christmas holiday and the ground was not clear of snow until the 29th. Christmas Day was, most unusually, an "ice-day" (maximum temperature only 32 degrees F.).

1970 There was snow on Christmas Eve; then snow and "snow lying" until 6th January (to a depth of four inches on Boxing Day). The only part of the British Isles where a White Christmas did not occur was in Scotland!

1964 Snow and "snow lying" from Christmas Day (another "ice-day") until the 28th.

1956 Slight snow on Christmas Eve. Snow and "snow lying" on Boxing Day. Then a thaw with melting snow and fog. Heavy rain on the 28th.

1938 A really spectacular one, with snow and "snow lying" from 18th December until Boxing Day. Snow lay up to eight inches deep, with considerable drifting.

As for the near misses, one was in 1968, when the snow did not start until Boxing Day; from then on there was snow and "snow lying" until New Year's Eve (up to five inches deep with considerable drifting). The other near miss was in 1962. Only a few flakes fell on Christmas Day and Boxing Day but from the 28th onwards we had weeks of heavy snow and "snow lying" in one of the most severe and snowy Winters of the century.

A White Christmas is never a merely local affair. In the Summer we might occasionally get a brief East Anglian heatwave all to ourselves but never an exclusive White Christmas. Our White Christmases invariably involve most of the rest of the country and are part of a broad pattern extending over most of Scandinavia, the Continent and often further afield.

A fixed date for Easter?

The Whitsun Bank Holiday has already been replaced by those in authority with a Spring Bank Holiday related to a fixed Monday in the year, thus denying the traditional Whit Monday celebrations and processions their earlier links with a religious holiday.

As things stand, the date of Easter Day can vary from as early as 22nd March to as late as 25th April. For purely social and recreational reasons there does seem to be a strong argument in favour of a holiday fixed later in the year. But would we gain so very much? There are those who pessimistically believe that, whatever the date, Easter has a wayward tendency to be chilly; often with hail, sleet or even snow. "More like Christmas" we are apt to grumble, as we shiver away from the deserted picnic spots.

Can Easter really be as cold as Christmas? Surveying the Rushmere St Andrew records (broadly representative of the rest of East Anglia) for the years 1951–1984, the following table gives details of all those occasions when either Good Friday, Easter Saturday, Easter Sunday or Easter Monday were as cold as or colder than the preceding Christmas Eve, Christmas Day or Boxing Day. It also shows all occasions when snow, sleet or hail fell during Easter. I have also included every night air frost at Easter (32 degrees F. or below) because it is the air frosts which can do the most damage to vegetation. I have ignored ground frosts as these are common enough in Spring. They are often fairly harmless and are Nature's way of making us pay just a little for the clear skies which give us fine picnic weather by day:

EASTER AND CHRISTMAS COMPARED, 1951–1983
Rushmere St Andrew

Easter						Previous Christmas	
Year	Day		Maximum day temp. °F.	Night air frost °F.	Snow, sleet or hail	Day	Maximum day temp. °F.
1983	1 Apr.	Good Friday	44	32	—	Christmas Eve	46
	2	Easter Saturday	47	—	Hail	Christmas Day	49
	3	Easter Day	46	32	Snow	Boxing Day	49
	4	Easter Monday	45	—	Sleet		
1980	4 Apr.	Good Friday	—	31		—	—
1978	24 Mar.	Good Friday	50	—	a few flakes sleet	Christmas Eve	54
	26	Easter Day	51	—	—		

Easter						Previous Christmas	
1977	8 Apr.	Good Friday	—	30	snow, sleet & hail	—	—
	9	Easter Saturday	—	28	Hail		
	10	Easter Day	—	28	—		
1975	28 Mar.	Good Friday	43	32	Snow	Christmas Eve	47
	29	Easter Saturday	44	31	Snow & hail		
	30	Easter Day	44	30	Snow lying to nearly half inch		
1971	12 Apr.	Easter Monday	—	32	—	—	—
1970	27 Mar.	Good Friday	46	30	Snow	Christmas Eve	47
	28	Easter Saturday	43	31	Slight snow	Christmas Day	47
						Boxing Day	44
1968	12 Apr.	Good Friday	—	32	—	—	—
1964	27 Mar.	Good Friday	43	—	—		
	28	Easter Saturday	43	—	—	Christmas Day	44
	29	Easter Day	41	—	—	Boxing Day	43
	30	Easter Monday	41	—	Sleet		
1961	3 Apr.	Easter Monday	45	32	—	Christmas Day	49
						Boxing Day	47
1958	5 Apr.	Easter Saturday	42	—	—	Christmas Eve	47
	6	Easter Day	43	—	—	Christmas Day	42
	7	Easter Monday	45	—	Hail	Boxing Day	47
1956	30 Mar.	Good Friday	45	—	—	Christmas Eve	48
	31	Easter Saturday	46	—	—	Christmas Day	51
	1 Apr.	Easter Day	47	—	—	Boxing Day	53
	2	Easter Monday	51	—	—		
1954	17 Apr.	Easter Saturday	51	—	—	Boxing Day	51
1951	24 Mar.	Easter Saturday	—	—	Snow, hail & thunder-storm	—	—
	25	Easter Day	—	31	Snow & hail		

The table does not attempt to show all the cold Easters we have suffered but specifically only those which have either given us a Wintry form of precipitation or have to some degree been colder than the preceding Christmas. The latter criterion, as in the cases of 1954, 1956 and 1978, is sometimes merely an indication of a very mild Christmas rather than a cold Easter, though we did, for example, have a few flakes of sleet at Easter in 1978.

What the table does show is that it was only when Easter was in March or the first half of April that it gave us Christmas weather out of season. There is, not surprisingly, evidence to suggest that a fixed, later Easter would tend to provide us with better — and certainly less cold — weather.

But there is no guarantee of that. A spectacular example of the variability of Easter occurred in 1979 (not included in the above table because it was not colder than the previous Christmas). The holiday got off to a spendid start. Easter Day (15th April) was pleasantly warm and sunny, an unobtrusive but influential ridge of high pressure lying across the country giving light south-easterly winds and a maximum shade temperature of 74 degrees F. at Rushmere St Andrew, the warmest Easter locally for thirty years. Alas, on the very next day (Easter Monday) a deepening low pressure system extending from the Continent up to Scandinavia suddenly put us in the track of a cold northerly blast, plunging our temperature to a miserable maximum of only 54 degrees F. There was worse to follow; by the following day the northerlies were

East Anglia and the

Some daily papers publish synoptic charts alongside the weather forecasts — and every day both the BBC and Anglia Television provide weather maps, analysed and explained by professional forecasters. The Anglia Television maps are particularly worth watching, not only because

David Brooks. *Anglia Television*

coming down almost directly from the Arctic Circle and on the Tuesday we suffered a bleak maximum of only 48 degrees F. — a drop in daytime temperature of 26 degrees F. in the space of only two days.

April is notoriously fickle. March is undoubtedly the backdoor to Winter and there is often a lot of ice and snow still to be shaken out in the April spring-clean. The late John H. Willis, commenting on the cold Spring of 1919, said:

> This long run of wintry weather trailed even into early April, with frosts in its opening week of 10 and 12 degrees; and though with its traditional fickleness April flirted with high summer for some 48 hours round Good Friday the 18th, when temperatures soared suddenly to 67 degrees, it coolly returned to its first love round the 27th, when a remarkable storm buried wide areas around London, and in Essex and Cambridge, under 12 to 18 inches of snow.

27th April is later than the present latest possible date for Easter Day, so that is cold comfort for those who would like a fixed Easter later in April!

daily weather maps

the forecaster has more time to deal with local details than the national forecasters but because in my opinion the local weather service instituted by the late Michael Hunt on Anglia and now run by David Brooks with Peter Walker and Jim Bacon is the best local service in the country.

Peter Walker. *Anglia Television*

When looking at the maps, it is a safe rule that the closer together are the isobars (the lines connecting all places of equal barometric pressure, thus showing the "highs" and the "lows" as with the lines of a contour map) the stronger will be the wind. The isobars frequently form themselves into familiar patterns. The following maps show some of the barometric situations which have particular significance for East Anglia and are worth looking out for. For the sake of simplicity I have not shown actual barometer readings against the isobars — it is not the actual height of the barometer which is important but the relative distribution of the highs and the lows. The arrows show the wind directions (as Buys Ballots law says: "Stand with your back to the wind and the low pressure will be to your left" — except, of course, in the case of the local sea breezes which are caused by thermal differentials).

I have classified the various patterns into the categories of "Good", "Poor", etc., according to the way in which they might usually affect East Anglia.

The late Michael Hunt receiving a presentation from his team of observers on his retirement as head of the Anglia Television weather department. He is flanked by his successor, David Brooks, left, and Gerald Rolfe, secretary of the C.O.L. organisation.

A — Good

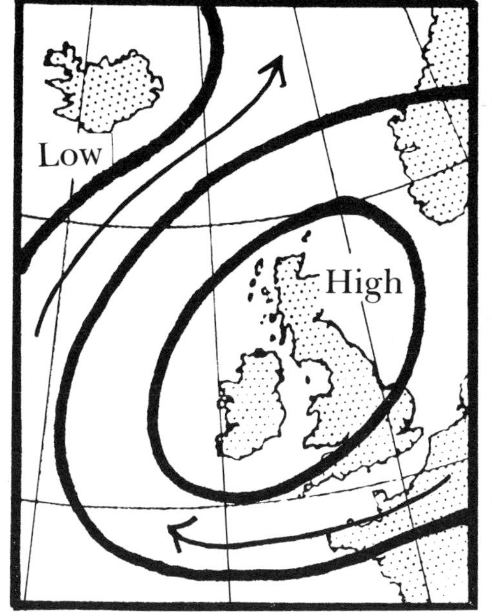

It is not often we get an anticyclone (high pressure area) completely covering the British Isles but when we do we can expect calm and settled weather, usually with clear skies. In these conditions, onshore winds often bring fog and cloud to coastal regions; in the accompanying example, East Anglia is vulnerable owing to easterly winds crossing the North Sea. If the anticyclone were situated further to the South-east, East Anglia would be within the SW airstream and sea fog would be less likely. (The west and south-west coasts would then be more vulnerable). With light winds and clear skies, ground frosts are almost inevitable from early Autumn until late Spring. This situation is best in Summer; in Winter, accumulation of cold surface air can cause a temperature "inversion", the warmer air above trapping the colder air below, often resulting in persistently dull, often foggy, weather.

B — Good

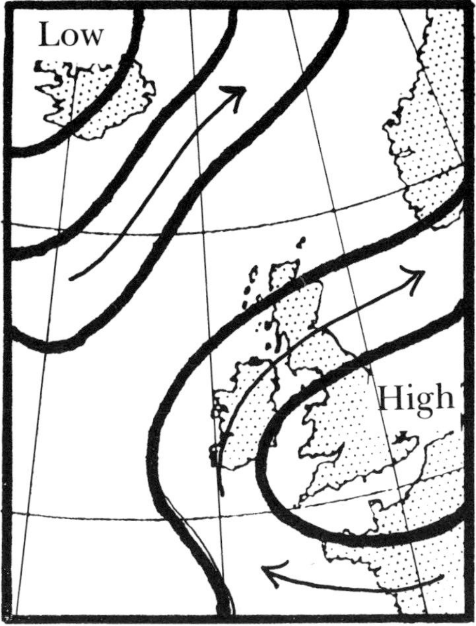

With high pressure extending from the Continent, dry weather is likely over the whole country with the probable exception of NW Scotland and Northern Ireland. Hot in Summer; cold in Winter. All coasts liable to fog. With clear skies and light winds, ground frosts are almost certain from early Autumn until late Spring. This pattern of pressure distribution frequently causes distortion and dislocation of television and radio reception.

C — Usually good

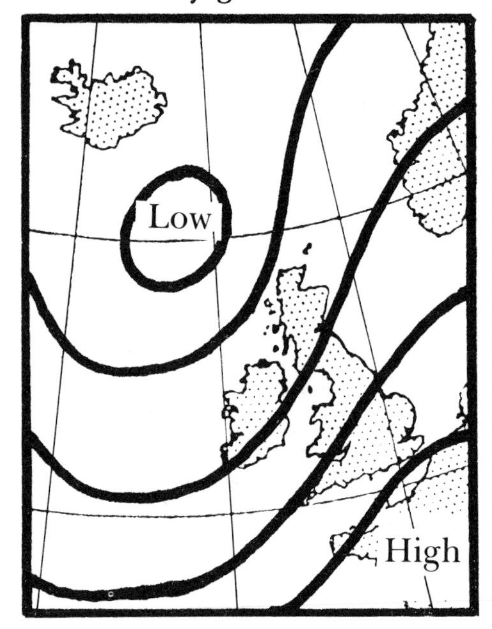

The low pressure near Iceland is probably giving rain over Scotland, Northern Ireland and NW England — but the high pressure over SE England should keep East Anglia under fair or fine conditions. There are benefits to East Anglia in this conjunction of a high and a low pressure system. While the anticyclone is maintaining dry weather, the depression is drawing air from probably as far south as the Azores. In the Summer, with the long track of landborne south-westerlies from Land's End to the Norfolk coast, Cromer and neighbourhood is very often the warmest holiday spot in the country — sometimes hotter even than in the Mediterranean and North Africa.

D — Usually good

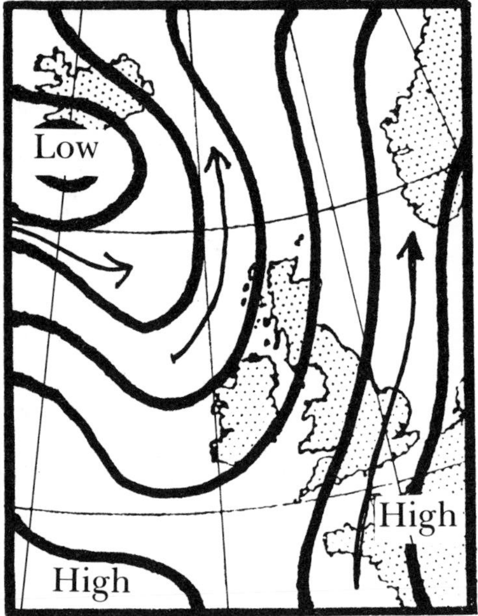

While a depression with cloud and rain is lurking off our western seaboard, a Continental anticyclone is giving fine weather over East Anglia and the South-east. On Sunday 13th April, 1980, the depression was too far away to give rain in East Anglia but near enough to give a thin, filmy layer of cirro-stratus cloud. A spectacular halo was visible throughout the day — but the barometer remained steady and the anticyclone maintained dry weather in East Anglia for the next few days, with temperatures into the 70s F., while it was already raining in the West.

E — Generally good

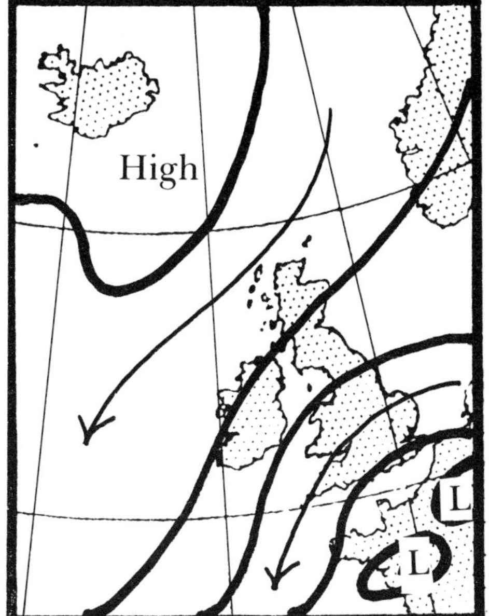

A large high-pressure system to the North dominates the scene, usually giving fine weather over the whole country. In the Summer, easterly winds off the Continent can bring very warm weather to East Anglia and SE England. But, with great heat over France and Spain, those small low pressure systems spell danger. They usually trigger off thunderstorms and the whole complex system often drifts northwards, bringing violent thunderstorms to East Anglia and the SE, often in the early hours of the morning and frequently followed by a damp, rainy (and often quite misty) day. This situation often brings an East Anglian heatwave to an end. Even in Winter this weather pattern carries a high thunder risk for East Anglia and the SE, though not so great as in the Summer.

F — Potentially poor

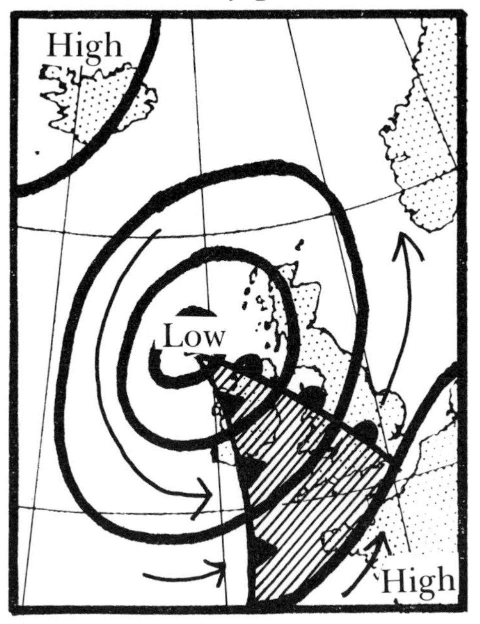

A very common situation. The Atlantic depression lying close to Scotland and Ireland is giving rain over many parts of the country, with the exception of East Anglia and the South-east (I have shaded the area between the warm and cold fronts). In East Anglia the weather is most likely to be fair or fine (warm in Summer), with thin, filmy cirro-stratus clouds just ahead of the warm front (marked ◓◓◓ on the map) — and most likely with a well-defined halo round the sun. If the depression remains stationary (which it often does), the barometer should also remain steady — and the halo is a good sign (the longer the halo lasts — sometimes several days — the better the prospects of prolonged fair weather). But if the depression is tracking eastwards, the barometer will be falling, the rain area (shaded on the map) will be approaching — and the halo is a bad sign (the quicker the clouds thicken, the sooner the halo will disappear). In the rear of the depression, behind the main rain area, a cold front (marked ▲▲▲ on the

G — Poor

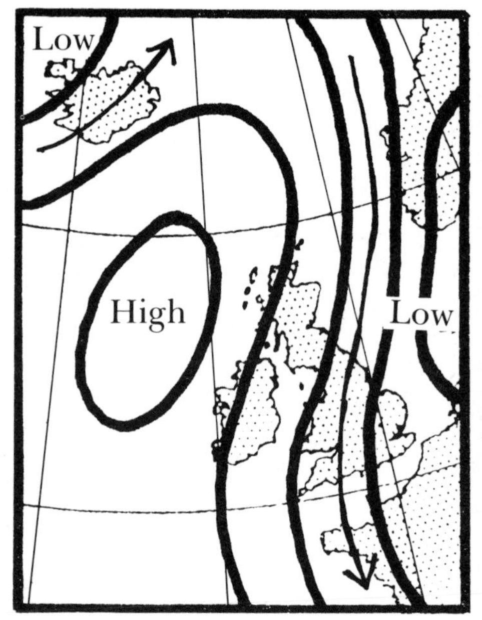

While the anticyclone is probably giving fair weather over the western half of the British Isles, the low over Scandinavia is feeding the more easterly half of the country with cold northerly winds direct from the Arctic — which, picking up moisture on their long maritime trek, usually give us cloudy, unsettled and miserable weather. "Fronts" and minor depressions in the rear of the low frequently travel south, bringing a sequence of bands of rain (snow in Winter) to East Anglia. This pattern frequently gives North Norfolk (and North Kent) quite considerable snowfalls, with drifting.

---

map) will bring colder NW winds with showery, squally weather. An unpleasant variation of this situation is when the depression is nearer to us and, as often happens, remains stationary for several days. "Fronts", with associated bands of rain, revolving anti-clockwise round the depression can give us a relentless sequence of often brief wet spells.

H — Poor

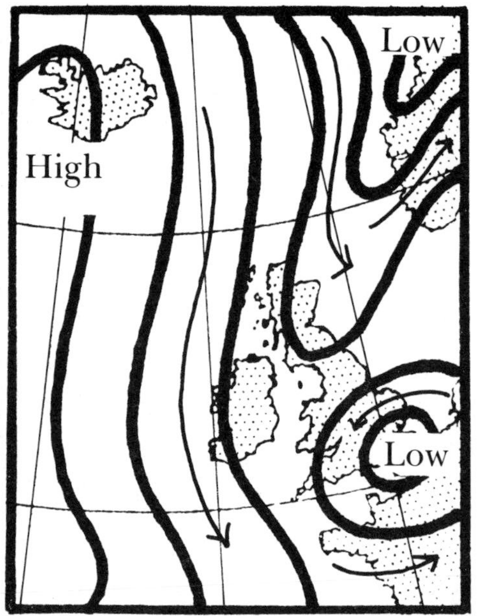

Low pressure to the South means an east wind — and even a small and shallow depression moving eastwards along the English Channel can bring 24 hours or so of continuous rain to East Anglia and the South ("when the wind is in the East, rain for twenty-four hours at least"). This was the situation on 9th March, 1975, when East Anglia was drenched with continuous rain (and some hail), up to an inch in places. On similar occasions, two inches or so have occurred. The slower the depression moves, the longer the rain continues and the heavier the total fall. A deceptive feature of this pattern is that, when the depression is moving parallel to East Anglia, the barometer usually remains steady — sometimes it even rises. Do not be deceived!

I — Very poor

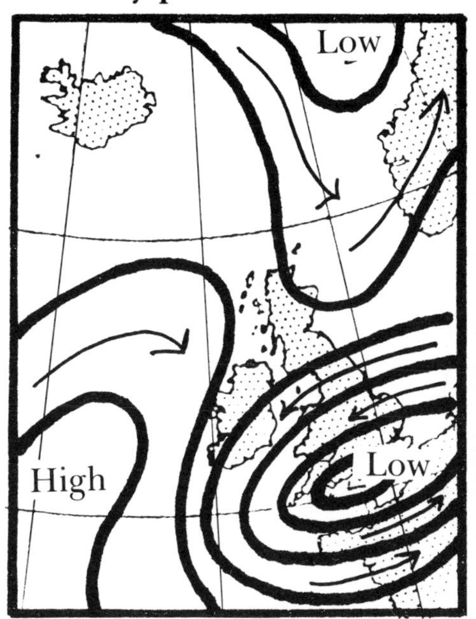

When the depression moving along the English Channel is well organised, intense and vigorous it brings trouble to East Anglia and the southern half of the country. With the isobars close together, easterly gales usually accompany the continuous rain. In the Winter, this situation has been responsible for some of our worst blizzards and snowdrifts. Snow warnings are often issued when this pattern develops in Winter.

J — Very dangerous

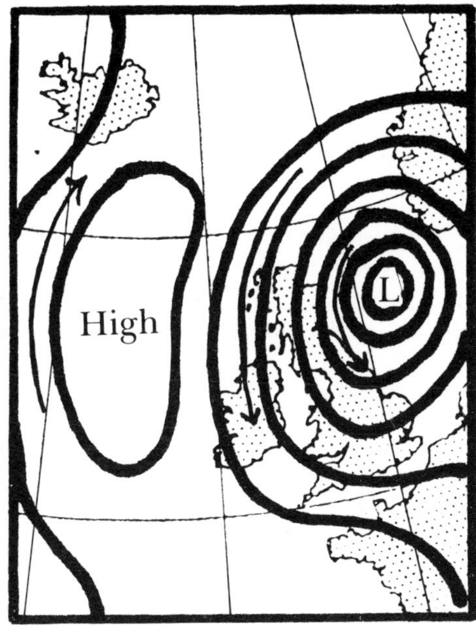

This alarming situation puts the entire East Coast at serious risk of North Sea flooding. It was responsible for the disastrous floods of 31st January and 1st February, 1953, which caused tragic loss of life — and also for the floods of 2nd–3rd January, 1976, and 11th–12th January, 1978. When an intense and rapidly moving depression travels eastwards across the North Sea it causes N or NW gales or even hurricanes to drive gigantic seas into the bottleneck of the funnel-shaped southern North Sea. The low barometric pressure over the North Sea allows the sea water to rise, while the level of the Atlantic is pressed down by the high pressure, causing a sea surge which forces additional Atlantic water down the already tumultuous North Sea and up the English Channel. Thus, the worst flooding usually occurs between the Wash and the Thames Estuary — but the entire coast is at risk. The situation becomes serious when the maximum effect of the depression coincides with a spring tide.

Something fishy?

Hamlet: Do you see yonder cloud that's almost in shape of a camel?
Polonius: By the mass, and 'tis like a camel, indeed.
Hamlet: Methinks it is like a weasel.
Polonius: It is backed like a weasel.
Hamlet: Or like a whale?
Polonius: Very like a whale.

Odd shapes often appear in the sky. The fairly commonplace "Mackerel sky" is formed by cirro-cumulus (20,000 to 40,000 feet high) or alto-cumulus clouds (6,000 to 20,000 feet). Sometimes this type of cloud develops a lens-like shape and is designated "lenticular". This development (caused by undulating waves in the upper air current) is very common in mountainous terrain but occasionally occurs over flatter

This series of photographs shows the development of lenticular alto-cumulus over the author's home at Rushmere St Andrew, near Ipswich. The development of such clouds is more common in mountainous areas than in East Anglia.

Not a flying saucer, but a circular cloud photographed by the author in 1970. Earlier stages in the development of this cloud can be seen on the previous page.

land such as East Anglia, now and again displaying iridescent mother-of-pearl colouring.

During the Summer of 1970 I was taking photographs from our garden of interesting formations of lenticular alto-cumulus. Having first appeared in orderly lines, the clouds began to disintegrate and dissolve. As they did so, one cloud detached itself from the rest and moved slowly towards us (slow movement is a feature of lenticular clouds). Eventually, almost all the rest of the clouds disappeared, leaving this one circular specimen hovering overhead. Anyone not having seen its development might well have wondered if he or she were observing some kind of flying saucer.

CHAPTER FOUR

Knowing the Weather

Independence is a fine thing — and owning one's own weather station, or at least having a few basic instruments and an elementary grounding of meteorological knowledge, provides interesting records and a personal back-up service to the official weather forecasts. When an official weather forecast occasionally goes wrong, some practical knowledge usually enables the amateur to diagnose the error and apply the appropriate correction.

Meteorology is a fascinating hobby — and, after the initial outlay, has virtually no running costs. Once one has bought one's weather instruments, rare specimens of weather happenings are limitless — and they all come free of charge!

A weather station can fit snugly into an ordinary garden and, although the basic equipment for a station up to Meteorological Office standards is fairly expensive, there is a wide range of cheap and sufficiently reliable instruments on the market to make it easy for anyone to install a station of quite useful efficiency. Intimate knowledge of the weather is particularly useful to all those involved in outdoor activities and hobbies and the following pages show some of the instruments available to give that knowledge.

Not everyone requires his or her weather station to be up to Meteorological Office standards. Here are some examples of simple and inexpensive equipment suitable for an informal weather station.

A Stevenson screen is expensive, although cheaper DIY kits are available. As a makeshift, a thermometer hung about 4 feet high on a north-facing post away from the house and where the sun cannot shine directly on the bulb will give a fair approximation of the "official" screen temperature. Many types of simple and inexpensive instruments are obtainable from leading manufacturers. For cheapness, I suggest a look around the garden centre shops, many of which have an Aladdin's cave of fascinating instruments for a whole variety of uses. They may not be up to Meteorological Office standards but are excellent for everyday purposes.

When buying a cheap thermometer, ensure that there is a good range of the type you have chosen. Then select a thermometer which

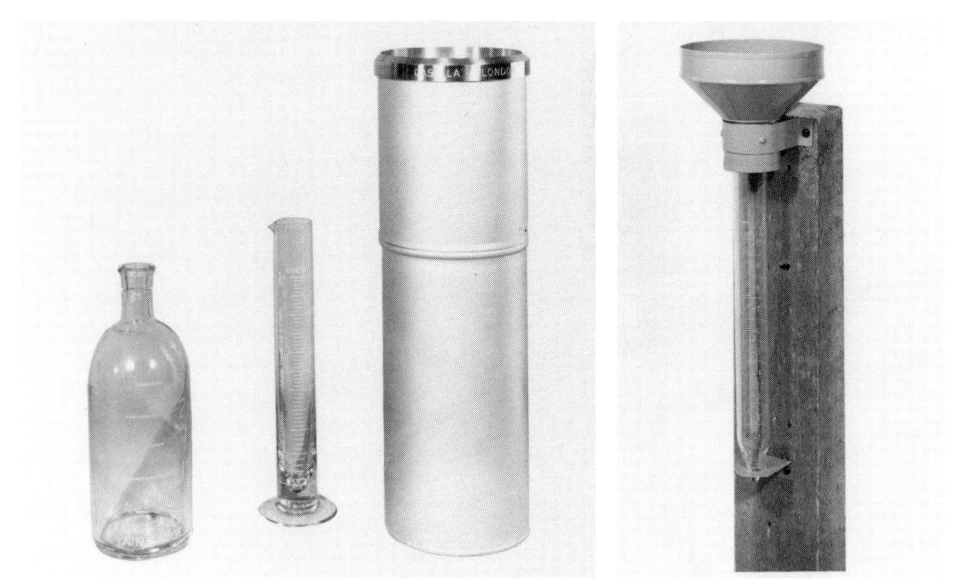

A rain gauge. The rain falling into the funnel is collected in a bottle from which it is poured into a measuring glass, enabling readings to be made to an accuracy of a hundredth of an inch. A cheaper form of rain gauge is seen at right. *Casella (London) Ltd.*

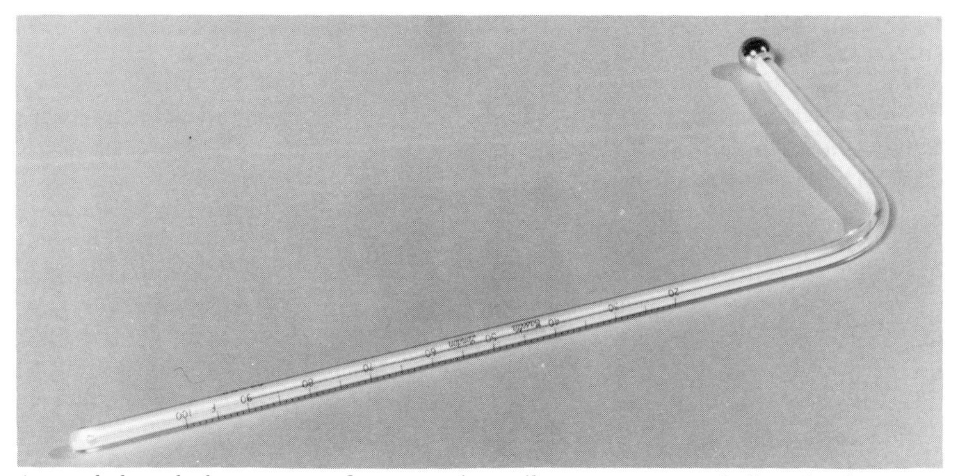

An angled earth thermometer for measuring soil temperature at shallow depths. *Casella (London) Ltd.*

gives a reading midway between the highest and the lowest of some of the others. In that way you are more likely to acquire a fairly accurate instrument (if the range you are looking at shows too wide a variation of temperature, choose a more reliable model).

Motorists

Black Ice

Of all the weather hazards, "black ice" is one of the most deadly. It can result from several causes, sometimes in combination. Black ice looks like water, and often occurs when the air temperature is misleadingly above freezing-point.

A good motorist should know the danger signs. Rain falling on a frozen surface and a sudden freeze-up of wet roads are obvious ones. More sinister, because they are less obvious, are the ones which occur when the air temperature is actually above freezing, with clear skies and/or dry air. Clear skies are conducive to ground frost (and black ice) on exposed surfaces. An added hazard is that country roads overhung with trees are often protected from ground frost; thus, driving out of a sheltered and wet country lane one may suddenly encounter an exposed main road covered with ice (a properly exposed grass thermometer in one's garden will have given a warning signal).

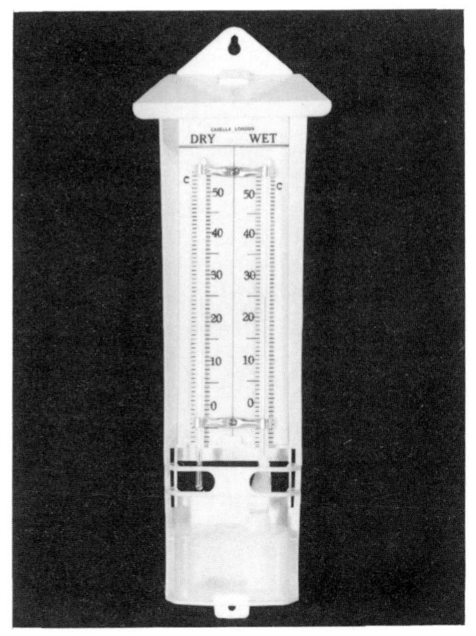

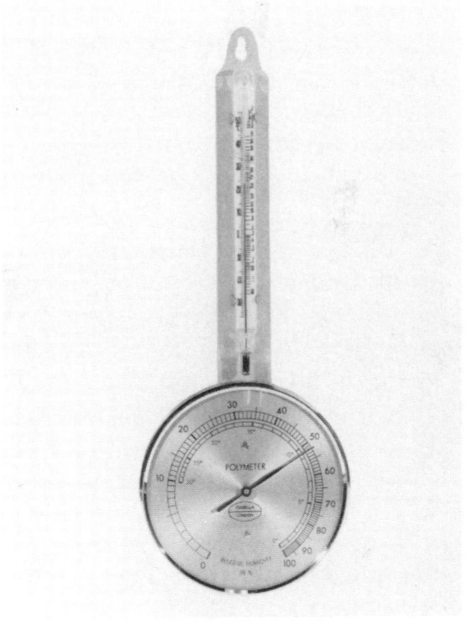

Two ways of measuring the relative humidity of the air: at left a wet and dry-bulb hygrometer and at right a dial hygrometer. *Casella (London) Ltd.*

The cooling effect of evaporation can cause wet surfaces to freeze, even though the air temperature is above freezing. For example, if the air temperature is, say 34 degrees F. but the air is dry (with a relative humidity of sixty per cent), the wet-bulb thermometer will read about 30 degrees F. — and wet roads may well be cooled (merely by evaporation) to below freezing. Whenever the wet-bulb is below freezing there is a danger of icy roads. A wet-bulb hygrometer is a useful indicator. But it needs special attention — and because of the ease of reading the humidity from a dial hygrometer, I have included in an appendix a table which is a dual conversion chart. Designed primarily to show the relative humidity for any given wet- and dry-bulb readings, it conversely shows the wet-bulb reading at any given air temperature and relative humidity. A word of caution; dial hygrometers do not always have a precise degree of accuracy but they are useful general indicators.

Black ice is particularly likely at dawn and sunset as well as during the night, often at the commuters' rush hour. The safest driving rule in cold weather is always to assume that wet-looking roads are actually frozen — and that other drivers are not so cautious.

Greasy roads

These are most dangerous after a long spell of dry weather during which oil and grease has accumulated on the road surface. Light rain or a damp fog can quickly turn the roads into skid-pans. The lighter the rain, the worse the grease. A torrential downpour is the most effective form of grease dispersal — and, fortunately, many hot dry spells are broken by violent thunderstorms.

Fog

One of our most frustrating hazards, the formation of fog is often complicated — particularly near coasts, estuaries and marshlands. A general fog, often occuring when the mild, moist air of a thaw flows across the cold earth, is perhaps the easiest for the forecasters to predict. The most difficult are the very local fogs which occur on "radiation" nights when a clear sky allows the earth's warmth to escape.

Radiation fogs are most frequent and dense in valleys and low-lying ground, calm conditions at night allowing the cold air to sink and settle into the lower levels. Such fogs are of a patchy nature, and the danger is not so much what lurks round the next bend as what lies in the next dip in the road. Hilltop fogs are commonplace but obviously not so frequent in the comparatively flat terrain of East Anglia, where "lakes" of fog occur in the shallow areas.

A sea fog can encroach some miles inland, the coast of East Anglia

Fog on the A45—caused by mild, moist air coming into contact with the cold earth.
East Anglian Daily Times

being particularly vulnerable in the Spring and early Summer when the North Sea is still cold from the Winter. A variety of conditions, including dull and windy weather, can accompany sea fogs when the wind is onshore. Motorists travelling north up the A12 from London are likely to find worsening conditions, both as regards radiation and sea fogs, from Chelmsford onwards.

A primary cause of fog is the mixing of air of differing temperatures. After a cold night, the rising sun adds a stimulant to the mixing process (the sun "stirring up its morning cup of tea"). Although the sun's warmth will usually clear away the fog, motorists should always be prepared for it to get a little worse before it clears. During the Winter, this temporary thickening often coincides with the early morning rush hour. Despite a natural tendency for commuters to wait for the fog to clear, an earlier start often pays off.

Holidaymakers

The chances of rain in East Anglia are considerably less than in most other parts of the British Isles. May is one of the driest months; June the sunniest and July and August the warmest. The many indentations of the eastern coast provide several beaches with pleasant south-easterly or southerly aspects. Along the beaches, particularly at low tide, a pungent and tangy air encourages people to take deep breaths and exclaim "Ah, this splendid smell of ozone!" As explained in chapter one, this is not true; it is more likely the smell of rotting seaweed and the like.

The ozone layer, many miles above us, gives vital protection from the burning ultra-violet rays . Dust and moisture near the earth's surface also

Holidaymakers who ignore the dangers of airbeds and inflatable boats when an offshore wind is blowing sometimes have cause to be grateful for the lookout kept by the coastguards in their watch-houses, like this one at Clacton perched on top of a martello tower.

play a part. Holidaymakers seeking a healthy-looking tan will find the East Anglian beaches happy hunting grounds. Most of East Anglia's coastal areas are well away from any large industrial conurbations; the prevailing south-westerly winds are landborne and not so moist as on the western side of the country; the easterlies off the Continent are usually dry, so the ultra-violet content of the sun's rays is comparatively high in East Anglia, where it is possible to acquire a tan on even a cloudy day.

The burning power of the ultra-violet rays has little to do with the actual heat of the sun's rays, which in excess can, according to one's bodily condition and the amount of clothing worn, cause sunstroke.

On the other hand, the North Sea is a comparatively cold one, particularly in Spring and early Summer. The onshore winds of East Anglia are generally cooler than elsewhere. If on the East Coast you sit in a deckchair facing inland towards the afternoon sun, beware of waking next morning with a sunburnt front and a stiff back.

Those with delicate skins wishing to acquire a tan without undue risk should restrict their sunbathing to morning and evening. At midday, the sun's rays have their shortest journey through the atmosphere and ultra-violet penetration is at its greatest. In the morning and evening, the much longer journey through the atmosphere allows more moisture, dust particles, etc., to obstruct the ultra-violet rays than at midday.

Exotic colouring of the sky at sunrise and sunset is largely due to the distortion of light through layers of moisture and impurities.

Sea breezes are harmless onshore winds. But any offshore wind must be treated with respect. Strong offshore winds are very dangerous to holidaymakers, handlers of small craft and the like. The dangerous sea currents at many points along the East Anglian coast are made even more hazardous when even a light offshore wind is blowing — and it is most unwise for anyone, particularly children, to use rubber dinghies or airbeds at any time without wearing life-jackets. If there is a fresh offshore wind it is foolish to take the slightest risk. Yet on Wednesday, 20th August, 1980 — with shade temperatures in the eighties and the entire East Anglian coast under the influence of a strong westerly wind of Force 5 to 6, gusting to 7 — the local coastguards were swamped by dozens of distress calls. Fortunately there was no loss of life, but such a situation shows inexcusably gross carelessness and almost criminal disregard for the personal safety of members of the rescue services.

The friendly sea breezes are not the only providers of relief on a hot day. The relative humidity and the wet-bulb factor play an important role. If the air is very dry, evaporation off a moist surface is rapid, causing the wet-bulb thermometer to read much lower than the dry-bulb (which registers the temperature of the air). On a hot day, perspiration helps. Evaporation of moisture off the skin reduces its temperature. For example, with an air temperature of 80 degrees F. in the shade and a dry air of only fifty per cent relative humidity, the evaporation temperature of the wet-bulb would be only 67 degreees F. — and that, if your skin is moist, would be the temperature you would feel (see Appendix twelve). The belief that on a hot day a few cups of hot tea are, in the long run, more cooling than an iced drink makes sense. A cold drink may give an immediate sense of cooling, but the hot tea will help us perspire, thus encouraging the wet-bulb factor of our skin.

In hot weather when the air is humid and there is little evaporation, perspiration gives little relief; we complain of the weather being close and muggy — and there is little we can do except to take advantage of any breeze we can. Temperature, humidity and wind strength are important factors in deciding whether conditions are pleasant, tolerable or downright uncomfortable.

Gardeners

A bad workman blames his tools but a good gardener will take steps to alleviate — and sometimes eliminate — the effects of some of our worst weather. A basic knowledge of the weather, close attention to the daily forecasts and a few simple instruments will often give warning of problems ahead, allowing evasive measures to be taken.

Rainfall and temperature are the main concern. There is little one can do about rain, apart from taking steps to store water against times of drought. But it is useful to own a rain gauge, even if only one of those very cheap and simple ones obtainable at many garden centres and garden shops. It does not really matter if exposure in your garden or the accuracy of the gauge are not up to Meteorological Office standards — it is the approximate amount of rain that falls in the garden which is the gardener's main concern.

The following simplified table shows composite averages for the whole of East Anglia. If you live in one of the comparatively wetter areas, you should add about two inches to the annual average; if in one of the drier areas, deduct two inches per annum (Appendix four will help identify in which rainfall area you live). Comparison of your own running total with this summary will give an indication as to the current state of affairs:

EAST ANGLIAN COMPOSITE RAINFALL AVERAGES*

	Average monthly rainfall Inches	Progressive average Inches
January	2	2
February	1½	3½
March	1½	5
April	1½	6½
May	1½	8
June	1¾	9¾
July	2¼	12
August	2	14
September	2	16
October	2¼	18¼
November	2½	20¾
December	2¼	23

*Average for first six months = 9¾ inches.
Average for last six months = 13¼ inches.

An inch of rain represents approximately 101 tons of water to the acre — headline news. Such bulk figures have little practical meaning. The fact that an inch of rain gives Ipswich, for example, over a hundred thousand tons of water merely boggles the mind.

More to the point, it is useful to know the rainfall equivalent of a few cans of water or the flow from a hosepipe. During a drought, assuming local water restrictions permit or there is sufficient rainwater in the butts, how can a gardener arrange the equivalent of an inch of rain in his garden? Some rather primitive conversions by my wife and me with our own 2½-gallon watering can show that, completely filled, it gives the equivalent of about 1½ inches of rain on an area approximately 2 feet by 1½ feet. (The area was dictated by the only straight-sided measuring tank we had available. Provided any container is straight-sided, the calculation is simple). Additionally, it might be worth while to calculate a hosepipe equivalent by checking the time it takes with the tap fully on to fill a container to a certain depth. Maybe a little complicated but I suggest the idea for what it is worth.

As regards temperatures, the thermal variations of the soil are of as much concern to gardeners as those of the air, and sometimes more. Soil temperatures at a depth of four feet have little operational significance in the day to day running of a garden — but they are of interest. The four-feet temperature is usually at its lowest in February and early March and at its highest in mid-August. There are no variations in the day and night readings — and throughout an entire month the changes are gradual, and such changes several days behind the temperature of the air. Throughout the whole of August, 1976, the four-feet temperature at Belstead only varied from 61.1 degrees F. to 61.4 degrees F. — and that is by no means exceptional.

The average monthly pattern of the four-feet temperature is shown in the table on page 98. The narrowness of the normal range within each month (over a period of eight years, 1973–1980) at Belstead, was as follows:

EARTH TEMPERATURES, 1973–1980
Average monthly range, Fahrenheit, four feet below the surface
Belstead

Winter		Spring			Summer			Autumn			Winter	
Jan	Feb	Mar	Apr	May	June	July	Aug	Sept	Oct	Nov	Dec	Year
3	1½	2	3	4½	4½	2½	1¼	2	4	5	3	19

The increased range during May and June shows the seasonal warming up process at its maximum, the end of each month being that much warmer than the beginning. The period of maximum cooling is similarly reflected in the October and November differentials. Note the time lag — the almost static midwinter and midsummer temperatures occur at four-feet depth during the last month of each season.

So much for the four-feet temperature range — which throughout an entire year can be considerably less than the variation occurring in the air temperature in a few hours. But in the upper soil, considerable short-term variations are commonplace as the topsoil quickly responds to the heat or cold of the air. The heat of the sun is accentuated by the protection from wind below ground — and frost can penetrate severely through the first few inches. As an indication, the following table shows the extremes of temperatures at various depths at Levington during the twenty years ended 1980 and at Belstead during the years 1914 to 1954:

TABLE OF EXTREMES OF EARTH TEMPERATURES, 0900 hours G.M.T.

Levington

Depth	Below grass				Below bare soil			
	Highest		Lowest		Highest		Lowest	
Cm	°F.	Date	°F.	Date	°F.	Date	°F.	Date
5	79	Jul, 1970	26	Jan, 1963	83	Jul, 1969	22	Jan, 1963
10	74	Jun–Jul, 1970	27	Jan, 1963	75	Jun, 1961	25	Jan, 1963
20	75	Jul, 1961	30	Jan, 1963	74	Jul, 1961	27	Jan, 1963

Belstead

Depth	Below grass			
	Highest		Lowest	
Feet	°F.	Date	°F.	Date
1	71.7	Jul, 1941	32.8	Mar, 1947
4	63.1	Aug, 1932	35.9	Mar, 1947

Bear in mind that the above soil temperatures refer only to the 0900 hrs GMT observations. Although readings four feet deep remain almost constant day and night, the temperature at a depth of one foot at 9 a.m. is usually at about its lowest for the twenty-four hours. Nearer the surface, temperatures at 9 a.m. are usually about halfway between their highest and lowest. The Levington figures clearly show the depths to which frost can penetrate and also the considerable heat generated by the sun long before the full heat of midday. An outstanding feature of the Belstead records was a very long run from 15th February to 6th March, 1929, when the 0900 hrs temperature at one foot depth remained almost unchanged within a few decimal points of 33 degrees F.

During 1980, I installed a set of thermometers suitable for the taking of temperatures from half an inch to four inches below the surface. The results are interesting. Even when screen temperatures are only in the mid-seventies it often happens that on a sunny day the first few inches of soil soar beyond 100 degrees F. even when the thermometer in full sunshine is managing only 80 degrees F. or so. Dry soil aids the heating process; if the soil is wet, warm sunshine may not bring the topsoil temperature up to that of the air. Water in the soil is a moderator, retarding both heating by day and cooling by night, so when there is a risk of frost the watering of a plot in the evening may prevent the

temperature of the topsoil falling below freezing point — but be careful to avoid wetting the plants themselves.

After a scorching Summer day, we water our gardens in the cool of the evening. But, owing to the time-lag, the cool of the evening for us is usually the hottest part of the day at a depth of one foot (the time-lag at four inches is about five hours; at one foot as much as seven or eight hours). For those who may be interested in the detailed pattern of one single day, I show on the next page hourly observations on Good Friday, 1981 (17th April). I chose this day chiefly because I was on the spot to take frequent readings but also because it shows so clearly the combined and conflicting effects of sun and a fresh, cool NE wind. It was a day of brilliant sunshine, with a slight ground frost the following night — or, more accurately, probably just before dawn next morning.

All this emphasises the extreme ranges of temperature to which small plants are frequently subjected. Hot sun by day greatly heats the topsoil; the same clear skies encourage sharp ground frost by night. If we complain of the discomfort of changeable temperatures, how much more should the plants grumble!

HOURLY PATTERN OF TEMPERATURES IN SHADE, SUN AND BELOW GROUND ON A SUNNY SPRING DAY, WITH A BRISK NE WIND. OBSERVATIONS ON GOOD FRIDAY, 17TH APRIL, 1981

Rushmere St Andrew

Time GMT	0800	0900	1000	1100	Noon	1300	1400	1500	1600	1700	1800	1900	2000	Minimum temperatures during night 17th–18th
Weather	← ALMOST CLOUDLESS →					← COMPLETELY CLOUDLESS →								
Wind direction and force	ENE 3	E 4	ENE 4	NE 4	ENE 3	E 4	NE 5	ENE 5	ENE 5	ENE 5	NE 4	NE 4	NE 3	
Screen (shade) temperature, °F.	46*	47	48	49	51	50	49	49	47	45	43	41	40	In screen 33
Relative humidity, %	68	66	63	63	56	52	51	51	59	64	70	76	79	
Temperature in sun (1 in. above	47*	49	54	51	57	57	56	54	52	45	40	38	36	On grass 28
Temperature, °F. 1 in. below bare soil	47*	47	55	62	68	73	72	70	61	Now in shade of nearby lilac tree 55	53	50	47	1 in. below surface 39
Temperature, °F. 4 in. below grass	47	47	48	50	51	53	54	55	55	54	54	53	52	
Temperature, °F. 1 ft below grass	50	50	50	50	50	50	50	51	51	51	51	51	51	

*It is interesting to note how the one-inch temperature—after starting off level with the shade and sun temperatures—quickly built up heat, due to the sun and complete protection from the wind.

During the following day (Easter Saturday, 18th April, 1981) conditions in our garden provided the following extremes — a typical and quite commonplace example:

WE SHOULD GRUMBLE!

24 hours in the life of a young bedding plant, RUSHMERE ST ANDREW, near IPSWICH, EASTER SATURDAY, 18th APRIL, 1981

Temperature extremes during the 24 hours 0900 GMT 18th April to 0900 GMT 19th April.

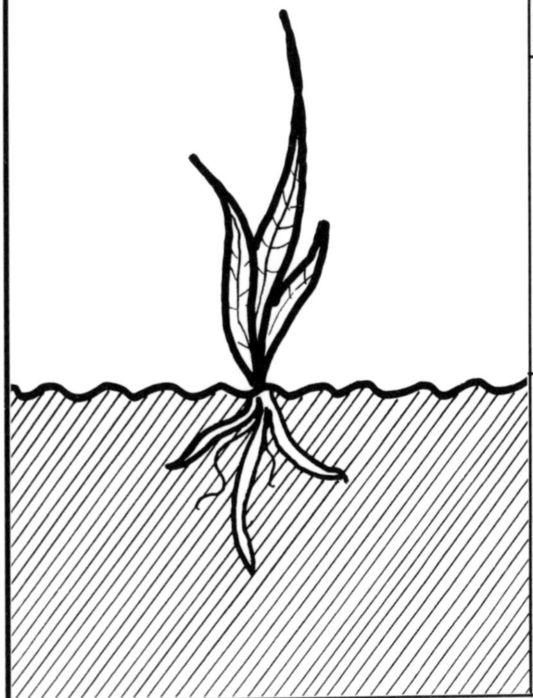

Maximum shade temperature 18th, 54°F. — about average for April. (Thermometer in screen about 4½ feet above ground.)

Minimum grass temperature during the night 18th–19th April, 29°F. — colder than an average January mid-day screen temperature. (Thermometer 1 inch above surface, fully exposed to clear sky.)

Maximum soil temperature during the 18th April, 76°F. — warmer than an average July mid-day screen temperature. (Thermometer 1 inch below surface of bare soil, fully protected from the wind.)

Difference in temperatures experienced by the roots (during the day) and the leaves (the following night) = 47°F.!

A few days later, all the bird baths in our garden were frozen over, following early morning radiation frosts.

A very important factor in horticulture is the "threshold" temperature of 42 degrees F. It is a complex subject outside the scope of this book, but, briefly, plant life tends to become dormant below 42 degrees F., resuming growth when 42 degrees F. is exceeded. The air temperature is significant but the "threshold" 42 degrees F. is more important as regards the temperature of the soil, affecting the roots of plants. Many gardeners do not reckon Spring to have begun until the temperatures are safely above 42 degrees F. The growth of grass is very closely linked with the "threshold" temperature, which can be a good indicator of when Spring growth can be expected. The late L. C. W. Bonacina wisely remarked that "cold weather in Spring merely holds back a little the rising tide of growth". After a long cold wintry spell, a substantial rise above 42 degrees F. in the soil temperature will tell you that Spring will soon be bursting out all over. In the Autumn, the "threshold" temperature can be a useful indicator as to when — other factors permitting — is the appropriate time to give the lawns their final cut.

Many garden centre shops sell special thermometers with metal points for safely pushing into the soil. For checking temperatures at greater depths, specially constructed thermometers are required.

The "threshold" temperatures can be evaluated in terms of "accumulated temperature". This is a method, based on daily readings, by which the number of degrees each day above or below the "threshold" are fed into a cumulative ± total. For example, if one took a reading of soil temperature at, say, 9 a.m. daily, starting in midwinter, the number of "day-degrees" above or below 42 degrees F. would by about mid-March give some idea as to whether growth was going to be early or late. Many gardening experts recommend that Spring outdoor sowing of seeds should be deferred until the temperature of the topsoil is above 42 degrees F. (in the mid-fifties for some varieties). Better to wait for 50 degrees F. or more is the general recommendation.

Proper study of "accumulated temperatures" is a complex operation, but to keep one's own rule-of-thumb records and compare them with the readings of previous years can provide useful information.

Frost is one of the gardener's most serious worries. There is nothing we can do to prevent an air frost but if the air temperature remains above freezing we can do a little to mitigate the effects of "clear sky" ground frosts. A grass minimum thermometer, fully exposed to the sky an inch above short grass, is a useful instrument. On a calm, clear night it will register several degrees lower than the screen temperature — and a big difference in late afternoon gives a useful hint. Rather than worrying about a red sky in the morning, gardeners should be more concerned with a clear sky at night. A cloudy sky will cut off radiation loss and often prevent frost.

In many fruitgrowing areas, such as California, a common frost deterrent is the lighting of a row of bonfires to windward of the orchards — not to provide warmth but to create a layer of smoke which, acting as a cloud, will help check the radiation loss. In a garden any particularly

"Brightly shone the moon that night . . . "

vulnerable plants would benefit a little by the branches of an overhanging tree. Sheets of muslin, newspapers, or a covering of straw all help.

East Anglia has its frost hollows — localities where cold surface air (heavy because of its low temperature) sinks into the hollows on calm nights. Many private gardens have miniature frost hollows. The effect of even a small and shallow hollow in one's garden should not be underestimated. On the lawn of my weather station there is a very slight hollow about five feet in diameter and in the centre no deeper than about two and a half inches. But on a clear, calm night a grass minimum thermometer sited in the hollow can give readings as much as 5 degrees F. lower than my standard thermometer exposed only a few feet away on level grass — which means that on many occasions anything growing in a frost hollow will be subject to a ground frost not experienced elsewhere in the garden.

Additionally, any sloping garden or allotment is subject to the sinking drift of cold air. A solid fence or close hedge at the top of the

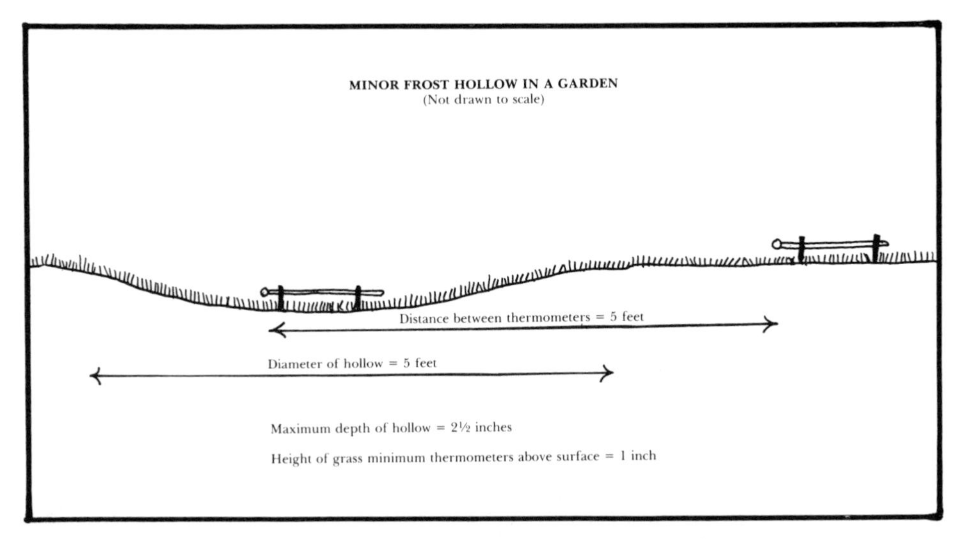

slope will help obstruct the downward flow. If one has to have a fence or hedge at the bottom of the slope it should be as open as possible to avoid trapping the cold, heavier air.

One frequent gardening question is: when can one feel safe from late Spring and early Autumn frosts? In East Anglia — unless close to the sea — a July frost has hardly ever happened and an August frost is very rare indeed. As a guide, I have compiled a chart showing the variable dates of the last ground frost of Spring and the first of Autumn at Belstead/Copdock during each decade from 1902 to 1979. This locality is ten to twelve miles from the sea, thus providing a useful halfway point

FENCING IN A SLOPING GARDEN OR ALLOTMENT

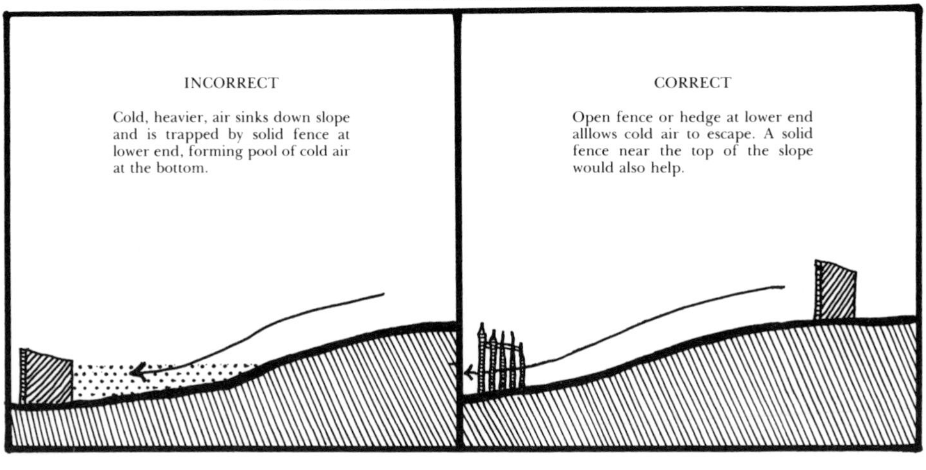

INCORRECT

Cold, heavier, air sinks down slope and is trapped by solid fence at lower end, forming pool of cold air at the bottom.

CORRECT

Open fence or hedge at lower end alllows cold air to escape. A solid fence near the top of the slope would also help.

between the coast (where frosts are far less frequent) and well inland where the risk is greater.

Precise definition of a ground frost has been the subject of varying criteria. Although freezing point is 32 degrees F., it was thought by many that damage to plants was negligible over 30 degrees F., but in 1961 the Meteorological Office revised the frost criterion from 30 degrees F. to 32 degrees F. But 32 degrees F. is a "threshold" temperature. For frozen water to thaw, the temperature must rise above 32 degrees F. For unfrozen water to freeze, the temperature must fall below 32 degrees F. So, for gardeners, I think 30 degrees F. is the more practical definition — and that is the one I have chosen for the following table.

LATEST SPRING AND EARLIEST AUTUMN GROUND FROSTS,* BY DECADE
Copdock/Belstead

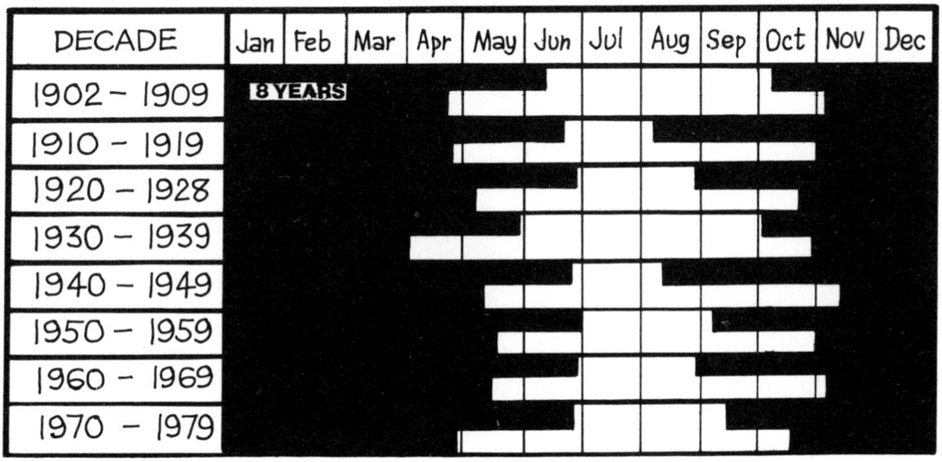

DECADE	Jan	Feb	Mar	Apr	May	Jun	Jul	Aug	Sep	Oct	Nov	Dec
1902 – 1909	8 YEARS											
1910 – 1919												
1920 – 1928												
1930 – 1939												
1940 – 1949												
1950 – 1959												
1960 – 1969												
1970 – 1979												

*For the purposes of this table the criterion for ground frost is a grass minimum temperature of 30 degrees F or less.
†Eight years.

The higher white bar of each decade shows the latest date of the last Spring frost and the earliest Autumn frost in the decade. The lower bar shows the earliest and latest dates, respectively, of the last Spring and first Autumn frost. So, as far as one can ever be certain about the weather, the shortest higher bar (i.e. 1910–1919) indicates the shortest frost-free period we can expect; the longest lower bar (i.e. 1930–1939) shows the longest we can hope for.

The last ground frost of Spring has varied from as early as 1st April, (1937) to as late as 30th June (1954). The first frost of Autumn has been as early as 7th August (1913) and as late as 15th November (1940). In the eighty years up to and including 1982, July has maintained its record locally of being the only "safe" month.

Bird lovers

The high mortality rate among birds due to lack of water is well known. Maintaining water supplies in a Summer drought presents no problem but in Wintry weather the bird baths often become frozen within minutes of thawing and refilling.

Even when a thermometer hanging outside tells you that the air temperature is above freezing, bird baths can freeze either by loss of heat to a clear sky or by the cooling effect of evaporation — or a combination of both. My wife and I have adopted measures which to some extent alleviate the problem of the former. In addition to existing bird baths in the garden, we have a few very shallow trays (tin serving trays from a public house, if your local landlord will oblige, are ideal). We place these

in the kitchen drainage area on top of the inspection covers of the drains so that they will benefit from the warmer air beneath the covers. If plenty of hot water is used in the house, the extra heat flowing under the trays will keep the water unfrozen after a conventional bird bath has frozen. But the trays must be shallow; too deep a tray will prevent the warmth reaching the surface, which always freezes first. This method cannot defeat a severe frost but it can delay freezing and, in the case of a light frost, may prevent freezing altogether. Dedicated bird lovers should take hot baths as often as possible!

In the case of radiation frosts, caused by clear night skies, measures can be taken to reduce the effects slightly. During a radiation frost, a bird bath exposed to the clear sky may freeze even though the sheltered air temperature is above freezing point. Give the bath some sort of overhead cover and it may escape the frost. On a clear night, any kind of roof over the bath may delay — and sometimes prevent — freezing. For that reason, if you have a bird table with a roof it is a good idea to put the food elsewhere in the Winter and place a shallow tray of water in its place.

Incidentally, the old saying that hot water freezes more quickly than cold water is a fallacy. Warm water poured into a bird bath will stay unfrozen just a little longer than cold water; though, alas, the small time-lag makes little practical difference.

Thunderstorms

East Anglia, with its low horizons, is a fine vantage place from which to observe thunderstorms. The tracking of a thunderstorm is simple because the time-lag between the lightning flash and the peal of thunder (being the difference between the speed of light and of sound) is roughly five seconds to the mile. There are rare exceptions to this rule, one occurring in a violent storm during the night of 19th September, 1980. After a disturbed night in the Ipswich area, conversations next day were of surprise that almost all the lightning was "sheet". One house was struck in Ipswich, but there were very few cloud-to-earth flashes. Even when I judged the storm to be directly overhead there was a five-second time-lag between flash and thunder — indicating a distance of a mile. The reason was simple but unusual. The clouds were at an unusually high level, with the tops towering to enormous heights. The lightning forks were mostly obscured, hence the "sheet" lightning, and the unusual height of the storm gave a vertical time-lag.

But that was an uncommon event. Sitting comfortably indoors near a window with a good view, the five-second-to-the-mile rule is a good indicator enabling one to track the progress of the storm easily. Using a map of reasonable scale (I like one issued by the East Anglia Tourist Board at a scale of six miles to the inch), one simply sets the map with its top to the North, waits for each successive flash, counts its distance and locates it on the map. A continuous sequence of observations will soon give a good idea as to the storm's direction.

It is usually reckoned that thunder is inaudible at more than about twelve miles distance but I have sometimes heard it farther away than that. Thunderstorms have been reported as being audible forty miles away — and during the Second World War we often heard at Rushmere St Andrew the bombing and gunfire in the London blitz seventy or so miles away.

If a heavy shower cloud has not yet developed into a thunderstorm, some alternative form of measurement is needed to indicate which direction it is taking. A few casual glances are not sufficient. The simplest method is to hold a finger, or pencil, at arm's length against a clearly defined marking in the cloud or, better still, to note the relationship of the cloud to some object like a flagpole or the corner of a roof. Scrutiny for a minute or two should indicate the cloud's movement. As a check, take a few sightings on widely separated parts of the cloud — in disturbed conditions swirling currents within the cloud often have no relation to its general movement. Never take sightings of the actual cloud tops — the vertical and horizontal spread of a vigorous and developing stormcloud often exceeds its speed. A storm whose actual movement is parallel to the observer may be developing and spreading towards him — a development usually made apparent by the behaviour of the cloud tops. Always beware of storms that come up against the wind. These deceptive ones are often most violent.

Safety precautions

Indoors is the safest place — but keep away from chimney-places, metal window frames and television sets (which are safest unplugged). If you are caught out of doors, discard metal objects such as steel-shafted umbrellas and golf clubs. In open country, make sure you yourself are not the highest point around — and never seek shelter from the rain under a tree.

Statistics indicate that the most vulnerable trees are the oak, the ash and the elm and that smooth-barked trees provide the minimum risk. If I were caught near some tall trees I would not question their variety nor the character of their bark; my concern would be a quick dash to some low-lying spot to avoid becoming another statistic. Having thrown away one's metal umbrella or golf clubs, it is sometimes best to throw away one's dignity as well. If your location is very exposed and the storm a bad one, seek sanctuary in a nearby ditch or bunker — being careful to avoid any wire fencing or other metal.

Water can add to the dangers of electricity. When bathing at the seaside it is better to come out of the water in a storm. Despite the vulnerability of metal, one of the safest places is inside a car. If the car is struck, the lightning would run round the outside metal and then earth through the tyres. But it is advisable to retract the car aerial just in case the lightning mistook it for a conductor and entered the car. It is usually wisest to pull up if driving through a thunderstorm, particularly in torrential rain, but avoid parking under tall trees, telegraph poles and the like.

The Role of the Amateur

The layman has always been interested in the weather. Old diaries abound with descriptive, often lurid, accounts of the weather. Instrumental records came later. Some of the earliest meteorological measurements in this country were taken at Wrentham, near Lowestoft, during 1673/74, and the famous Marsham, Norfolk, phenological records date from 1736. Elsewhere in this book, I freely quote from the nineteenth century records of Orlando Whistlecraft at Thwaite, Suffolk, and of the Rev. L. Jenyns at Swaffham Bulbeck, Cambridgeshire. The observations and writings of the latter are particularly respected by today's professionals.

The existence of old records, however sketchy, is invaluable to the professional climatologist. It was an amateur who, as long ago as 1863,

At his weather station at Rushmere St Andrew, the author takes his daily readings of the maximum and minimum thermometer and wet and dry-bulb thermometer in the Stevenson screen. *Tony Ray*

suggested that the motivation of a barometric depression might be a clash between polar and equatorial air, but it was not until the 1914–18 war that Norwegian scientists rediscovered and developed the theory. Before that we had never heard of warm and cold fronts, despite that nineteenth century hint from an amateur.

Today a worldwide network of official weather stations, conforming to strict standards of accuracy and uniformity, provides essential information on which the official forecasts are based. Observations and photographs taken by satellites, together with various scanning devices such as radar, play an increasingly important role. Apart from the daily forecasts, the measurement of weather at ground level provides the public with much useful information.

Left: Mr Gerald Rolfe, secretary of the Climatological Observers' Link, taking readings at his weather station at Ely.

Opposite: A map of East Anglia showing the twenty-seven stations operated by members of the Climatological Observers' Link, each one being marked with a circle.

Standard weather stations are not necessarily maintained by professionals. Many, often less comprehensively equipped, are owned by private individuals, and there is a large and increasing number of amateurs who, as well as enjoying their hobby, play a useful role in the measurement and collation of meteorological data. One of the most useful contributions is made by the Climatological Observers' Link (COL for short), an organisation created in 1970. Its comprehensive monthly bulletin includes detailed reports of the previous month's weather from about two hundred observers, mostly in this country but including several from other parts of the world. In 1982 there were more than twenty observers in Norfolk, Cambridgeshire, Suffolk and Essex alone. Members of COL include professionals as well as amateurs — many professional meteorologists have their own private weather stations and

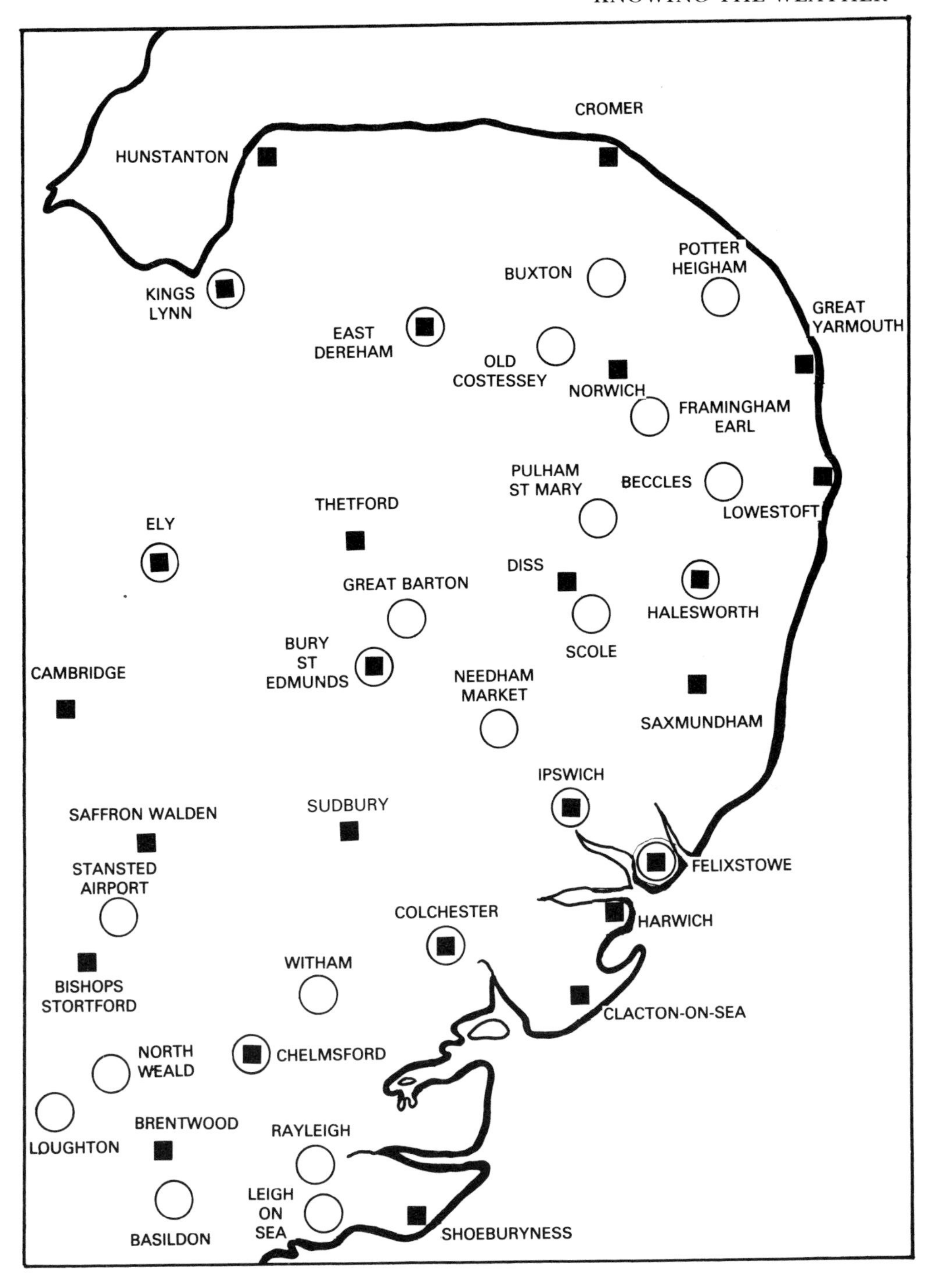
CROMER
HUNSTANTON
KINGS
LYNN
BUXTON
POTTER
HEIGHAM
GREAT
YARMOUTH
EAST
DEREHAM
OLD
COSTESSEY
NORWICH
FRAMINGHAM
EARL
PULHAM
ST MARY
BECCLES
LOWESTOFT
THETFORD
ELY
DISS
GREAT BARTON
HALESWORTH
BURY
ST
EDMUNDS
SCOLE
CAMBRIDGE
NEEDHAM
MARKET
SAXMUNDHAM
IPSWICH
SAFFRON WALDEN
SUDBURY
FELIXSTOWE
STANSTED
AIRPORT
COLCHESTER
HARWICH
WITHAM
BISHOPS
STORTFORD
CLACTON-ON-SEA
NORTH
WEALD
CHELMSFORD
BRENTWOOD
RAYLEIGH
LOUGHTON
LEIGH
ON
SEA
SHOEBURYNESS
BASILDON

share the enthusiasm of the amateurs. The COL correspondence column provides a fascinating forum for amateur and professional contributors alike. The secretary of COL, Mr G. W. Rolfe, lives at Ely, where he maintains his own weather station. In 1981 he founded the Cambridgeshire Rainfall Organisation, on similar lines to the long-established and much larger Norfolk Rainfall Organisation.

Founded by George Copeman in 1860, this pioneer organisation had only a small early membership, rising to about three dozen by the end of the First World War. Later, the organisation was taken over by one of East Anglia's leading amateur meteorologists, T. B. (Tom) Norgate, and as a result of his enthusiasm and dedication membership is now over 200; their collated rainfall figures are published monthly in the Norfolk press. Tom Norgate, active to the end, died in August, 1985; a revered character whose name will long be remembered. His successor is Norman Brooks, of Old Costessey, Norfolk.

Mr Ken Blowers of Ipswich, weatherman of the *East Anglian Daily Times* and the Ipswich *Evening Star*.
East Anglian Daily Times

Mr Terry Mayes of Colchester, who in 1982 inaugurated the Rainfall Organisation of Suffolk and Essex.
Adrian Rushton

Above left: Mr Reg Snowling of Pulham St Mary, Norfolk, an enthusiastic member of the Climatological Observers' Link and the Rainfall Organisation of Suffolk and Essex, checks the sunshine record on a fine day.
P. R. Lange

Above right: Stephen Bartholomew of Beccles, also a member of the same two organisations and a contributor of weather reports to the *Beccles and Bungay Journal*, completes his daily register.
Beccles and Bungay Journal

Right: The late Mr T. B. Norgate, of Lyng, who was secretary of the Norfolk Rainfall Organisation from 1963 until his death in 1985, taking one of his daily readings.
Eastern Daily Press

When two or three are gathered . . .

Under the protective eye of Belstead Church, with which the Wilson family have long and close associations, Richard Wilson watches the weather at his well-equipped climatological station at Belstead Hall, just a few miles south of Ipswich.

He has two Stevenson screens. The one on the left contains the standard meteorological equipment — maximum and minimum thermometers and the wet and dry-bulb hygrometer. In the second is a self-recording thermograph which, with a pen and ink tracing on a revolving drum, maintains a continuous record of temperature in which every change, day and night, is faithfully and accurately preserved for posterity. Just visible in front of the church tower is a wind vane and Robinson cups anemometer, (registering the direction and speed of the wind. Not to be seen in the pictures are a self-recording rain gauge

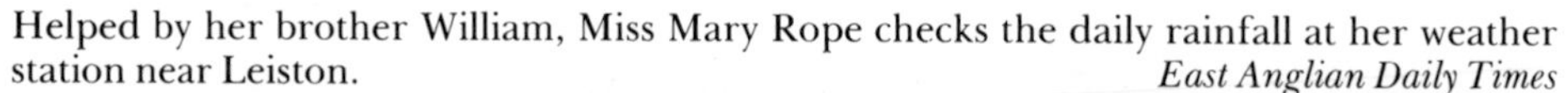

Helped by her brother William, Miss Mary Rope checks the daily rainfall at her weather station near Leiston. *East Anglian Daily Times*

Mr Richard Wilson takes his daily readings from the instruments in one of his two Stevenson screens. *Hazel le Rougetel*

(registering both the total and the rate of fall) and earth thermometers at depths of a foot and four feet. There is, too, the obligatory grass minimum thermometer which indicates the nightly loss of heat by radiation and which measures the incidence and intensity of ground frosts.

Richard Wilson's equipment was originally sited at Copdock, a little over a mile from Belstead, where they were maintained from 1902 until 1941 by the late Mr F. L. Bland, a well-known banker and public figure. Following Mr Bland's death, the entire station was moved to Belstead. The very close proximity and similar environment of the two sites allows acceptable comparisons between the two sets of records, thus providing one of the most useful examples of long-term amateur weather records in the country.

This long-term and accurate measurement of East Anglian weather — and the unfailing courtesy and co-operation of Richard Wilson — has provided me with a wealth of valuable information for this book.

A life of dedication

In 1908, twelve-year old Mary Rope, of Lower Abbey Farm, Leiston, Suffolk, was given a rain gauge by a friend, embarking her on a hobby involving a lifetime of regular reports of her daily 9 a.m. readings and their monthly submission to the Meteorological Office.

Seventy years later, Miss Mary Rope, who shared with her eighty-one-year old brother William and other members of the family the task of daily readings, had her devotion recognised by the award of the BEM in the 1980 New Year's Honours List. At the presentation ceremony I suggested to her that, with an annual rainfall of about 23 inches, she must in her lifetime have measured rainfall to a depth of something like 45 yards. Amused, she said "You know, I had never thought of it like that!"

Few people ever think of the hardships of the vast army of rain gauge readers when — sometimes in blinding blizzards — they have, on the hour, to grope with frost-numbed fingers for their half-buried gauges, carefully melt the snow and measure the water. Dedication indeed!

Orlando Whistlecraft, 1803–1883

Perhaps the most famous of all Suffolk's weather observers, Orlando Whistlecraft was born at Thwaite, where, from 1840 to almost the end of 1882, he maintained his weather station. He was a prolific writer on weather matters, a frequent contributor to the local press and the author of several books, including an annual almanack, *A Tabular Statement of the Thermometer*, *Climate of England*, *Rural Gleanings* and his richly titled *The Very Hot and Magnificent Summer of 1846* (from which I quote on pages 74–77. He was particularly interested in the effect of the weather on agriculture. He was also something of a poet, with strongly expressed Christian beliefs.

Orlando Whistlecraft, who described himself as farmer, school-master and shopkeeper, lived at Thwaite Post Office. He was the son of a Thwaite churchwarden and was buried in Thwaite churchyard.

CHAPTER FIVE

East Anglia at Risk

ALL PARTS of the British Isles are vulnerable to occasional damage, sometimes with fatalities, due to the weather. Often weather disasters are of a local nature, and East Anglia, apart from its rather higher risk of thunderstorms, differs little from the rest of the country.

But the more serious disasters, however localised their effect may be, are usually due to a combination and concentration of surrounding factors. In the West Country, the terrible Lynmouth tragedy of 15th August, 1952, was the result of a twelve-hour deluge of nine inches of rain over the whole of Exmoor and district; nine inches of rain at Lynmouth alone would not have caused so terrible a disaster. It was millions of tons of water from the higher ground sweeping down the narrow River Lyn, bringing with it fallen trees and tons of debris, which virtually swept away tiny Lynmouth and its picturesque little pier and caused such a dreadful death toll.

Many areas of the British Isles have their own particular weather risks. East Anglia's most serious danger is that of flooding from the North Sea. This peculiar and continuing vulnerability of the North Sea coast is recognised by international climatologists as a major risk in the world-wide weather scene. One of the worst North Sea tragedies ever known occurred on the night of 31st January and 1st February, 1953 — vividly described and documented in Michael Pollard's *North Sea Surge* (Terence Dalton, 1978) and *The Flooding of Eastern England*, by M. G. and H. J. Harland (Minimax Books Ltd). The latter also gives a comprehensive and historical survey of earlier and later North Sea floods.

A situation similar to, though not so serious as, that of 1953 occurred during the night of 2nd–3rd January, 1976; another flood during the night of 11th–12th January, 1978, was almost as severe as that of 1953, but damage and loss of life were greatly reduced, largely because of improvements in sea defences and warning systems following the 1953 disaster. All these disastrous North Sea floods were caused by a well recognised and notorious combination of adverse weather factors — so clearly defined as to make it impossible for the forecasters to be caught off their guard.

The basic ingredients of a dangerous North Sea flood (which affects the coasts of the Netherlands as much as those of East Anglia) are a fierce and deepening depression crossing the North Sea and an area of high pressure over the Atlantic. With steep pressure gradients (many isobars on the weather map) between the Atlantic high and the North Sea low, north-west to north gales up to and exceeding hurricane force sweep down the North Sea. The low barometric pressure over the North Sea can allow the level of the sea to rise several inches, while in dangerous contrast high pressure on the Atlantic is forcing down the level of the ocean, sending a surge of water into both ends of the North Sea. The build-up of water in the North Sea — already made turbulent by the

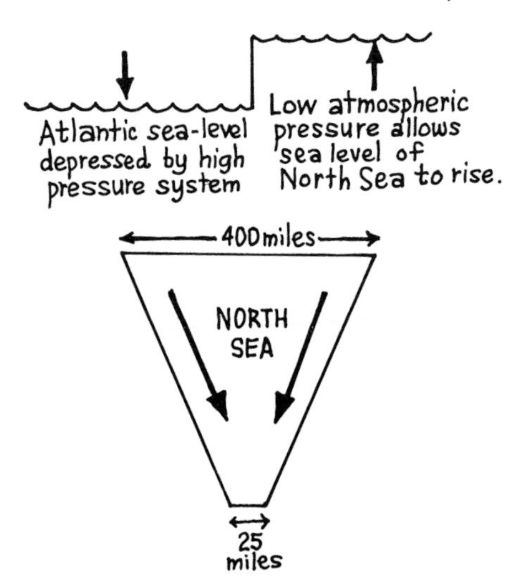

stormy depressions — is worsened as water is driven southwards by hurricane winds down the North Sea, which narrows to a mere 25 miles at the entrance to the English Channel.

On the accompanying map I have summarised the basic situation resulting in the 1978 floods; the pattern is almost identical to that which caused previous North Sea floods and it can be taken as a blueprint for disaster. The map shows the situation about noon on 11th January, 1978. During that night the depression deepened as it moved South-east, the central barometric pressure during the worst of the storm being 28.9 inches, compared with 30.7 inches at the centre of the Atlantic anticyclone. It was this all-too-familiar sharp difference in barometric pressure which caused hurricane force northerly winds and adverse differentials between the levels of the Atlantic and the North Sea.

On 1st February, 1983, a situation arose which was almost identical

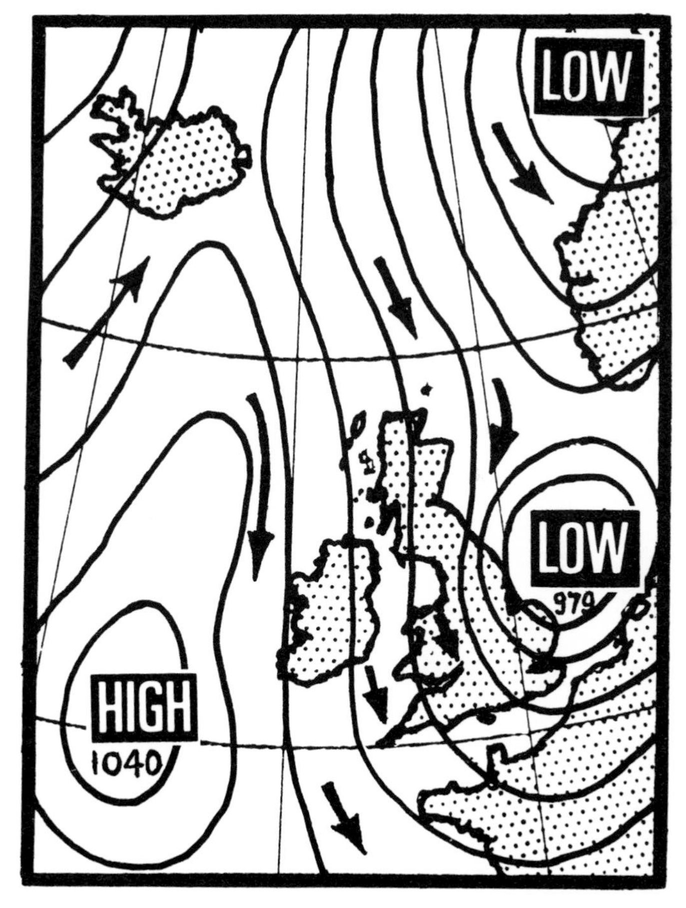

to that of 1953 (also 1st February) and that of 1978. As before, the villain was a very deep depression crossing the northern North Sea with gale to hurricane force north-westerly winds in its rear sweeping down the North Sea which, coinciding with an unusually high Spring tide, whipped up the sea and re-created the all-too-familiar "funnel" situation.

Fortunately, three factors helped to save East Anglia from tragedy. Firstly, barometric pressure over the Atlantic was not nearly so high as on previous occasions, thus reducing the "surge" effect; secondly, wind speeds dropped miraculously minutes before high tide; the third and most significant factor was the great improvement in sea defences and alarm systems. Flood damage did occur in several localities, but the fact that a major disaster was averted fully justified the heavy costs incurred in the erection of the new East Anglian coastal defences.

Less disastrous flooding can, of course, come from sources other

Rescuers at work among the flooded prefabs at Felixstowe in the aftermath of the 1953 flood. *East Anglian Daily Times*

than the North Sea. Rural areas are particularly vulnerable when continuous rain has fallen on already sodden ground or melting snow, the water pouring from surrounding fields and overflowing rivers to inundate low-lying towns and villages. Melting snow is a serious factor, particularly when accompanied by heavy rain, as people living in the Fens know to their cost; disastrous flooding occurred in the Fenland when the deep snow melted in the great thaw of 1947.

For farmers, soil erosion is an East Anglian risk, especially in a dry Spring when strong north-easterly winds frequently persist for weeks on end. Visiting motorists may be surprised when they sometimes have to switch on their headlights to negotiate a local dust-storm as soil blows off the fields across the road. The bleak flatness of the Fens makes them most vulnerable to soil erosion; a situation aggravated wherever there is an absence of hedges. Although the blizzards of February, 1979, were by no means unprecedented road conditions were the worst ever known because there were fewer hedges and more traffic than in days gone by.

The controversional burning of stubble by farmers has been blamed for many road accidents as dense smoke drifts across adjacent roads. Considerate farmers, about to choose a day when the wind is blowing in the right direction for safety, should remember that if they are in a coastal or nearby region a brisk sea breeze may completely alter the picture and put the roads at risk. Pollution of the air by stubble-burning is the subject of some public complaint, but it is unlikely that the pollution is sufficient to affect our weather.

Black smoke rises high in the air as a field of stubble is burnt off in Autumn. Hot air rising over the burning stubble can sometimes cause cumulus clouds to form, but such operations are unlikely to affect the weather.
East Anglian Daily Times

CHAPTER SIX

Where do we go from here?

THE question is a universal one and popularly focuses on two main interests — is our climate changing, and when are we going to get consistently reliable weather forecasts?

Maybe time does not march on so much as move in circles. So far as the weather is concerned, it has usually all happened before — but the timing is variable, with no reliable patterns. Sometimes very definite rhythms or "moods" develop — both in the long and short term, ranging from days to years — but the difficulty lies not so much in recognising the various patterns as in knowing when (and why) they are going to break down.

So far as the climate is concerned, I see no indications of any appreciable lasting changes. But the effect of man's activities cannot be ignored either in terms of modification or actual alteration of our climate. There are those who think that nuclear explosions on a large scale must disturb our atmosphere and affect the weather. But even the horrific energy released in the Hiroshima explosion was less than the power of a normal English thunderstorm and the immediate barometric pressure distribution and its associated weather remained unaffected. The potential dangers, short or long-term, of radio-active fall-out and the like is another matter.

Man's pollution of the atmosphere by everyday activities seems a more likely influence on the weather. There is much concern that some types of propellant gases used in aerosols, having risen to the upper atmosphere, might be destroying the vital ozone layer without which life would be impossible on earth. Fortunately it appears that by one of nature's excellent control systems it is the dangerous ultra-violet rays themselves which, mixing with the oxygen of our atmosphere, actually create ozone — and it is reassuring to believe that as fast as we reduce the protective ozone layer by our carefree use of aerosols, nature is patiently repairing the damage. At least, that is what we thought until a hole appeared in the ozone layer above the Antarctic.

Be that as it may, pollution of the upper atmosphere could be a serious factor. Whether it arises from such local rural activities as stubble-burning or from the production of vast quantities of industrial fumes on a world-wide scale, pollution of the upper air is almost certainly taking place. After a succession of juggernauts has swept past us on the road, we breathe a sigh of relief as the fumes disappear. Disappear to where? As likely as not into the upper atmosphere where, in the universal rubbish tip, they form a layer of impurities — thus causing the "greenhouse effect".

Just as the glass of a greenhouse allows entry of the short-wave rays of the sun during the day and impedes the long-wave return of heat by radiation at night, so any layer of impurities in the earth's upper atmosphere will disturb nature's balance of payments arrangements in the equalisation of daily gain and nightly loss of heat.

It may also be that if pollution of the upper air impedes the entry of solar energy into our atmosphere the circulation of our weather machine might slow down, leading to slower-moving weather systems with an increasing persistence of "blocking highs" and similar static tendencies.

One's first assumption might be that a build-up of upper air pollution would reduce the warmth of the sun's rays entering our atmosphere, thus causing a cooler global climate. On the contrary; although the daily intake (short wave) of heat might be reduced, the nightly loss (long wave) would be reduced to an even greater extent and

It is said that the sound of the guns in Flanders could be heard in Brandon during the 1914–18 War, and people blamed the gunfire for the severe weather. Today they blame atomic explosions. *Suffolk Record Office*

this trapping of the sun's heat (as in a greenhouse) would actually raise the global temperature.

Hurrah! A warmer climate to come? Alas, no. The first significant result of a higher global temperature would be extensive melting of the polar ice. And if that happened to a considerable degree, ice-cold water from both Poles would flood the oceans — with a chilling effect on the weather. And, with the inevitable rise in the general level of the seas, low-lying areas such as East Anglia would probably disappear altogether.

Fortunately, despite the persuasive nature of some of the theories, there are so far no reliable indications of any appreciable global changes in temperature.

Will we ever be able to control, or to some degree modify, our weather? On a quiet summer evening, with stubble-burning at its height, one can often see cumulus-type clouds forming at the top of some of the

A heath fire at Rushmere St Andrew actively creating cumulus-type cloud heads.

columns of smoke — but they rarely last. On the other hand, vapour trails (contrails) from high-flying aircraft often persist and quite frequently develop into well-established and recognisable cloud formations. The firing of ice-pellets into clouds, or lining them with silver dioxide, has had small-scale success, but in most cases the rain factor was already there and the pellets merely acted as a minor booster. During the drought of 1976 there were, for days on end, no clouds into which to fire anything. Squeezing a dry sponge will not eject water.

Where do we go from here in terms of improved weather forecasts? In the mid-nineteenth century, the invention and development of the synoptic weather chart, whereby meteorologists were able for the first time to identify the existence and characteristics of high and low areas of barometric pressure, was an enormous step forward, leading to the regular issue of official daily weather forecasts. During the 1914–18 War, Norwegian scientists discovered the existence of "cold" and "warm" fronts which gave the answer to many discontinuities in our weather which had previously puzzled the experts.

Serious gaps in knowledge still persist, despite great technological advances in the measuring of our weather by such devices as satellites, radar, computers and so on. The use of satellite photographs (frequently shown on television by the weathermen) has not only given meteorologists greater insight into the structure of the barometric systems but has also given descriptive advance information as to the character of approaching Atlantic depressions which, not many years ago, were merely hinted at by the surface observations of a few weather ships. Although satellite photographs have added a new dimension to the scene (and much interest to television forecasts), their benefit so far largely concerns the current forecast and we have yet to see any marked improvement in our ability to make long-term forecasts. A helicopter aloft on a summer holiday weekend can transmit useful information as to current traffic flow and the location of serious jams — but it cannot tell us, for instance, what conditions will be like on the M1 on Tuesday week.

The computer, which is programmed with (probably 85 per cent) information of what we really know about the weather, also has to cope with (probably 15 per cent) lack of knowledge. Even today's computerised forecasts lack accuracy. A well-known television weatherman once said in a documentary programme: "There is no doubt about our uncertainty". A cynic might add that the computer makes the same errors as a human being but with a greater degree of detail.

Bob Prichard (whose informed explanations are so interesting on Radio 4's London Weather Centre forecasts) hit a significant nail on the head when he said: "There is a danger that we let computers take away our initiative. I do not decry the computer; it is a wonderful tool if used wisely. But computers do not have souls, they do not have feelings — we must make them our slaves, not our masters, as we sometimes seem in danger of doing" (*Journal of Meteorology*, January, 1985).

One of the most important advances of the present century, the full understanding of which must eventually lead to greatly improved weather forecasts — particularly the long-term ones — has been the discovery of the "jet streams". Their existence was accidentally and rather sketchily discovered in the mid-1920s but they did not engage serious attention until after the Second World War (during which they had

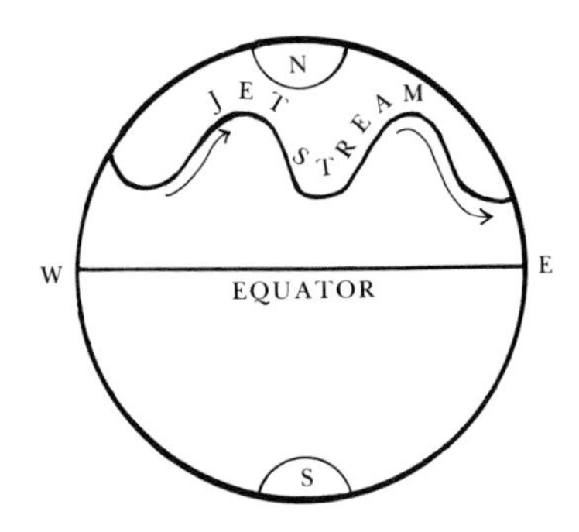

greatly affected high-flying aircraft on bombing raids). The jet streams have, however, nothing to do with jet aircraft but are high-speed winds of 100 to well over 200 m.p.h. which curve and twist about in the atmosphere about seven miles above us. They are rather weird, tube-like masses of air which whizz along horizontally from west to east in a swirling pattern, sometimes to the South and sometimes to the North of the British Isles.

When the jet streams travel to the South of us we tend to get low barometric pressure with cool unsettled weather. When they are to the North, high pressure and warmer more settled weather is likely. But that is a very broad generalisation greatly over-simplifying a situation which is full of complexities. Sometimes the pattern gets stuck. During the famous hot summer of 1976 the jet streams were persistently to the North; in the low temperatures of December 1981, and in recent cold springs and early summers they were firmly to the South.

Nature is full of contradictions, contrasts and compensatory factors. An intriguing aspect of the atmosphere is that, although our weather is largely controlled by the deployment of areas of high and low barometric pressure (in which temperature only modifies the situation), the jet streams which appear to control — or at any rate greatly affect — the

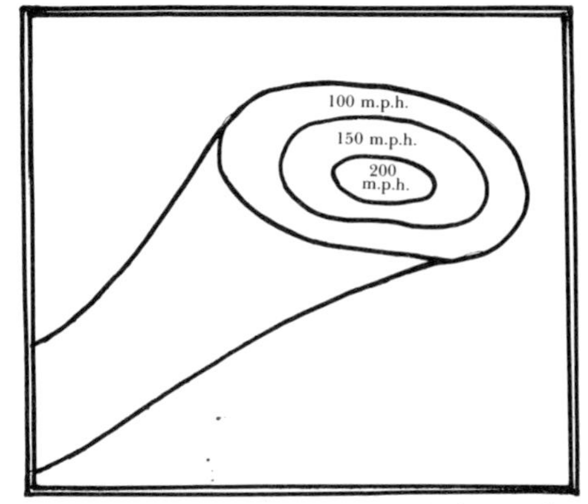

Diagram of a jet stream. Usually some 100 to 200 miles in width but only a few miles in depth, these jet streams have a considerable effect on our weather as they go snaking through the atmosphere. The fact that the core usually has a higher speed than the outside edges causes complications.

barometric structure are themselves actually thermal in origin. The initiation of this thermal imbalance is not yet fully understood.

Such questions as "What was the reason for the famous 1976 drought and the notoriously severe winters of 1947 and 1962/63?" remain largely unanswered. The cause of these unusual (and many other very ordinary) events can be explained by the tactical disposition of the various highs and lows of barometric pressure. But what are the strategic reasons behind each set of causes? If the jet streams which motivate our barometric weather systems are created by thermal differentials, where does the original motivation for all this begin?

In a BBC Television series "God and the Scientist" Sam Berry, Professor of Genetics at University College, London, said: "To assume chance is really a statement of ignorance. It is possible to think of purpose in the world in a way that doesn't contradict our understanding of the mechanism behind an event". Does nature decide, at some particular time, that drought or a severe winter would serve a useful purpose — and then simply use the weather systems as pawns in the game? It is an interesting hypothesis.

In chess, "check" is the name of the game. A pawn can be as important as a queen and the cause of the check lies simply in the positioning of the pieces — but the reason behind the cause is in the mind of the player. In 1976 "drought" was the name of the game — and the famous dry spell can be accurately but superficially explained by the day-to-day deployment of the various barometric systems — chiefly, in 1976, by a hard shoulder of high pressure which, lying across the British Isles, kept the Atlantic depressions in check. That was the cause—but what was the reason behind the cause? Maybe it was not the weather systems that produced the drought; perhaps the need for a drought produced the systems.

So: where does it all begin . . . and where, if ever, will it end?

Miracles without End

At sunset on Good Friday, 29th March, 1929, a shining cross appeared in the sky directly over the dying sun. It was hailed as a miracle by many awe-inspired witnesses, who were promptly put in their place by know-alls explaining that it was nothing more than a sun-pillar, caused by light reflected off ice crystals in the upper atmosphere, intersected by a short band of high cirrus cloud also illuminated by the

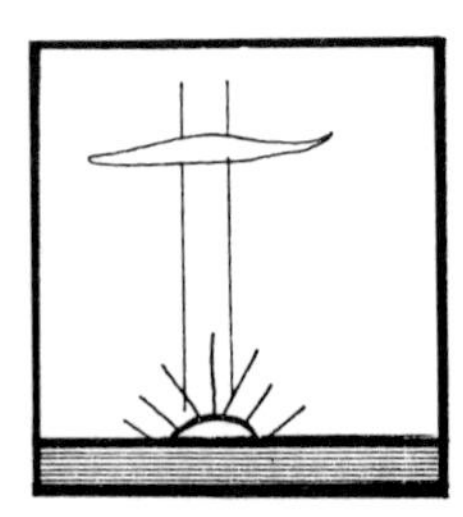

sun. That explanation was a scientific truism — but, if a "miracle" can be factually explained, does that make it any less wonderful? On the contrary, within some weather miracles there is often an inner miracle more remarkable than the event itself. In a snowdrift there may be countless millions of snowflakes; the inner mystery is that, by a strict law of nature, every flake (however intricate and elaborate and with no two alike) conforms to a six-pointed design.

By day, the sun pumps heat and energy into our atmosphere to make it work. By night, heat is radiated back into space. If this exchange were not carefully controlled we would, over the centuries, have either frizzled or frozen to death. If, one day, we are clever enough to discover the scientific explanation of the hexagonal snowflake and nature's careful balance of payments act with heat and cold, would that make nature any less amazing? And what further wonders might we discover in the process?

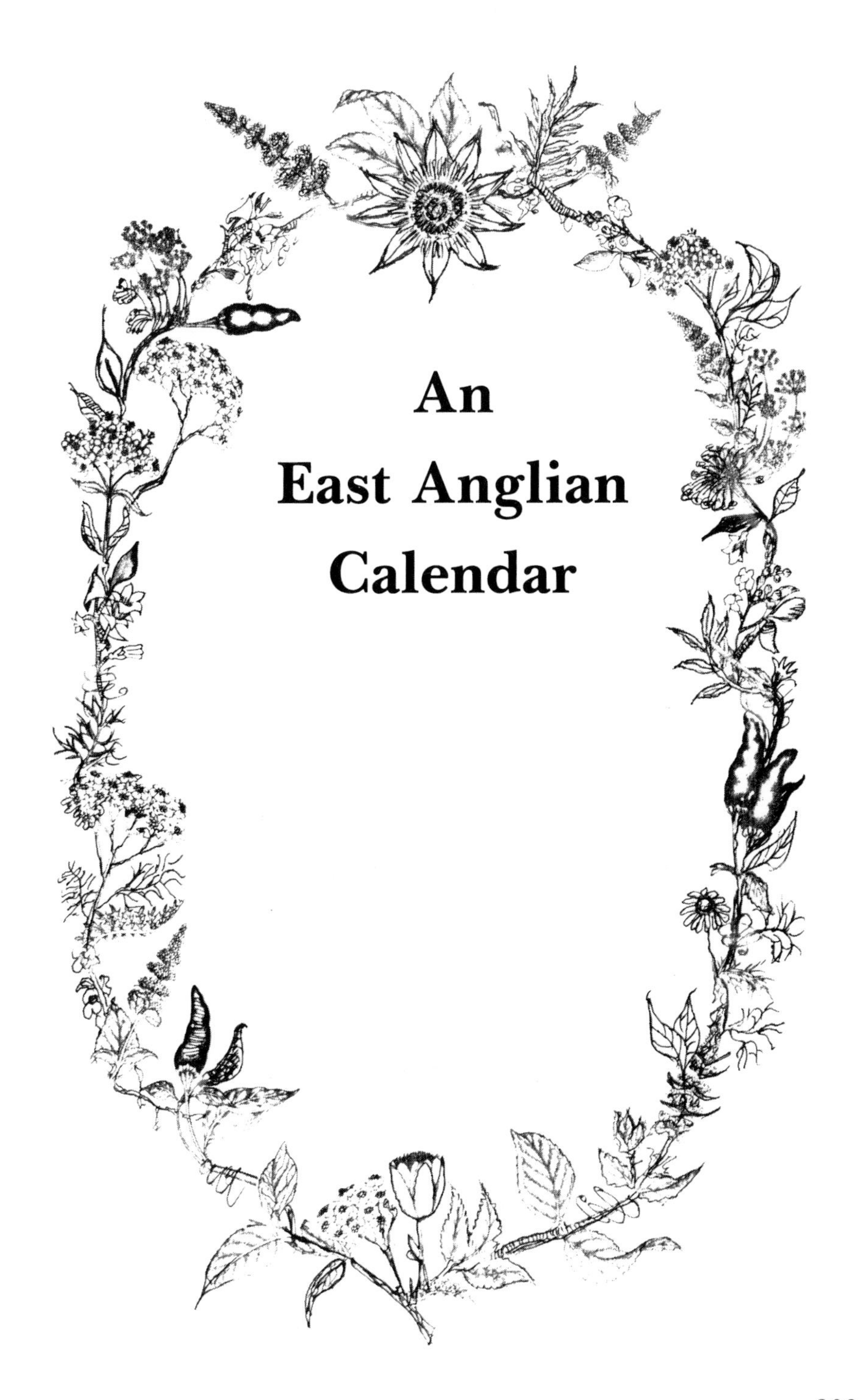

An East Anglian Calendar

An East Anglian Calendar

THE orthodox calendar attaches significance to the solstices and the equinoxes (and several old weather proverbs attach misleading importance to them). They do have associations with our weather but belong more to astronomy than to meteorology. The summer solstice, with the sun at its farthest North from the equator, gives us our longest days (about 21st June) and the winter solstice, when the sun is farthest South, gives us our shortest days (about 21st December).

The equinoxes are when the sun is in its halfway position directly over the equator, giving us days and nights of equal length. The spring equinox occurs about 21st March; the winter equinox about 22nd September. Midsummer is generally reckoned to be around 21st June although many diaries and nautical almanacks describe the Summer Solstice as the commencement of summer. With more romantic associations, Midsummer's Day is celebrated on 24th June; less poetically, it is also a financial Quarter Day.

"Why, this is the very midsummer madness" protests Olivia at Malvolio's strange antics in *Twelfth Night*. Rabies in dogs was often supposed to be caused by midsummer heat — and from ancient times a form of madness has been attributed to midsummer. Whether such behaviour derives from the heat, over-indulgence at the festival or over-reaction to the financial shocks of Quarter Day is arguable.

What is clear is that, weather-wise, June is too early to be considered midsummer. Another meteorological drawback of the standard calendar is the setting out of the months from January to December, the disadvantage being that it splits the winter into two, making later references and comparisons confusing. It would be nice to think that the year starts with Spring; and, indeed, for meteorological purposes the months are divided as follows:

Spring — March, April and May
Summer — June, July and August
Autumn — September, October and November
Winter — December, January and February

A practical example of the application of the meteorological calendar is seen in Chapter Four in the table of Spring and Autumn frosts. In that table, a frost in June is designated as a late Spring frost. An August frost is reckoned to belong to the Autumn. In the very rare event (in East Anglia) of a frost in July (the meteorological midsummer), we would blame neither Spring nor Autumn; but simply give July a black mark for giving us a frost when, as we might say, it didn't ought to have done.

Although the temperature and sunshine values are only generalisations, I have separated the coastal from the inland areas because of the marked differences between the two. Variations in rainfall are more likely to be related to local contours; hence I have not separated the inland from the coastal. As an approximate guide, two inches could be deducted from the overall figure to evaluate the drier parts of East Anglia (e.g., parts of Essex) and two inches added for the wetter parts (e.g., the higher countryside in Norfolk). The wettest and driest readings for each month have been culled from a variety of East Anglian records, the earliest of which dates back to 1839. Higher rainfalls may well have occurred of which I have no record. Similarly, entries under the heading "A Few Notable Events" are by no means comprehensive – merely a few snatches of information indicative of the variable climate in which we live.

"If the grass grows in January it grows the worse for it all the year."
Peterborough proverb

JANUARY

SECOND MONTH OF WINTER

Averages

TEMPERATURE °F.

	Inland	Coastal
Maximum	43°	43°
Minimum	33°	35°
Number of air frosts	13	8

RAINFALL

2 inches

Wettest	Driest
5½ inches (1939)	1/10 inch (1855)

Number of rain days 15

SUNSHINE

Hours

Inland	Coastal
50	55

Sunless days 12

GENERAL

No of days snow/sleet	5
„ „ snow lying	4
„ „ thunder	0–1

Characteristic Tendencies

On average, the coldest month of the year. Often fine and settled early; this pattern occasionally develops into a longer period of cold, fine weather — but more often unsettled conditions return after a few days and persist well into the month. Fourth week often characterised by quieter weather before a return to stormy weather by the end of the month — this being a period with the highest gale frequency of the year.

A FEW NOTABLE EVENTS

1953 A night of dreadful North Sea flooding on 31st January/1st February. Severe damage and many lives lost.

1963 Minimum air temperature of 4 degrees F. at Mildenhall on the 23rd.

1976 Hurricane on the 2nd/3rd with gusts of over 100 mph.

1978 Hurricane during night 11th/12th with serious North Sea flooding.

1985 Coldest weather ever known in East Anglia; minimum air temperature minus 4 degrees F. at Loddon, Norfolk, on the 8th.

"When gnats dance in February, the husbandman becomes a beggar."
Suffolk proverb

FEBRUARY

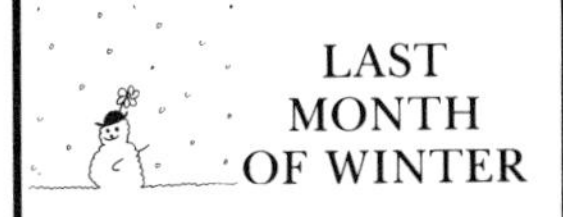

LAST MONTH OF WINTER

Averages

TEMPERATURE °F.

	Inland	Coastal
Maximum	45°	43°
Minimum	33°	35°
Number of air frosts	12	9

RAINFALL

1½ inches

Wettest	Driest
3¾ inches	Nil
(1881)	(1857)

Number of rain days 13

SUNSHINE

Hours

Inland	Coastal
70	75

Sunless days 8

GENERAL

No of days snow/sleet	5
„ „ snow lying	4
„ „ thunder	0–1

Characteristic Tendencies

Mild and stormy weather typical of late January often extends into February, but quieter colder weather frequently occurs in mid-month, returning to changeable weather later with a rise in gale frequency. Noted for its occasional heavy snowstorms. Fog frequency lowest of the winter months. Driest of the winter months.

"February, fill dyke, be it black or be it white;
But if it be white, it's better to like"

This version of a widely paraphrased saying clearly indicates that it is an exhortation — not an assessment of February weather. The preference for white expresses the soaking effect of snow-cover. If the dykes had been full in February, 1976, the effects of the subsequent historic drought would have been less severe.

A FEW NOTABLE EVENTS

1947 Minimum air temperature of minus 5 degrees F. at Writtle, Essex.

1979 On the 15th, the worst blizzards and road conditions in living memory. Entire communities cut off by drifts; traffic at a standstill.

"March dry, good rye; March wet, good wheat."
"Cold March, wet April & hot May,
Will make a fruitful year they say."
Two Suffolk proverbs

MARCH

FIRST MONTH OF SPRING

Averages

TEMPERATURE °F.

	Inland	Coastal
Maximum	51°	47°
Minimum	35°	37°
Number of air frosts	9	5

RAINFALL

1½ inches

Wettest	Driest
4½ inches	Less than ¼ in
(1914)	(1840)

Number of rain days 12

SUNSHINE

Hours

Inland	Coastal
115	125

Sunless days 6

GENERAL

No of days snow/sleet	3
„ „ snow lying	1
„ „ thunder	0–1

Characteristic Tendencies

Its "March hare" reputation is widespread throughout the temperate zones of the northern hemisphere. The polar regions (after nearly six months' night) are at their coldest; the equatorial regions, with the sun overhead, are at their hottest. Often changeable and stormy, but mid-month in southern England is frequently characterised by anticyclonic weather. The combination of better weather and longer days gives a marked increase in the hours of sunshine. Rainfall becomes more showery, and heavy snowfalls are not uncommon.

A FEW NOTABLE EVENTS

1947 Continuing one of the most severe winters of the century, snow remained lying during the first 13 days, with maximum air temperature at Rushmere St Andrew remaining below freezing point for two succesive days.

1968 On the 9th, maximum air temperatures at Cromer 74 degrees F., and 77 degrees F. on the 29th.

"If the first three days of April be foggy, there will be a flood in June."
Huntingdon proverb

APRIL

SECOND MONTH OF SPRING

Averages

TEMPERATURE °F.

	Inland	Coastal
Maximum	57°	53°
Minimum	39°	41°
Number of air frosts	4	1

RAINFALL

1½ inches

Wettest	Driest
5¼ inches	Nil
(1871)	(1855)

Number of rain days 12

SUNSHINE

Hours

Inland	Coastal
155	165

Sunless days 3

GENERAL

No of days snow/sleet	2
" " snow lying	—
" " thunder	0–1

Characteristic Tendencies

Despite "April showers", it is one of the driest months. Decline in frequency of strong winds but the frequency of northerly and easterly winds increases towards the second half of month, often producing late spring snowfalls. (April showers bring forth May flowers but also false hopes.) Surface temperature of North Sea continues its slow rise.

A FEW NOTABLE EVENTS

1884 Severe earthquake on the 22nd centred near Colchester, Essex. Much damage in Essex and Suffolk.

1893 Air temperature at Cambridge reached 83 degrees F.

1917 Minimum air temperature at Norwich on the 2nd fell to 17 degrees F. — on the grass, 6 degrees F.

1919 On the 27th heavy snow to a depth of eighteen inches in Suffolk, Essex and Cambridgeshire.

1949 Air temperature reached 82 degrees F. at Mildenhall on 16th.

"Cold May, good for corn and hay;
Rain in May makes plenty of hay."
Peterborough proverb

MAY

LAST MONTH OF SPRING

Averages

TEMPERATURE °F.

	Inland	Coastal
Maximum	63°	58°
Minimum	44°	46°
Number of air frosts	Less than 1	Very rarely

RAINFALL

1½ inches

Wettest	Driest
5½ inches (1878)	¼ inch (1959)

Number of rain days 11

SUNSHINE

Hours

Inland	Coastal
200	210

Sunless days 2

GENERAL

No of days snow/sleet	—
" " snow lying	—
" " thunder	2

Characteristic Tendencies

Tends to be a dry, quiet month. A very high frequency of northerly and easterly winds — and clear nights can lead to late frosts, particularly when fine weather follows a period of northerly winds.

A FEW NOTABLE EVENTS

1698 3rd: "There fell snow from two o'clock in the afternoon to six in the evening." (Congregational Church Book of Guestwick, Norfolk).

1947 31st: air temperature reached 89 degrees F. at Mildenhall

*"A dry May and a dripping June
Bring all things into tune."*
Bedfordshire proverb

JUNE

FIRST MONTH OF SUMMER

Averages

TEMPERATURE °F.

	Inland	Coastal
Maximum	69°	65°
Minimum	49°	52°
Number of air frosts	—	—

RAINFALL

1¾ inches

Wettest	Driest
8¼ inches	Less than ¼ inch
(1982)	(1921 & 1962)

Number of rain days 11

SUNSHINE

Hours

Inland	Coastal
210	220

Sunless days 1

GENERAL

No of days snow/sleet	—
„ „ snow lying	—
„ „ thunder	2–3

Characteristic Tendencies

On average the sunniest month, especially the first week which is also one of the driest of the year. Occasionally June comes as a disappointing anticlimax to a fine sunny May. There is often a period of unsettled weather in the earlier part of the month, associated with west to north-west winds.

A FEW NOTABLE EVENTS

1944 On the 6th, the D-Day invasion of Normandy by Allied Forces, with a fleet of over 4,000 vessels, jeopardised by very strong north-westerly winds.

1970 Over 3½ inches of rain within two hours at Wisbech on the 28th.

1975 On the 2nd, snow stopped play in County cricket match at Colchester. First June snowfall ever known in parts of Suffolk.

1976 During last week air temperature reached 93 degrees F. at Honington, Suffolk. Relative humidity on the 30th the lowest of the century — less than 10% in places.

1982 4½ inches of rain in 100 minutes at West Bradenham, Norfolk, on the 5th, contributing to a record June rainfall of 9 inches.

"If the 15th be wet, St Swithin is christening the apples."
Suffolk proverb

JULY

SECOND MONTH OF SUMMER

Averages

TEMPERATURE °F.

	Inland	Coastal
Maximum	71°	69°
Minimum	53°	56°
Number of air frosts	—	—

RAINFALL

2¼ inches

Wettest	Driest
6¼ inches	Less than ¼ inch
(1875)	(1878 & 1955)

Number of rain days 13

SUNSHINE

Hours

Inland	Coastal
185	200

Sunless days 2

GENERAL

No of days snow/sleet	—
" " snow lying	—
" " thunder	3

Characteristic Tendencies

On average the warmest month of the year but usually less sunny than June, greater heating causing more convectional clouds. Rainfall totals vary considerably from place to place and from year to year because of the showery and thundery nature of much of the rain. Can be very dry but the seasonal tendency for occasional torrential thundery downpours raises the average monthly rainfall. The last week of the month is often wet and unsettled. A few very warm nights often occur.

A FEW NOTABLE EVENTS

1902 Over 3¼ inches of rain within two hours at Ipswich on the 1st.

1911 Air temperature at Cambridge reached 96 degrees F.

1941 Nearly 4 inches of rain within two hours at Writtle, Essex, on the 26th.

1946 Severe hailstorms in West Suffolk, causing much damage to crops.

1948 Air temperature at Mildenhall reached 93 degrees F. during last week.

1949 4 inches of rain within two hours at March on the 15th.

1959 Air temperature at Cromer reached 94 degrees F.

"St Bartlemy's mantle wipes dry
All the tears that St. Swithin can cry." Anon.

AUGUST

LAST MONTH OF SUMMER

Averages

TEMPERATURE °F.

	Inland	Coastal
Maximum	71°	68°
Minimum	53°	56°
Number of air frosts	—	—

RAINFALL

2 inches

Wettest	Driest
6½ inches	1/10 inch
(1916)	(1940 & 1947)

Number of rain days 12

SUNSHINE

Hours

Inland	Coastal
180	190

Sunless days 2

GENERAL

No of days snow/sleet	—
„ „ snow lying	—
„ „ thunder	3

Characteristic Tendencies

On average the wettest of the summer months, the sometimes cool, thundery weather of late July often continuing. The mid-month period frequently becomes warm and settled. A few very warm nights often occur.

A FEW NOTABLE EVENTS

1843 On the 9th a thundersorm of reputedly unprecedented violence struck the Cambridge area. Hailstones "as large as ordinary walnuts"; hundreds of birds killed and much damage to fruit and crops.

1911 Air temperature at Cambridge reached 96 degrees F.

1912 7¼ inches of rain on the 25th/26th turned Norwich into "a miniature Venice".

1932 Air temperature on the 19th reached 97 degrees F. at Halstead, Essex, and 95 degrees F. at Norwich.

1953 Air temperature reached 91 degrees F. at Mildenhall on the 12th.

1972 4½ inches of rain within two hours at Costessey, Norfolk, on the 1st.

"There are generally three consecutive windy days about the middle of September which have been called by Midland millers the windy days of barley harvest."
Anon.

SEPTEMBER

FIRST MONTH OF AUTUMN

Averages

TEMPERATURE °F.

	Inland	Coastal
Maximum	67°	65°
Minimum	49°	53°
Number of air frosts	—	—

RAINFALL

2 inches

Wettest	Driest
7 inches	Nil
(1927)	(1865)

Number of rain days 12

SUNSHINE

Hours

Inland	Coastal
140	155

Sunless days 2

GENERAL

No of days snow/sleet	—
" " snow lying	—
" " thunder	1–2

Characteristic Tendencies

Often unsettled early but with a very marked tendency for a dry, settled spell in mid-month. Frequently changeable again from the third week onwards. Thunderstorm frequency now very much lower than in July and August. Marked seasonal reduction in hours of sunshine.

A FEW NOTABLE EVENTS

1901 Over 3¼ inches of rain within two hours at Fingringhoe, Essex, on the 11th.

1949 Air temperature reached 90 degrees F. at Rushmere St Andrew and Mildenhall on the 5th.

1950 "Blue" sun caused by high-level layer of ash particles from extensive forest fires in Canada.

"October always has twenty-one fine days."
Suffolk proverb

OCTOBER

SECOND MONTH OF AUTUMN

Averages

TEMPERATURE °F.

	Inland	Coastal
Maximum	59°	57°
Minimum	44°	47°
Number of air frosts	1	Very rarely

RAINFALL

2¼ inches

Wettest	Driest
8¼ inches	Less than ¼ inch
(1865 & 1939)	(1947 & 1969)

Number of rain days 13

SUNSHINE

Hours

Inland	Coastal
105	115

Sunless days 5

GENERAL

No of days snow/sleet	—
„ „ snow lying	—
„ „ thunder	0–1

Characteristic Tendencies

Often unsettled and reckoned to be one of the wettest months of the year — but some very dry Octobers in the 1970s decade have reduced the average. With quieter weather in the first half of the month the first serious autumn fogs can occur. But October can also produce some very warm days with temperatures in the high 70s F.

A FEW NOTABLE EVENTS

1836 Severe blizzards and drifting snow during last week. Newmarket Heath had to be cleared before the race-horses could run.

1959 Air temperature reached 82 degrees F. at Mildenhall during the first week.

"Wind north-west at Martinmas, severe winter to come."
Huntingdonshire proverb

"If trees show buds in November, the winter will last until May."
Suffolk proverb

NOVEMBER

LAST MONTH OF AUTUMN

Averages

TEMPERATURE °F.

	Inland	Coastal
Maximum	49°	50°
Minimum	39°	41°
Number of air frosts	6	2

RAINFALL

2½ inches

Wettest	Driest
8½ inches	½ inch
(1878)	(1867 & 1879)

Number of rain days 16

SUNSHINE

Hours

Inland	Coastal
60	65

Sunless days 10

GENERAL

No of days snow/sleet	1
„ „ snow lying	<½
„ „ thunder	0–1

Characteristic Tendencies

Usually wet; often changeable and stormy in the early weeks. Settled weather in mid-month can lead to fog and frost, making it on average one of the foggiest periods of the year. Snow or sleet occur only briefly.

A FEW NOTABLE EVENTS

1938 Air temperature reached 70 degrees F. at Cambridge and Mildenhall on the 5th.

"Thunder in December prophesies fine weather."
Suffolk proverb

DECEMBER

FIRST MONTH OF WINTER

Averages

TEMPERATURE °F.

	Inland	Coastal
Maximum	45°	45°
Minimum	35°	37°
Number of air frosts	11	5

RAINFALL

2¼ inches

Wettest	Driest
6 inches	Less than 1/10 inch
(1914)	(1843 & 1852)

Number of rain days 15

SUNSHINE

Hours

Inland	Coastal
45	50

Sunless days 13

GENERAL

No of days snow/sleet	3
„ „ snow lying	1½
„ „ thunder	0–1

Characteristic Tendencies

Least sunny month of the year with a tendency to foggy spells. Frequently stormy and unsettled both early and late with a quieter spell of weather in the pre-Christmas period. By twentieth-century experience, the chances of a White Christmas are only about one in ten.

A FEW NOTABLE EVENTS

1770 Severe hurricane on the 28th. Much shipping lost off Harwich and Lowestoft.

1906 Air temperature dropped to 2 degrees F. at Woodbridge, Suffolk, on the 30th.

1962 Air temperature dropped to 8 degrees F. at Mildenhall.

1981 Coldest December for over 100 years; mean temperature about 7 degrees F. below normal.

APPPENDIX ONE

FAHRENHEIT versus CENTIGRADE/CELSIUS

AFTER initial difficulties, the public soon adapted to decimal currency. Not so in the case of the Centigrade scale of temperature, even though it had long been the accepted currency of the scientists. And who wants Centigrade? The scientists, yes, but what of the general public for whom this book is written?

In an article in the *Journal of Meteorology*, July/August, 1979, David C. Trout reported that in a survey in the Torbay area in April, 1978, 72% of those questioned preferred Fahrenheit, with 22% in favour of Centigrade and 6% happy with either. During my talks to various organisations (of all age groups) I often ask for a show of hands. Years after the Torbay survey, the preference for Fahrenheit is overwhelming — often 100%. Old records, and many people's memories, are in Fahrenheit. "Eighty in the shade they say,/Very, very warm for May" sang someone in *The Arcadians*. "Twenty-seven in the shade" sounds daft and lacks character. (In a heatwave, even the professional weathermen start talking of temperatures "in the 80s" or "soaring into the 90s"!). My book is full of comparisons with the past and — sentimental though it may be — when I have quoted temperatures from the observers of long ago I have felt it almost an impertinence to think of converting the well-understood Fahrenheit.

Professional weathermen a few years ago started to talk about "Celsius" instead of Centigrade. They are, in my view, wrong; the Celsius scale (invented by a Swedish scientist of that name in 1742) had 100 degrees as freezing point and zero as boiling-point. The Centigrade scale (which appeared a year later) used exactly the same degree marks but was modified so that freezing point became zero and boiling-point 100 degrees. So, although the size of each degree was introduced by Celsius, Centigrade is the only correct way of describing the present modified scale — and it seems a pity that the professionals confused the public by some unnecessary and incorrect hair-splitting.

So, with no apologies and with deference to strongly held public views, I have used the Fahrenheit scale throughout — and the following table makes conversion easy:

TEMPERATURE
CONVERSION OF CENTIGRADE TO FAHRENHEIT

°C.		+0·2	+0·5	+0·8	°C.		+0·2	+0·5	+0·8
	°F.	°F.	°F.	°F.		°F.	°F.	°F.	°F.
37	99	99	99	100	8	46	47	47	48
36	97	97	98	98	7	45	45	45	46
35	95	95	96	96	6	43	43	44	44
34	93	94	94	95	5	41	41	42	42
33	91	92	92	93	4	39	40	40	41
32	90	90	91	91	3	37	38	38	39
31	88	88	89	89	2	36	36	37	37
30	86	86	87	87	1	34	34	35	35
29	84	85	85	86	0	32	32	33	33
28	82	83	83	84	−0	32	32	31	31
27	81	81	81	82	−1	30	30	29	29
26	79	79	80	80	−2	28	28	27	27
25	77	77	78	78	−3	27	26	26	25
24	75	75	78	78	−4	25	24	24	23
23	73	74	74	75	−5	23	23	22	22
22	72	72	73	73	−6	21	21	20	20
21	70	70	71	71	−7	19	19	19	18
20	68	68	69	69	−8	18	17	17	16
19	66	67	67	68	−9	16	15	15	14
18	64	65	65	66	−10	14	14	13	13
17	63	63	63	64	−11	12	12	11	11
16	61	61	62	62	−12	10	10	9	9
15	59	59	60	60	−13	9	8	8	7
14	57	58	58	59	−14	7	6	6	5
13	55	56	56	57	−15	5	5	4	4
12	54	54	55	55	−16	3	3	2	2
11	52	52	53	53	−17	1	1	1	0
10	50	50	51	51	−18	0	−1	−1	−2
9	48	49	49	50	−19	−2	−3	−3	−4

APPENDIX TWO

THE BEAUFORT SCALE OF WIND FORCE

Specification (for use on land)	Beaufort no.	Speed limits m.p.h.	Average speed m.p.h.	Pressure (lbs per sq. foot)
CALM. Smoke rises vertically.	0	0	0	0
LIGHT AIR. Direction of wind shown by smoke drift, but not by wind vanes.	1	1–3	2	0.01
LIGHT BREEZE. Wind felt on face; leaves rustle; ordinary vane moved by wind.	2	4–7	5	0.08
GENTLE BREEZE. Leaves and small twigs in constant motion; wind extends light flag.	3	8–12	10	0.28
MODERATE BREEZE. Raises dust and loose paper; small branches are moved.	4	13–18	15	0.67
FRESH BREEZE. Small trees in leaf begin to sway; crested wavelets form on inland waters.	5	19–24	21	1.31
STRONG BREEZE. Large branches in motion; whistling heard in telegraph wires; umbrellas used with difficulty.	6	25–31	28	2.30
NEAR GALE. Whole trees in motion; inconvenience felt when walking against the wind.	7	32–38	35	3.60
GALE. Breaks twigs off trees; generally impedes progress.	8	39–46	42	5.40
STRONG GALE. Slight structural damage occurs (chimney pots and slates removed).	9	47–54	50	7.70
STORM. Seldom experienced inland; trees uprooted; considerable structural damage occurs.	10	55–63	59	10.50
VIOLENT STORM. Very rarely experienced; accompanied by widespread damage.	11	64–72	68	14.00
HURRICANE.	12	Over 72	—	Over 17.00

APPENDIX THREE

BAROMETER CONVERSION TABLE

Millibars	Inches	Millibars	Inches	Millibars	Inches
948	27.99	982	29.00	1016	30.00
949	28.02	983	29.03	1017	30.03
950	28.05	984	29.06	1018	30.06
951	28.08	985	29.09	1019	30.09
952	28.11	986	29.12	1020	30.12
953	28.14	987	29.15	1021	30.15
954	28.17	988	29.18	1022	30.18
955	28.20	989	29.21	1023	30.21
956	28.23	990	29.23	1024	30.24
957	28.26	991	29.26	1025	30.27
958	28.29	992	29.29	1026	30.30
959	28.32	993	29.32	1027	30.33
960	28.35	994	29.35	1028	30.36
961	28.38	995	29.38	1029	30.39
962	28.41	996	29.41	1030	30.42
963	28.44	997	29.44	1031	30.45
964	28.47	998	29.47	1032	30.47
965	28.50	999	29.50	1033	30.50
966	28.53	1000	29.53	1034	30.53
967	28.56	1001	29.56	1035	30.56
968	28.59	1002	29.59	1036	30.59
969	28.61	1003	29.62	1037	30.62
970	28.64	1004	29.65	1038	30.65
971	28.67	1005	29.68	1039	30.68
972	28.70	1006	29.71	1040	30.71
973	28.73	1007	29.74	1041	30.74
974	28.76	1008	29.77	1042	30.77
975	28.79	1009	29.80	1043	30.80
976	28.82	1010	29.83	1044	30.83
977	28.85	1011	29.85	1045	30.86
978	28.88	1012	29.88	1046	30.89
979	28.91	1013	29.91	1047	30.92
980	28.94	1014	29.94	1048	30.95
981	28.97	1015	29.97	1049	30.98

APPENDIX FOUR

AVERAGE ANNUAL RAINFALL AT SIXTY LOCATIONS IN EAST ANGLIA
(Averages in inches for 1916–1950 by courtesy of the Meteorological Office)

Inland (more than 25 miles from coast)		Marginal (5–25 miles from coast)		Coastal (Situated on, or less than 5 miles from, the coast)	
PETERBOROUGH, Cambs	21½	FAKENHAM, Norfolk	26½	HOLME-NEXT-THE-SEA, Norfolk	22¼
CHATTERIS, Cambs	21½	AYLSHAM, Norfolk	27½	BRANCASTER, Norfolk	23½
LITTLEPORT, Cambs	20¾	WISBECH, Cambs	21	WELLS-NEXT-THE-SEA, Norfolk	23½
THETFORD, Norfolk	24½	DOWNHAM MARKET, Norfolk	23½	CLEY-NEXT-THE-SEA, Norfolk	26
HAUGHTON (ST. IVES), Hunts	22	SWAFFHAM, Norfolk	27½	CROMER, Norfolk	26¾
ISLEHAM, Cambs	21¼	EAST DEREHAM, Norfolk	26¼	BACTON, Norfolk	24
HONINGTON, Suffolk	24	NORWICH, Norfolk	25½	GREAT YARMOUTH	24
ST NEOTS, Hunts	21½	DITCHINGHAM, Suffolk	25¾	GORLESTON	24
CAMBRIDGE	21¾	BROME, Suffolk	25½	LOWESTOFT, Suffolk	23½
NEWMARKET, Suffolk	23½	HALESWORTH, Suffolk	25	SOUTHWOLD, Suffolk	23
BURY ST EDMUNDS, Suffolk	24	FRAMLINGHAM, Suffolk	25½	ALDEBURGH, Suffolk	23
COCKFIELD, Suffolk	24¼	STOWMARKET, Suffolk	25	HOLLESLEY, Suffolk	23
HAVERHILL, Suffolk	24¾	IPSWICH, Suffolk	23½	FELIXSTOWE, Suffolk	21¼
ROYSTON, Herts	22¼	BELSTEAD, Suffolk	23½	DOVERCOURT, Essex	21½
SAFFRON WALDEN, Essex	23¼	BOXTED, Suffolk	23¾	WALTON-ON-NAZE, Essex	21½
THAXTED, Essex	23½	HALSTEAD, Essex	24½	LITTLE HOLLAND, Essex	22
BISHOP'S STORTFORD, Herts	25	BRAINTREE, Essex	23½	CLACTON-ON-SEA, Essex	21½
DUNMOW, Essex	24	TIPTREE, Essex	22½	MERSEA ISLAND, Essex	21¼
GOOD EASTER, Essex	24½	MALDON, Essex	20¾	BRADWELL-ON-SEA, Essex	22
CHESHUNT, Herts	24¾	GALLEYWOOD, Essex	23¾	SHOEBURYNESS, Essex	20¼
AVERAGE	23	AVERAGE	24½	AVERAGE	23

The locations are classified in regions according to their distance from the nearest coastline and, to facilitate identification on a map, are listed in geographical order (north at the top; south at the bottom). Although of little effect on rainfall, sea-breeze occurrence in each region is approximately as follows — Inland: occasionally. Marginal: frequent. Coastal: very frequent.

Two factors contributing to higher rainfall totals are usually topography (comparatively high ground) and convection (showers often being more frequent inland).

Those interested in the variability of averages will notice some differences from those for a different period of time (1931–1960) in the next table. At many places the 1916–1950 averages were higher than the 1931–1960 figures. Compare, for example, the 1916–1950 Cromer rainfall with that of 1931–1960 in the following tables. Similarly, the 1916–1950 average for Honington is 24 inches, whereas official figures for the 42 years 1936–1977 at Mildenhall/Honington show an average of only 21½ inches.

Such differences are not indicative of any developing change in climate. They do, however, stress the importance, when using averages for comparative purposes, of uniformity in the period of time selected.

APPENDIX FIVE

Rainfall and Humidity

Based on averages mainly for the 30 years 1931–1960

EAST ANGLIA — COASTAL

Cromer

	Relative humidity		Precipitation		
	Average of observations at 0900	1500	Average monthly fall	Maximum fall in 24 hours	Average no of rain days*
	per cent		*inches*		
January	91	—	2.28	1.07	18
February	90	—	1.81	1.46	16
March	86	—	1.45	0.87	13
April	82	—	1.54	0.99	13
May	81	—	1.89	1.73	11
June	80	—	1.54	1.34	11
July	81	—	2.48	1.89	13
August	83	—	2.20	2.83	12
September	85	—	2.13	1.18	14
October	87	—	2.40	1.14	16
November	90	—	2.52	1.38	18
December	91	—	2.69	1.34	18
Year	86	—	24.33	2.83	173

*In this and the following tables, the criterion in the UK for a rain day is about 0.01 inches or more; in Orenburg, USSR, the criterion is about 0.004 inches or more.

Gorleston

	Relative humidity		Precipitation		
	Average of observations at 0900	1500	Average monthly fall	Maximum fall in 24 hours	Average no. of rain days
	per cent		*inches*		
January	88	83	2.24	1.30	16
February	87	80	1.65	0.94	14
March	86	79	1.46	0.83	12
April	79	73	1.42	1.14	12
May	79	77	1.50	0.94	10
June	75	73	1.73	1.38	11
July	77	74	2.24	2.32	12
August	81	74	2.20	1.62	12
September	83	73	2.05	1.81	13
October	87	78	2.56	1.73	14
November	89	83	2.72	1.18	17
December	89	85	2.05	0.91	16
Year	83	78	23.82	2.32	159

Felixstowe

	Relative humidity		Precipitation		
	Average of observations at		Average monthly fall	Maximum fall in 24 hours	Average no of rain days
	0900	1500			
	per cent		*inches*		
January	89	85	1.97	1.57	16
February	89	81	1.57	0.91	14
March	86	76	1.34	0.79	12
April	78	70	1.22	0.63	12
May	78	71	1.46	1.38	10
June	76	71	1.38	1.65	11
July	78	71	1.85	1.34	12
August	79	73	1.85	1.42	11
September	81	73	1.81	1.57	12
October	87	76	2.28	2.36	14
November	90	83	2.21	0.94	16
December	90	86	1.81	0.98	16
Year	83	76	20.75	2.36	156

Clacton

	Relative humidity		Precipitation		
	Average of observations at		Average monthly fall	Maximum fall in 24 hours	Average no of rain days
	0900	1500			
	per cent		*inches*		
January	90	—	2.17	1.69	16
February	89	—	1.50	0.91	14
March	86	—	1.46	0.75	12
April	81	—	1.38	0.87	12
May	80	—	1.57	1.34	11
June	78	—	1.61	1.77	11
July	80	—	1.85	1.57	11
August	81	—	1.89	2.05	11
September	83	—	1.97	1.81	12
October	86	—	2.28	1.54	13
November	89	—	2.28	1.02	15
December	90	—	1.89	0.91	15
Year	84	—	21.85	2.05	153

EAST ANGLIA — INLAND
Cambridge

	Relative humidity		Precipitation		
	Average of observations at		Average monthly fall	Maximum fall in 24 hours	Average No. of rain days
	0900	1500			
	per cent		*inches*		
January	90	91	1.93	1.06	15
February	88	89	1.38	0.98	13
March	84	86	1.42	0.98	10
April	73	74	1.46	0.79	11
May	71	79	1.77	1.22	11
June	70	80	1.77	1.26	11
July	73	80	2.28	2.24	12
August	76	82	2.16	1.46	12
September	79	86	2.01	1.77	11
October	84	88	2.01	1.14	13
November	89	90	2.13	1.10	14
December	91	91	1.65	0.91	14
Year	81	85	21.97	2.24	147

GREAT BRITAIN — COASTAL
Bournemouth

	Relative humidity		Precipitation		
	Average of observations at		Average monthly fall	Maximum fall in 24 hours	Average no of rain days
	0900	1500			
	per cent		*inches*		
January	—	—	3.23	1.50	17
February	—	—	2.21	1.46	13
March	—	—	2.21	0.91	12
April	—	—	1.77	0.87	12
May	—	—	2.05	1.85	11
June	—	—	1.85	1.54	11
July	—	—	2.28	1.97	12
August	—	—	2.40	1.57	12
September	—	—	2.83	2.13	13
October	—	—	3.50	1.97	14
November	—	—	3.74	1.97	16
December	—	—	3.43	1.65	17
Year	—	—	31.50	2.13	160

Ilfracombe

	Relative humidity		Precipitation		
	Average of observations at		Average monthly fall	Maximum fall in 24 hours	Average no of rain days
	0900	1500			
	per cent		*inches*		
January	84	—	4.06	1.46	19
February	84	—	2.87	1.30	14
March	82	—	2.48	1.89	13
April	81	—	2.44	1.06	12
May	81	—	2.40	1.34	13
June	82	—	2.21	1.34	11
July	83	—	3.23	1.97	15
August	84	—	3.62	3.46	15
September	82	—	3.50	2.20	15
October	83	—	4.29	2.20	17
November	84	—	4.76	1.89	17
December	84	—	4.53	2.17	19
Year	83	—	40.39	3.46	180

GREAT BRITAIN — INLAND
Central, similar latitude to East Anglia
Birmingham

	Relative humidity		Precipitation		
	Average of observations at		Average monthly fall	Maximum fall in 24 hours	Average no of rain days
	0900	1500			
	per cent		*inches*		
January	89	82	2.91	1.65	17
February	89	76	2.12	1.02	15
March	85	68	1.97	1.30	13
April	75	58	2.09	1.50	13
May	74	58	2.52	1.30	14
June	74	59	1.97	1.30	13
July	75	62	2.72	1.42	15
August	80	64	2.72	1.93	14
September	84	67	2.40	1.54	14
October	88	73	2.72	1.61	15
November	90	80	3.30	1.50	17
December	90	84	2.64	1.85	18
Year	83	69	30.08	1.93	178

USSR — INLAND (CONTINENTAL)
Similar latitude to East Anglia
(Based on mainly 8-year averages 1962–1969)
Orenburg

	Relative humidity		Precipitation		
	Average of observations at		Average monthly fall	Maximum fall in 24 hours	Average no. of rain days
	0900	1500			
	per cent		*inches*		
January	75	69	0.94	0.55	15
February	75	67	0.83	0.55	11
March	78	70	0.83	0.55	12
April	56	41	0.98	1.06	7
May	44	33	1.46	1.18	10
June	51	39	1.85	1.30	12
July	52	39	1.50	1.38	9
August	45	32	1.30	0.71	9
September	55	41	1.06	0.34	9
October	70	57	1.69	0.91	14
November	81	71	1.34	0.51	14
December	76	72	1.10	0.55	14
Year	63	53	14.88	1.38	136

APPENDIX SIX

Sunshine

Based on averages mainly for the 30 years 1931–1960

EAST ANGLIA — COASTAL

Cromer

	Bright sunshine			
	Average monthly duration	Average per cent of possible	Maximum duration in one day	Average no. of days with no sun
	hours		*hours*	
January	55	22	8.1	11
February	73	26	9.7	9
March	125	34	11.6	6
April	162	39	13.5	3
May	197	40	15.3	3
June	203	40	15.3	2
July	195	38	15.4	2
August	180	39	13.9	2
September	150	39	12.2	2
October	111	34	10.1	5
November	60	23	8.3	9
December	50	21	7.2	12
Year	1561	35	15.4	66
No. of years	30	30	30	30

Gorleston

	Bright sunshine			
	Average monthly duration	Average per cent of possible	Maximum duration in one day	Average no. of days with no sun
	hours		*hours*	
January	54	21	7.8	13
February	69	25	9.7	9
March	125	34	11.2	6
April	166	40	13.4	3
May	209	43	15.0	2
June	215	43	15.9	1
July	210	42	15.9	1
August	189	42	14.5	2
September	152	40	12.3	2
October	111	34	10.3	5
November	57	22	8.6	11
December	46	19	6.8	14
Year	1603	36	15.9	69
No. of years	30	30	30	30

Felixstowe

	Bright sunshine			
	Average monthly duration	Average per cent of possible	Maximum duration in one day	Average no. of days with no sun
	hours		*hours*	
January	59	23	7.8	11
February	74	27	9.5	8
March	133	36	11.3	5
April	176	42	13.7	2
May	218	45	14.9	2
June	224	45	15.7	1
July	205	41	15.4	1
August	193	42	14.2	1
September	156	41	12.9	2
October	115	35	10.6	4
November	65	24	8.7	9
December	49	20	7.3	13
Year	1667	37	15.7	59
No. of years	30	30	30	30

Clacton

	Bright sunshine			
	Average monthly duration	Average per cent of possible	Maximum duration in one day	Average no. of days with no sun
	hours		*hours*	
January	57	22	7.8	12
February	76	27	9.9	8
March	131	36	11.3	6
April	169	41	13.3	2
May	210	44	14.9	2
June	231	47	15.7	2
July	212	43	15.5	1
August	199	44	14.6	1
September	161	42	12.5	2
October	116	35	10.6	5
November	64	24	8.5	11
December	48	19	7.4	13
Year	1674	37	15.7	64
No. of years	27	27	27	27

EAST ANGLIA — INLAND
Cambridge

	Bright sunshine			
	Average monthly duration	Average per cent of possible	Maximum duration in one day	Average no. of days with no sun
	hours		*hours*	
January	52	20	7.4	12
February	69	25	9.5	8
March	117	32	11.2	6
April	153	37	13.2	3
May	192	40	14.9	3
June	202	41	15.6	2
July	186	37	15.3	2
August	177	39	14.0	2
September	138	36	12.3	2
October	105	32	9.5	5
November	57	21	8.3	11
December	42	17	7.1	14
Year	1490	33	15.6	70
No. of years	30	30	30	30

GREAT BRITAIN — COASTAL

Bournemouth

	Bright sunshine			
	Average monthly duration	Average per cent of possible	Maximum duration in one day	Average no. of days with no sun
	hours		hours	
January	65	25	7.8	11
February	82	29	9.5	8
March	133	36	11.3	5
April	185	45	13.5	3
May	218	45	15.1	2
June	230	47	15.5	1
July	213	43	15.4	2
August	206	46	14.2	2
September	150	39	12.0	3
October	116	35	10.6	5
November	71	26	8.7	9
December	57	23	7.0	12
Year	1726	39	15.5	63
No. of years	30	30	30	30

Ilfracombe

	Bright sunshine			
	Average monthly duration	Average per cent of possible	Maximum duration in one day	Average no. of days with no sun
	hours		*hours*	
January	51	19	8.0	13
February	72	26	10.2	9
March	135	37	11.6	6
April	179	43	13.6	4
May	218	45	15.0	2
June	230	47	15.6	2
July	198	40	15.3	3
August	193	43	14.1	3
September	142	37	12.7	3
October	101	30	10.4	7
November	57	21	8.5	11
December	42	17	6.9	14
Year	1618	36	15.6	77
No. of years	30	30	30	30

GREAT BRITAIN — INLAND

Central, similar latitude to East Anglia

Birmingham

	Bright sunshine			
	Average monthly duration	Average per cent of possible	Maximum duration in one day	Average no. of days with no sun
	hours		*hours*	
January	43	16	7.3	14
February	58	21	9.0	9
March	98	27	11.2	8
April	139	33	13.1	3
May	167	34	15.3	3
June	180	36	15.3	2
July	166	33	15.4	2
August	159	35	14.0	2
September	117	31	11.9	3
October	86	26	9.9	6
November	48	18	7.7	12
December	38	16	7.0	14
Year	1299	29	15.4	78
No. of years	30	30	30	30

USSR — INLAND (CONTINENTAL)

Similar latitude to East Anglia

Orenburg

	Bright sunshine			
	Average monthly duration	Average per cent of possible	Maximum duration in one day	Average no. of days with no sun
	hours		*hours*	
January	89	34	7	11
February	119	43	9	8
March	154	42	12	7
April	241	58	13	2
May	289	60	15	1
June	286	57	16	1
July	326	65	15	0
August	299	66	15	1
September	214	56	13	2
October	130	39	11	9
November	85	32	9	13
December	71	29	7	13
Year	2303	51	16	68
No. of years	4	4	4	4

APPENDIX SEVEN

Air Temperature

(Averages for 30 years 1931–1960, with the exception of Clacton-on-Sea and Orenburg).

EAST ANGLIA—COASTAL
Cromer 52°56′N, 1°17′E

1931–1960	Average daily		Average monthly		Absolute	
	Max	Min	Max	Min	Max	Min
	°F	*°C*	*°F*	*°C*	*°F*	*°C*
January	43	34	53	25	57	18
February	44	34	55	27	65	16
March	49	37	61	29	74	20
April	54	40	67	33	80	30
May	59	45	73	37	83	30
June	65	51	80	44	90	39
July	69	54	81	48	94	44
August	68	55	80	49	92	45
September	65	52	78	45	90	43
October	58	46	68	36	79	32
November	50	40	58	32	66	25
December	45	37	53	29	58	21
Year	56	44	85*	23*	94	16
No. of years	30	30	30	30	30	30

*Average of highest/lowest each year. Average seasonal range = 62°F.

Gorleston 52°35′N, 1°43′E

1931–1960	Average daily		Average monthly		Absolute	
	Max	Min	Max	Min	Max	Min
	°F	°C	°F	°C	°F	°C
January	43	36	53	25	58	16
February	44	36	54	27	61	17
March	47	37	59	28	72	18
April	52	41	64	33	76	30
May	56	47	68	37	82	31
June	63	52	75	44	84	39
July	67	56	77	47	84	43
August	67	56	77	48	88	43
September	64	53	74	43	79	38
October	57	48	66	35	74	30
November	50	42	58	32	68	24
December	45	38	54	27	59	22
Year	55	45	80*	23*	88	16
No. of years	30	30	30	30	30	30

*Average of highest/lowest each year. Average seasonal range = 62°F.

Felixstowe 51°57′N, 1°20′E

1931–1960	Average daily		Average monthly		Absolute	
	Max	Min	Max	Min	Max	Min
	°F	°C	°F	°C	°F	°C
January	42	36	51	25	57	19
February	43	35	52	26	58	11
March	47	37	58	28	71	16
April	53	41	64	33	75	29
May	59	46	70	37	76	31
June	65	53	75	44	82	37
July	69	57	78	49	86	45
August	69	57	77	49	83	41
September	65	54	74	44	82	40
October	58	48	66	36	73	30
November	50	42	58	32	67	26
December	45	38	53	28	60	22
Year	56	45	80*	23*	86	11
No. of years	30	30	30	30	30	30

*Average of highest/lowest each year. Average seasonal range = 57°F.

Clacton-on-Sea 51°47′N, 1°09′E

Mainly 1931–1942 and 1946–1960	Average daily		Average monthly		Absolute	
	Max	Min	Max	Min	Max	Min
	°F	*°C*	*°F*	*°C*	*°F*	*°C*
January	43	35	51	25	56	18
February	43	34	52	26	57	15
March	47	37	57	29	71	19
April	53	41	62	33	70	29
May	58	47	68	37	74	28
June	65	53	75	43	81	39
July	69	56	78	48	84	42
August	69	56	76	48	85	42
September	65	53	73	44	80	38
October	57	47	65	34	71	29
November	50	41	57	31	70	26
December	45	37	53	27	58	21
Year	55	45	80*	22*	85	15
No. of years	25	25	27	27	27	27

*Average of highest/lowest each year. Average seasonal range = 58°F.

EAST ANGLIA — INLAND
Cambridge 52°12′N, 0°08′E

1931–1960	Average daily		Average monthly		Absolute	
	Max	Min	Max	Min	Max	Min
	°F	*°C*	*°F*	*°C*	*°F*	*°C*
January	43	33	54	20	58	8
February	45	33	56	21	64	1
March	51	35	63	24	71	11
April	57	39	69	28	79	24
May	63	44	77	31	87	24
June	69	49	82	40	93	34
July	72	53	83	43	94	38
August	72	53	83	43	96	38
September	67	49	78	37	88	32
October	58	43	68	29	80	21
November	50	38	59	27	70	17
December	45	35	55	22	60	13
Year	58	42	87*	17*	96	1
No. of years	30	30	30	30	30	30

*Average of highest/lowest each year. Average seaonal range = 70°F.

Bournemouth 50°43′N, 1°54′W

1931–1960	Average daily		Average monthly		Absolute	
	Max	Min	Max	Min	Max	Min
	°F	°C	°F	°C	°F	°C
January	45	35	53	24	55	12
February	46	35	54	25	58	14
March	51	37	60	26	70	14
April	56	41	67	32	79	28
May	62	45	74	35	87	29
June	67	51	79	43	88	38
July	70	55	80	47	90	44
August	70	55	79	46	93	41
September	66	51	75	41	82	35
October	59	46	66	33	73	27
November	51	41	59	29	62	24
December	47	38	54	25	58	18
Year	58	44	84*	20*	93	12
No. of years	30	30	30	30	30	30

*Average of highest/lowest each year. Average seasonal range = 64°F.

Ilfracombe 51°12′N, 4°08′W

1931–1960	Average daily		Average monthly		Absolute	
	Max	Min	Max	Min	Max	Min
	°F	°C	°F	°C	°F	°C
January	47	40	55	30	58	19
February	47	39	55	30	61	20
March	50	41	59	32	68	27
April	53	44	64	37	75	32
May	59	48	69	41	79	35
June	63	54	75	48	86	43
July	66	57	75	52	84	49
August	67	58	75	52	86	47
September	64	55	72	48	80	42
October	58	50	65	41	76	34
November	53	45	59	37	65	30
December	49	42	55	32	60	25
Year	56	48	80*	27*	86	19
No. of years	30	30	30	30	30	30

*Average of highest/lowest each year. Average seasonal range = 53°F.

Birmingham/Edgbaston 52°29′N, 1°56′E

1931–1960	Average daily		Average monthly		Absolute	
	Max	Min	Max	Min	Max	Min
	°F	°C	°F	°C	°F	°C
January	42	35	53	24	56	11
February	43	35	54	25	60	16
March	48	37	60	28	69	19
April	54	40	66	32	75	29
May	60	45	74	36	85	30
June	66	51	79	43	87	37
July	68	54	80	47	90	43
August	68	54	79	47	91	43
September	63	51	74	42	81	37
October	55	45	65	35	77	28
November	48	40	57	31	67	24
December	44	37	53	26	58	21
Year	55	44	84*	22*	91	11
No. of years	30	30	30	30	30	30

*Average of highest/lowest each year. Average seasonal range = 62°F.

Orenburg (Chkalov) 51°45′N, 55°06′E

1962–1969	Average daily		Average monthly		Absolute	
	Max	Min	Max	Min	Max	Min
	°F	°C	°F	°C	°F	°C
January	14	0	31	−29	35	−46
February	15	−2	32	−23	39	−39
March	32	15	43	−14	55	−28
April	54	33	75	14	85	−7
May	72	47	87	33	95	24
June	78	55	95	40	103	35
July	83	60	95	48	102	42
August	80	56	93	42	99	38
September	70	45	86	28	92	22
October	49	33	67	14	73	0
November	34	23	46	6	53	−14
December	20	6	36	−18	39	−31
Year	50	31	98*	−30*	103	−46
No. of years	8	8	8	8	8	8

*Average of highest/lowest each year. Average seasonal range = 128°F.

The shorter period covered at Orenburg does not invalidate the comparisons but a longer period would doubtless reveal a wider range of extremes.

APPENDIX EIGHT

NUMBER OF DAYS WHEN SNOW OR SLEET FELL AT RUSHMERE ST ANDREW
40 years — 1942–1981

(A "day of sleet or snow" includes anything from a few flakes to a heavy fall.)

	Jan	Feb	Mar	Apr	May	Jun	Jul	Aug	Sep	Oct	Nov	Dec	Year
1942	15	12	1	—	—	—	—	—	—	—	—	—	28
1943	4	—	—	—	—	—	—	—	—	—	1	1	6
1944	6	6	1	—	—	—	—	—	—	—	1	2	16
1945	9	—	1	2	2	—	—	—	—	—	—	1	15
1946	3	2	7	—	—	—	—	—	—	—	—	4	16
1947	8	19	5	—	—	—	—	—	—	—	2	1	35
1948	1	5	—	—	—	—	—	—	—	—	—	—	6
1949	—	—	3	2	—	—	—	—	—	—	—	3	8
1950	4	2	—	2	—	—	—	—	—	—	—	13	21
1951	3	1	7	3	—	—	—	—	—	—	—	—	14
1952	6	8	5	1	—	—	—	—	—	—	7	5	32
1953	4	11	—	—	—	—	—	—	—	—	—	—	15
1954	7	6	3	1	—	—	—	—	—	—	—	—	17
1955	7	12	10	—	—	—	—	—	—	—	—	—	29
1956	5	19	2	—	—	—	—	—	—	—	—	2	28
1957	2	3	—	2	—	—	—	—	—	—	—	1	8
1958	6	6	9	5	—	—	—	—	—	—	—	1	27
1959	6	—	—	—	—	—	—	—	—	—	—	—	6
1960	9	3	—	—	—	—	—	—	—	—	—	2	14
1961	—	—	3	—	—	—	—	—	—	—	—	4	7
1962	2	8	10	1	—	—	—	—	—	—	2	7	30
1963	19	14	1	—	—	—	—	—	—	—	—	2	36
1964	2	3	4	1	—	—	—	—	—	—	1	5	16
1965	4	7	6	1	—	—	—	—	—	—	5	1	24
1966	8	5	2	2	—	—	—	—	—	—	1	2	20
1967	4	—	1	2	3	—	—	—	—	—	—	2	12
1968	9	9	3	2	—	—	—	—	—	—	1	3	27
1969	1	16	5	1	—	—	—	—	—	—	4	6	33
1970	3	8	8	8	—	—	—	—	—	—	—	7	34
1971	1	3	6	—	—	—	—	—	—	—	5	3	18
1972	4	—	2	—	—	—	—	—	—	—	1	—	7
1973	1	5	1	5	—	—	—	—	—	—	2	3	17
1974	—	1	3	—	—	—	—	—	—	2	—	2	8
1975	1	—	8	6	—	1*	—	—	—	—	—	2	18
1976	2	2	4	1	—	—	—	—	—	—	—	4	13
1977	7	2	3	1	—	—	—	—	—	—	1	—	14
1978	8	6	4	5	—	—	—	—	—	—	2	3	28
1979	14	6	5	1	5	—	—	—	—	—	—	2	33
1980	8	—	2	—	—	—	—	—	—	—	5	5	20
1981	7	9	2	1	—	—	—	—	—	—	1	11	31
40-year-average	5.3	5.5	3.4	1.4	<0.25	—	—	—	—	—	1.1	2.7	19.4

*Snow stopped play at Colchester County cricket match

APPENDIX NINE

NUMBER OF DAYS OF SNOW LYING AT RUSHMERE ST ANDREW
40 years — 1942–1981

(The official definition of “snow lying” is that, at the 0900 hrs GMT observation, at least half the ground representative of the point of observation is covered with snow.)

	Jan	Feb	Mar	Apr	May	Jun	Jul	Aug	Sep	Oct	Nov	Dec	Year
1942	13	—	—	—	—	—	—	—	—	—	—	—	13
1943	3	—	—	—	—	—	—	—	—	—	—	—	3
1944	—	1	—	—	—	—	—	—	—	—	—	—	1
1945	12	—	—	1	—	—	—	—	—	—	—	—	13
1946	—	1	3	—	—	—	—	—	—	—	—	6	10
1947	10	28	13	—	—	—	—	—	—	—	—	—	51
1948	—	5	—	—	—	—	—	—	—	—	—	—	5
1949	—	—	2	—	—	—	—	—	—	—	—	—	2
1950	—	—	—	—	—	—	—	—	—	—	—	3	3
1951	—	—	—	—	—	—	—	—	—	—	—	—	—
1952	1	4	4	1	—	—	—	—	—	—	—	1	11
1953	4	3	—	—	—	—	—	—	—	—	—	—	7
1954	5	2	3	—	—	—	—	—	—	—	—	—	10
1955	7	10	3	—	—	—	—	—	—	—	—	—	20
1956	2	18	1	—	—	—	—	—	—	—	—	2	23
1957	—	—	—	—	—	—	—	—	—	—	—	—	—
1958	7	4	—	—	—	—	—	—	—	—	—	—	11
1959	4	—	—	—	—	—	—	—	—	—	—	—	4
1960	8	—	—	—	—	—	—	—	—	—	—	—	8
1961	—	—	—	—	—	—	—	—	—	—	—	—	—
1962	3	2	1	—	—	—	—	—	—	—	—	3	9
1963	29	27	4	—	—	—	—	—	—	—	—	—	60
1964	1	—	—	—	—	—	—	—	—	—	—	4	5
1965	4	2	1	—	—	—	—	—	—	—	1	—	8
1966	8	—	—	—	—	—	—	—	—	—	—	—	8
1967	4	—	—	—	—	—	—	—	—	—	—	3	7
1968	8	1	—	1	—	—	—	—	—	—	—	6	16
1969	2	17	—	—	—	—	—	—	—	—	4	4	27
1970	4	4	3	—	—	—	—	—	—	—	—	5	16
1971	6	1	3	—	—	—	—	—	—	—	2	1	13
1972	—	2	—	—	—	—	—	—	—	—	—	—	2
1973	—	2	—	—	—	—	—	—	—	—	2	3	7
1974	—	—	—	—	—	—	—	—	—	—	—	—	—
1975	—	—	1	1	—	—	—	—	—	—	—	—	2
1976	4	—	—	—	—	—	—	—	—	—	—	—	4
1977	2	—	1	—	—	—	—	—	—	—	—	—	3
1978	2	6	1	—	—	—	—	—	—	—	3	4	16
1979	19	11	1	—	—	—	—	—	—	—	—	1	32
1980	—	—	—	—	—	—	—	—	—	—	3	4	7
1981	2	5	—	—	—	—	—	—	—	—	—	22	29
40-year-average	4.3	3.9	1.1	<0.25	—	—	—	—	—	—	<0.5	1.8	11.6

APPENDIX TEN

NUMBER OF "ABSOLUTE" DROUGHTS BY DECADES

(15 or more consecutive rainless days)

Belstead/Copdock

Decade	Jan	Feb	Mar	Apr	May	Jun	Jul	Aug	Sept	Oct	Nov	Dec	Year
1902–1909 (8 years)	—	—	—	1	—	1	2	—	1	—	—	—	5
1910–1919	—	—	—	1	4	1	—	2	—	—	—	—	8
1920–1929	—	—	1	—	—	4	3	—	1	1	—	—	10
1930–1939	—	—	2	1	3	2	4	3	—	—	—	—	15
1940–1949	—	—	1	1	3	2	—	3	—	1	—	—	11
1950–59	—	1	1	2	2	—	1	2	2	1	—	—	12
1960–1969	—	—	—	—	1	2	2	—	—	—	—	—	5
1970–1979	—	—	—	2	2	3	2	1	3	2	—	1	16
Total 1902–1979	—	1	5	8	15	15	14	11	7	5	—	1	82

APPENDIX ELEVEN

THE "WET-BULB" FACTOR

Air Temperature (°F.), Relative Humidity (%) and Wet-Bulb Temperature (°F.)

The table, which shows the inter-relation between air temperature, wet-bulb temperature and relative humidity, can be used in a variety of ways. When the air is saturated (relative humidity 100%), the air and wet-bulb temperatures are identical. The drier the air, the bigger the difference between the two temperatures.

From this table, owners of a wet- and dry-bulb hygrometer can calculate the relative humidity (more detailed tables or a slide-rule are obtainable from instrument suppliers). Owners of an ordinary thermometer and a dial hygrometer (showing the relative humidity) can, by using the table (with both instruments in the open air in the shade), calculate the approximate wet-bulb temperature.

1. The shaded squares indicate danger conditions in which, although a thermometer hanging outside indicates a temperature above freezing-point, wet surfaces (e.g. roads) may be cooled by evaporation to a state of freezing.
2. More pleasantly, the table also indicates the cooling effect of evaporation on moist skin in hot weather. The drier the air the greater the cooling effect. Thus, with a shade temperature of 80° degrees F., dry air with a humidity of only 40% would reduce the temperature of evaporation off the skin to a refreshing 64° degrees F. In very humid conditions, the cooling effect can be slight or nil, thus creating a close and muggy feeling. (See table 13 "The Discomfort Factor").

THE INTER-RELATION OF AIR TEMPERATURE (°F.), RELATIVE HUMIDITY (%) AND WET-BULB TEMPERATURE (°F.)

Air temperature (dry-bulb) °F.	Relative humidity 100%	90%	80%	70%	60%	50%	40%	30%
	Wet-bulb temperature (°F.)							
90°	90°	88°	86°	83°	80°	77°	73°	68°
80°	80°	78°	76°	74°	71°	68°	65°	60°
70°	70°	68°	66°	64°	62°	59°	56°	52°
60°	60°	58°	57°	55°	53°	50°	47°	43°
50°	50°	49°	47°	45°	43°	41°	39°	36°
40°	40°	39°	37°	36°	35°	33°	31°	28°
38°	38°	37°	36°	34°	33°	31°	29°	27°
36°	36°	35°	34°	33°	31°	30°	28°	26°
34°	34°	33°	32°	31°	30°	28°	27°	25°
33°	33°	32°	31°	30°	29°	27°	26°	24°

Unless very accurate and properly exposed instruments are used, this table should be taken as an approximate guide only.

THE DISCOMFORT FACTOR

(caused mainly by a combination of high temperature and high relative humidity)

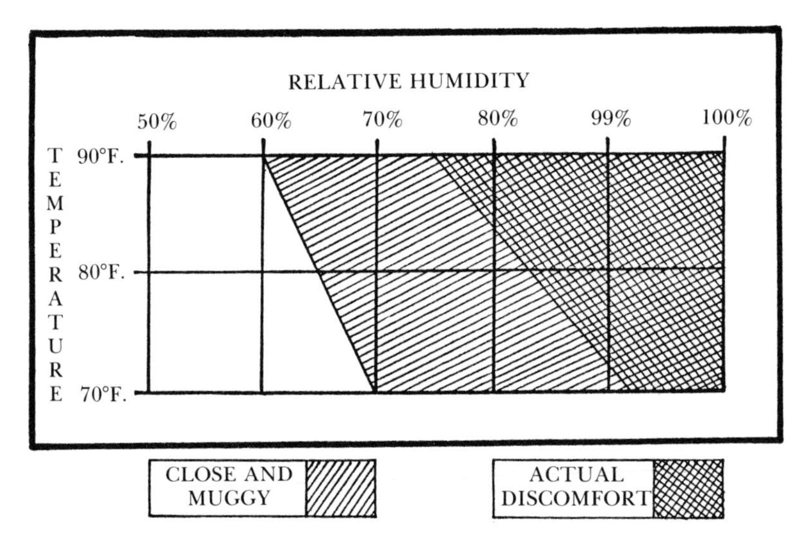

Several scientific formulae have been published, based variously on meteorological, physiological and other considerations, which seek to define the causes of physical discomfort arising from oppressive warmth. In the concept of the above table I have adopted a simple empirical approach, based on my own and friends' experiences and concerned mainly with the shade temperature and the relative humidity. But increased wind speed greatly lessens discomfort and is an important factor. On an otherwise calm, warm summer day anywhere within at least ten miles of the East Anglian coast might well — as a result of a sea-breeze — enjoy the benefits of a higher wind speed than at places further inland. (The sea-breeze is, in any case, cooler than the inland temperature.)

The above table is generally operative for light winds of Force 2 (4–7 m.p.h.) and less. An approximate adjustment for the modifying effect of wind speed (accelerating the "wet-bulb" effect of increased evaporation off the skin) is, I find by personal observation, as follows:

If the wind has reached Force 3 to 4 (8–18 m.p.h.), move both shaded areas up to 5% humidity to the right.

If the wind is Force 5 (19–24 m.p.h.) or more, move both shaded areas 10% humidity to the right.

An absolutely dead calm greatly increases the discomfort factor. But all this is arbitrary, particularly as it is impossible to include the human factor.

Individual reactions vary greatly; some people positively revel in a sweltering heat. Generally speaking, however, when the relative humidity on a warm day is as high as 90% or more, even slight physical effort, if sustained, may become unduly tiring. At that point, evaporation from the skin (the "wet-bulb" effect) is so slight as to provide no appreciable effect. (See table 12 of wet- and dry-bulb temperatures and relative humidity.)

The "70s rule" is a good generalisation. If the shade temperature is 70°F. or more and the relative humidity 70% or more, oppressive discomfort will usually be felt.

APPENDIX THIRTEEN

WIND CHILL

I have compiled this table from a variety of sources, with varying degrees of emphasis on the meteorological, physiological and other factors involved. The result is a fair approximation of the total effect of wind chill. Wind chill can work both for and against us — note the advantages of a sea-breeze on a hot day as compared with the dangerous effects of a strong wind in severely cold weather.

WIND-CHILL TABLE

Wind speed m.p.h.	Air temperature °F.						
	80°	70°	60°	50°	40°	30°	20°
	Equivalent wind-chill temperature						
Calm	80°	70°	60°	50°	40°	30°	20°
5	77°	67°	57°	47°	36°	26°	15°
10	73°	63°	52°	41°	29°	17°	5°
15	70°	60°	49°	36°	22°	10°	−4°
20	68°	58°	46°	32°	18°	4°	−10°
25	66°	56°	43°	30°	15°	0°	−14°
30	64°	54°	41°	28°	13°	−2°	−18°
35	62°	52°	40°	27°	11°	−4°	−20°
40	61°	51°	39°	26°	10°	−6°	−21°

Wind speeds greater than 40 m.p.h. have very little additional effect.

INDEX